Essential
Anatomy & Physiology

Third Edition 2011
Second Edition 2006
First published 2002

Published by Essential Training Solutions Ltd.
PO Box 12565
Sawbridgeworth
Hertfordshire
CM21 1BL

www.essential-training.co.uk

This page has intentionally been left blank.

ISBN 0-9553425-0-3
ISBN 978-0-9553425-0-9

Contents

This page has intentionally been left blank.

Introduction

This page has intentionally been left blank.

Structural Organization

The **anatomy** (structure) and **physiology** (function) of the body is highly complicated. Chemicals combine to form various structures, all of which function together to form the whole being.

The human body consists of several levels of structural organization:

1. Chemical Level

This is the **lowest** level. It includes all **atoms** (e.g. carbon, hydrogen, oxygen, nitrogen, calcium, potassium, sodium) and **molecules** essential for maintaining life.

The numerous chemical reactions that take place in the body sustain life. All chemical reactions that occur in the body fall under the heading **metabolism**. When large, complex molecules are broken down **energy** is released (**catabolism**). The energy released enables chemical reactions to take place that **build up** the body's structural and functional components (**anabolism**).

Metabolism is covered in more detail later in this section. The Chemistry section introduces you to some basic chemistry that will help you to further understand the anatomy and physiology of the body. You will find this really useful. Please pay particular attention to the main **chemical elements** that are found in the body.

2. Cellular Level

Molecules combine to form **cells**. The study of cells is called **cytology**.

Cells are the basic structural and functional units that make up the body. They are surrounded by **intercellular fluid** and are capable of performing **all** the activities vital to life, including metabolism, respiration, excretion, responsiveness, growth, repair and reproduction.

There are **many types**, e.g. nerve cells, blood cells and muscle cells. Each type of cell has its own specialized structure and function but they all have some general features.

A typical cell is shown on the next page. The cell is surrounded by a **cell membrane** which encloses the content of the cell. There are a number of components within the cell membrane that serve a particular function. These structures are called **organelles**.

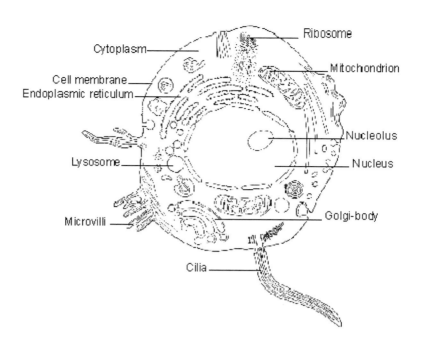

Here's a short description for each of the main components of a typical cell.

Cell membrane: The outer lining that forms the barrier between the cell and the extracellular fluid (fluid outside the cells). 20% of extracellular fluid is made up of plasma and so the cell membrane is also referred to as the plasma membrane. The cell membrane protects the contents of the cell and regulates the movement of substances into and out of it.

Cytoplasm: Semi-fluid within the cell membrane that surrounds the organelles. It contains water, ions and many organic compounds including enzymes. It is the medium in which many of the cell's chemical reactions occur.

Endoplasmic reticulum: A network of channels running through the cytoplasm. It performs many roles including intracellular transport and support. It also provides the surface area for many types of chemical reactions. Its surface is often covered with protein-synthesizing ribosomes, forming "rough" endoplasmic reticulum. It is here that most of the cell's enzyme activity takes place under the influence of ribonucleic acid. Endoplasmic reticulum lacking ribosomes is called "smooth" and is involved in lipid (fat) synthesis, including steroids.

Cilia: Tiny hair-like structures that protrude from the cell membrane. They aid movement and absorption.

Mitochondrion: A large double-membraned organelle, also known as the "powerhouse". It is responsible for producing the majority of the cell's adenosine triphosphate (ATP), which is the energy-carrying molecule, used to capture and store energy.

Nucleus: Literally means 'central part'. In a cell, the nucleus is the oval-shaped organelle that contains the chromosomes (the hereditary factors) consisting of deoxyribonucleic acid (DNA). The nucleus controls cellular activities. The fluid within the double nuclear membrane is called nucleoplasm. The nuclear membrane has water-filled pores that allow most ions and water-soluble molecules to move between the nucleus and the cytoplasm.

Nucleolus: A part of the nucleus that functions in the synthesis and storage of ribonucleic acid (RNA).

Golgi-body: A structure looking similar to a stack of plates. Its functions include processing proteins and lipids (fats) and controlling the enzyme activity of the endoplasmic reticulum.

Lysosome: A single membraned organelle that contains digestive enzymes. Lysosomes break down metabolic substances, foreign particles and worn out cell parts.

Ribosome: An organelle in the cytoplasm that may attach to the endoplasmic reticulum. It contains ribonucleic acid (RNA) and proteins. Ribosomes are the site of protein synthesis.

Microvilli: Finger-like projections of the cell membrane that increase the surface area for absorption.

Now you've got all that, there are just a few more components of the cell to be aware of:

Vacuoles: Membrane-bound organelles in cells that frequently function as temporary storage or transportation.

Vesicles: Small secretory bladders or sacs situated at the cell membrane. They secrete cellular substances.

Centrosomes and Centrioles: A centrosome is a dense area of cytoplasm near the nucleus. It has a part to play in cell division. The centrosome contains a pair of cylindrical structures called centrioles. Each centriole contains clusters of microtubules. Microtubules are made of protein and they provide support, structure and transportation.

As the body's building blocks, cells must perform many roles. For example, the body is dependent on specialised cells to fight disease, transport oxygen, manufacture proteins, store nutrients and to even move! To perform these roles every cell needs to be able to carry out a number of **functions** to stay alive. They are:

1. **Metabolism and Respiration**
2. **Excretion**
3. **Sensitivity**
4. **Repair, Growth and Reproduction**

We'll look at these functions next.

1. Metabolism and Respiration

All metabolic reactions take place **in cells**. The energy released when complex molecules are broken down is used to build up the body's structural and functional components. These vital metabolic reactions require **fuel** which is provided by food. The food we eat is broken down during the digestive process and the nutrients are absorbed **from** the **intestine into** the **blood**. Tiny molecules (including glucose) derived from the food eventually pass from the blood into the intercellular fluid and are then transported through the **cell membrane** into the **cell**.

Once in the cell, **glucose** can be broken down to produce **energy**. This is often as a result of a reaction with **oxygen**. Oxygen is inhaled into the **lungs**, absorbed into the **blood** and is then passed into the **intercellular fluid**. When the oxygen arrives in the **cell**, the oxygen and the glucose react to produce **energy**, **carbon dioxide** and **water**. This is called **aerobic cellular respiration** and is often expressed as an equation:

Glucose + Oxygen = Energy + Carbon Dioxide + Water

Note: Cellular respiration is covered in greater detail in the Muscular Section.

2. Excretion

Waste products from metabolic reactions, such as carbon dioxide, have to be **excreted** from the cell. If not, the cell becomes **toxic**. Waste products from the cell are transported through the cell membrane into the intercellular fluid. They then make their way into the **blood**.

Both respiration and excretion require the movement of substances into and out of the cell. The ability for substances to move between the cell and the intercellular fluid is vital for **homeostasis** (covered later in this section). The movement of **solutes** through the cell membrane can only occur because it is **semi-permeable**. This means that it is not impenetrable and can **selectively allow** some substances through.

Substances that can pass through the semi-permeable cell membrane may do so in a number of different ways:

Diffusion

When there is a greater concentration of a solute on one side of the cell membrane than the other, the solute may move **passively** (without using energy) through the cell membrane until the concentration on either side of the membrane is equal. This process of solutes moving **from an area of high concentration to an area of low concentration** is called diffusion. Diffusion is dependent on the size of the solute's molecules. If the molecules are too large to pass through the cell membrane then clearly diffusion cannot take place. Diffusion of molecules across the cell membrane may be aided by membrane proteins that serve as transporters. This is called **facilitated diffusion** and is still a **passive** process.

Osmosis

Osmosis is the process in which **water** passes **passively** through a semi-permeable membrane to equalise the concentration of dissolved substances. The water moves **from** the side of **low** chemical concentration **to** the side of **high** chemical concentration. Osmosis therefore allows the chemical levels inside and outside of the cell to be equalised when the chemicals themselves are too large to diffuse through the cell membrane.

Filtration

Substances may be **forced** across the cell membrane by **gravity** or **water pressure**. This **passive** process always forces substances **from** the area of **higher pressure** into the area of lower pressure.

Active Transport

Some substances cannot move through the cell membrane passively. They require energy to move into or out of the cell. Active transport is the term given to the ways in which substances can, **with the use of energy**, pass into and out of the cell. Some substances are **pushed or pumped** through and others are literally **"carried"** across.

Sometimes the cell membrane **wraps around** solid particles or fluid and literally **engulfs** them into the cell. This occurs by one of the following active processes:

Phagocytosis

Some cells are capable of "eating" a **solid particle**. The cell membrane and cytoplasm **extend**, causing **projections** called **pseudopods**. These extensions **engulf** the particle and the pseudopods fuse, effectively **encapsulating** the particle within the cell. Once inside the cell the particle is **digested** by enzymes. Phagocytosis plays a role in **immunity** and is covered in more detail in the Lymphatic System in the non-specific immunity section.

Pinocytosis

Pinocytosis is "**cell drinking**". It is similar to phagocytosis but the cell engulfs droplets of **extracellular fluid** rather than solid particles. No pseudopods are formed. Instead the membrane **folds inwards**, forming a **pinocytic vesicle** that allows the liquid to flow inward and then the cell surrounds the liquid. The pinocytic vesicle can then **detach** from the cell membrane. While only certain types of cells are capable of phagocytosis, **most cells** can perform pinocytosis.

3. <u>Sensitivity</u>

All cells are sensitive and therefore have the ability to **respond to a stimulus**. This allows them to pick up messages from other parts of the cell or other parts of the body and respond accordingly.

4. <u>Repair, Growth and Reproduction</u>

Cells can produce proteins and can therefore **repair** themselves and **grow**. However, they do become irreparably damaged, diseased or worn out and die. Growth and repair are largely under the hormonal control of the endocrine system but are affected by many other factors including nutrition, environmental influences and disease. Billions of cells are lost in an average day. It is therefore vital that new cells are produced to **replace** the old and to enable **growth** to occur.

Cell division is the process by which cells reproduce themselves. It consists of **nuclear division** (division of the nucleus) and **cytoplasmic division** (division of the cytoplasm and organelles). Cytoplasmic division is called **cytokinesis**.The nucleus and cytoplasm divide to produce new cells.

There are two main types of nuclear division.

1. Mitosis
The cell divides to produce **two identical** cells. Mitosis ensures that the new cells have the same number and kind of chromosome as the parent. It is an ongoing process that replaces dead or injured cells and adds new cells for growth.

2. Meiosis
The cell divides to produce **four** cells, each with **half** the **genetic complement** of the parent cell. Meiosis is the process by which the sex cells are produced. These are the ova in the female and the sperm in the male. We look at meiosis in more detail in the Reproductive System section.

Let's take a closer look at mitosis.

Mitosis is the nuclear division that occurs in all **non-sex** cells to produce **two identical** cells. The chromosomes in the nucleus of the cell **first replicate**. Each chromosome is then made up of **2 identical chromatids**, joined at a point called a **centromere**.

Chromosome **REPLICATION** Chromatids

There are then 4 phases of mitosis:

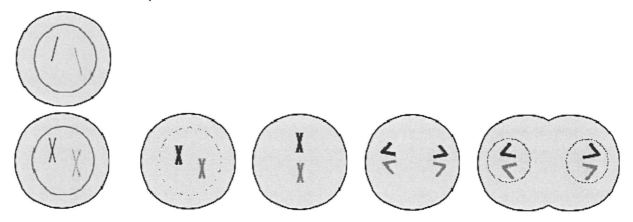

Replication   **1. Prophase 2. Metaphase 3. Anaphase 4. Telophase**

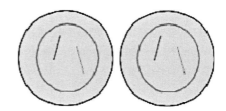

Prophase: The chromosomes, that have already replicated to consist of two chromatids, appear to shorten and thicken. The nuclear membrane disintegrates.

Metaphase: The chromosomes align down the centre of the cell.

Anaphase: The chromatids split into two groups, each group containing identical genetic information, and move to opposite ends of the cell.

Telophase: A nuclear membrane forms around each group of chromosomes.

During late anaphase or early telophase, the **cell membrane** begins to indent at opposite sides of the cell. The opposite sides of the cell membrane eventually make contact, **dividing** the **cytoplasm** (cytokinesis) around each new nucleus. The **two** new **identical** cells can then **split**.

Mitosis ensures that the new cells have the same **number** and **kind** of chromosome as the parent. It is an **ongoing** process that replaces dead or injured cells and adds new cells for growth. However, cells are not always in a state of mitosis. They are said to be in **interphase** when they are carrying on their usual processes but not dividing.

We have completed our look at cells, so let's move on to the next level of structural organization...

14

3. Tissue Level

Many **cells** of the **same type** make up tissue e.g. muscle cells make up muscle tissue. The study of tissues is called **histology**.

There are **four** main types of tissue – (A) epithelial, (B) connective, (C) muscle and (D) nervous. Let's look at each in turn.

A. Epithelial Tissue

Epithelial tissue generally consists of **closely packed** cells, arranged in **layers**, with little extracellular material between them. Epithelial tissue forms the linings and coverings of many organs and vessels in the body.

There are two main types of epithelial tissue:

Simple Epithelium

Simple epithelium is comprised of a **single layer** of cells. It is used to line body cavities such as the heart, blood vessels, lungs, and digestive tract. Although due to its thinness simple epithelium is fragile it does allow substances to be **absorbed quickly** through it.

Compound Epithelium

Compound epithelium contains **more than one layer** of cells. As it is thicker and stronger than simple epithelium it **protects** areas that are subjected to wear and tear. For example, compound epithelium lines the oesophagus and forms the epidermis.

There are 3 main types of simple epithelium and 2 main types of compound epithelium.

Simple Squamous

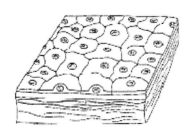

Simple squamous epithelium is also referred to as **pavement** epithelium due to its appearance. The cells are **flat** with a central nucleus. The **thinness** of this tissue is highly adapted for diffusion, osmosis and filtration but it is **fragile** and so is found in areas which are not subjected to wear and tear. It lines the alveoli, Bowman's capsule of the kidney, heart, blood vessels and lymph vessels. It also forms the walls of capillaries where it is called endothelium.

Simple Cuboidal

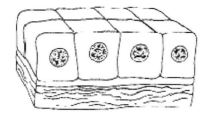

The **cube-shaped** cells of simple cuboidal epithelium are arranged in rows. Cuboidal epithelium performs the functions of **secretion** and **absorption**. It covers the surface of the ovaries, lines the back of the eye and the kidney tubules. It is also found in the smaller ducts of many glands.

Simple Columnar

The cells of columnar epithelium are **tall**, column-shaped. They offer a little more protection than the flat cells of squamous epithelium. Columnar epithelium lines the ducts of most glands and much of the digestive tract. Columnar epithelium may also contain **goblet cells**. Goblet cells secrete **mucus** which serves to **protect** and **lubricate**. Columnar epithelium may be ciliated or have microvilli.

Simple Ciliated Columnar

Columnar epithelium may have **cilia** (minute hair-like projections). Ciliated columnar epithelium can be found in the upper respiratory tract where the cilia trap and help to carry unwanted particles and mucus along the passageways. It is also present in the fallopian tubes, uterus and the central canal of the spinal cord.

Simple Columnar with Microvilli

The cell membrane of columnar epithelium may have **microvilli**. This type of epithelium is found in the small intestine where the microvilli **increase** the **surface area** for absorption.

Compound Stratified

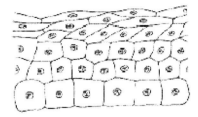 Compound stratified epithelium is composed of a **number of layers** of cells of different shapes and its role is mainly to **protect**. Stratified epithelium can be squamous, cuboidal or columnar depending on the shape of the cells that make up the **surface layer**, but squamous (shown left) is by far the most common.

In compound stratified squamous epithelium the basal layer cells **replicate** and new cells **push up** to the surface. If the top layer is **dry** and **dead** it is called **keratinised** stratified squamous epithelium (shown right), e.g. the epidermis.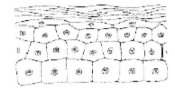

Non-keratinased stratified squamous epithelium (as shown top left) is found on wet surfaces such as the conjunctiva, lining of the mouth, pharynx and oesophagus.

Compound Transitional

Compound transitional epithelium permits **stretching**. It can therefore vary in appearance depending upon whether it is relaxed or distended. When relaxed the upper cells look large and rounded. Due to its ability to stretch, transitional epithelium is found in **hollow structures** that are subjected to expansion such as the urinary bladder and portions of the ureters and urethra.

Relaxed   Stretched

As we have said, there are four main types of tissue –

   A. **epithelial**
   B. **connective**
   C. **muscle and**
   D. **nervous**

Let's move on to connective tissue.

B. Connective Tissue

Connective tissue is the most **abundant** tissue. It binds, protects, strengthens and supports other tissues, protects and insulates internal organs and compartmentalises some structures.

Connective tissue consists of cells, ground substances and fibres. The ground substances and fibres, called the **matrix**, are located outside the cells. Generally, connective tissue consists of relatively few cells in a great deal of intercellular substance. The matrix can be liquid, gel-like or solid and so connective tissue can range from fluid (e.g. blood) to bone which is the hardest.

There are several types:

Areolar - Areolar tissue is the **most widely distributed** connective tissue in the body. It consists of large, flat cells in a **watery gel** supported by a network of fine, white collagen fibres and elastic fibres. This white tissue **surrounds blood vessels**, **nerves** and **muscles** and **connects** the **skin** to the underlying tissues and muscles.

Adipose - Adipose is "**fatty**" tissue and is semi-solid. The cells are specialised for the storage of fat. Adipose tissue **supports**, **protects** and **insulates**. It also provides a **store of energy**. Adipose tissue is found throughout the body but particularly in the subcutaneous layer of the skin and around the kidneys.

White fibrous - White fibrous connective tissue contains closely packed collagen fibres. It is **strong** and forms **attachments**. For example, white fibrous tissue is found in **tendons** (that attach muscle to bone) and **ligaments** (that attach bone to bone).

Yellow elastic - As the name suggests, yellow elastic connective tissue consists of **yellow elastic fibres**. It allows organs to **stretch** and then return to normal size. For example, yellow elastic tissue is found in the **walls** of the arteries.

Lymphoid - Lymphoid tissue - commonly called **lymph** - is **semi-solid** and contains cells called lymphocytes. This tissue forms a part of the lymphatic system which is concerned with the control of disease.

Blood - Blood is a connective tissue. It contains 45% **blood cells** and 55% **plasma** (the matrix). The composition of the blood is detailed in the Cardiovascular System.

Bone - Bone consists of **widely separated** cells within a **matrix**. The matrix consists of approximately 25% **water**, 25% **protein** and 50% **mineral salts** (see Bone Tissue). There are two types of bone – **compact** and **cancellous**. As the name suggests, compact bone tissue contains **few spaces**. Compact bone tissue is strong, providing **protection** and **support**. Cancellous (spongy) bone tissue is arranged in an interlacing network in which **red bone marrow** may be found in the spaces. Bone types are covered in detail in the Skeletal System.

Cartilage - Cartilage is firm and the matrix is quite solid. It contains cells called **chondrocytes**. Cartilage **connects** and **protects**. There are 3 types:

Hyaline: This is the **most common** and is also called **articular** cartilage. It is firm, elastic and reduces shock and friction in the **joints**. It is also used to connect **bone to bone** in joints such as those between the ribs and the sternum. Hyaline cartilage also forms the rings that keep the **trachea** open.

White fibrous: White fibrous cartilage is made up of bundles of white collagenous fibres with chondrocytes in between. It is very strong but slightly flexible. It is found in **some pelvic joints** and makes up the **intervertebral discs**.

Yellow elastic: This flexible cartilage consists of yellow elastic fibres. It forms the **epiglottis** and can be found at the **tip of the nose** and in the upper part of the **pinna** (external part of the ear).

Before we move on to look at the third tissue type - muscle tissue - let's quickly discuss **membranes**.

A membrane is a thin, flexible sheet of tissue that encloses a cell (e.g. the cell membrane) or a structure (e.g. the pleural membranes of the lung). There are 3 types of membrane:

Mucous membranes

Mucous membranes are comprised of a layer of **epithelial** tissue and an underlying **connective** tissue. They line body cavities that **open to the exterior** and line the entire **digestive**, **respiratory** and **reproductive** systems and most of the **urinary** system. Mucous membranes secrete a fluid called **mucus** that **lubricates** and **protects** the underlying cells.

Serous membranes

Like mucous membranes, serous membranes are also comprised of a layer of **epithelial** tissue and an underlying **connective** tissue. The connective tissue in serous membranes is **areolar**. Serous membranes line body cavities that **do not open** to the exterior and **cover** many **organs**. For example the pleura (covering the lungs) and the pericardium (covering the heart) are serous membranes. The epithelial layer secretes **serous fluid** that **lubricates** and allows the organs to **glide** against each other or against the walls of the cavities.

Synovial membranes

These line the cavities of **freely moveable** (synovial) **joints**. Synovial membranes do not contain epithelium. They are composed of areolar connective tissue, elastic fibres and fat. Synovial membranes secrete **synovial fluid** to **lubricate** and **nourish** the cartilage that protects the bone at the joints.

C. Muscle Tissue

Muscle tissue consists of **elongated** cells capable of **expanding** and **contracting**. The contractile fibres are usually arranged in bundles and surrounded by connective tissue.

Muscle tissue facilitates **movement**, maintains **posture** and generates **heat**. It is categorized into 3 types: **skeletal (voluntary)**, **smooth (involuntary)** and **cardiac (involuntary)**. For detailed information see the Muscular System.

D. Nervous Tissue

Nervous tissue is made up of **nerve cells**. There are 2 types - **neurons** and **neuroglia** (see the Nervous System).

Neurons are sensitive to stimuli and are capable of initializing and transmitting **nerve impulses**. Nervous tissue therefore helps to **co-ordinate** body activities.

Tissues are just the third level of structural organization. Let's move on…

4. Organ Level

Tissues of **varying type** make up an **organ**. The stomach, for example, is an organ as it consists of more than one tissue type. The outer layer of the stomach is comprised of connective tissue, the middle layer is muscle tissue, and the inner layer is epithelial tissue. Organs have specific functions and usually have distinctive shapes.

5. System Level

Several related **organs**, with a **common function**, make up a **system**. For example, the cardiovascular system, responsible for circulating the blood around the body, consists of the heart, veins and arteries – all of which are organs, as they all comprise of more than one tissue type.

6. Organism Level

All parts of the body (from the chemicals to the cells, tissues, organs and systems) are structured to function together to make up the **organism** - the **living individual**. This is the **highest** level of structural organization.

Before we go any further, let's **summarize** structural organization.

➤ There are 6 levels of structural organization – chemical, cellular, tissue, organ, system and organism.

➤ Chemical level - includes all atoms and molecules.

➤ Cellular level - cells, made from molecules, form the basic structural and functional units of the body.

➤ The main functions of the cells are metabolism, respiration, excretion, sensitivity, repair, growth and reproduction.

➤ Substances pass through the semi-permeable cell membrane by diffusion, osmosis, filtration or active transport.

➤ Cell division is the process by which cells reproduce themselves. It consists of nuclear division and cytoplasmic division.

➤ Mitosis is nuclear division in non-sex cells. It produces two identical cells. There are 4 phases, prophase, metaphase, anaphase and telophase.

➤ Meiosis is nuclear division in sex cells. The cell divides to produce four cells, each with half the genetic complement of the parent cell.

➤ Tissue level - cells of the same type make up tissue.

➤ There are 4 main types of tissue, epithelial, connective, muscle and nervous.

➤ The main types of epithelial tissue are simple squamous, cuboidal and columnar, and compound stratified and transitional.

➤ Connective tissue has 8 main types – areolar, adipose, white fibrous, yellow elastic, lymphoid, blood, bone and cartilage (hyaline, white fibrous and yellow elastic).

➤ The 3 types of membranes are mucous, serous and synovial.

➤ Organ level - tissues of varying type make up an organ.

➤ System level - several organs with a common function make up a system.

➤ Organism level - all parts of the body (chemicals, cells, tissues, organs and systems) function together to make up the organism.

Anatomical Position

The body is a highly complicated structure and in this package we will look at its anatomy (structure) and physiology (function) in some detail. However, to accurately describe the location of a body part, there are a number of general **anatomical terms** to become familiar with.

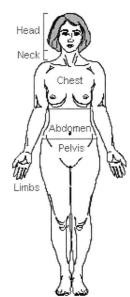

For descriptive purposes, the body is split into **regions** - the head, neck, chest, abdomen, pelvis and the four limbs. The abdomen is the area between the diaphragm and the pelvis. The chest, also called the thoracic area or thorax, is above the abdomen, the pelvis is below it.

To describe the location of any body part, it is always assumed that the body is in the upright position, facing the observer, feet flat on the floor, arms at the sides, with the palms of the hands turned forward as shown here. This is called the **anatomical position**.

Anterior

The **frontal** view of the body is called the **anterior** view. This term is also used to describe the location of a body part in comparison to another.

For example, anatomically, the ribs are positioned in front of the heart. The ribs are therefore described as being anterior to the heart.

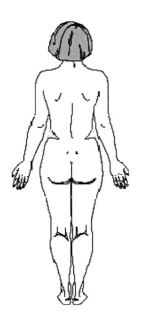

The **rear** view is called the **posterior** view. Again this term is also used comparatively.

For example, the spine is positioned behind the lungs. The spine is therefore posterior to the lungs.

Posterior

A part of the body that is positioned **higher** than another is said to be **superior**. The **lower** part is referred to as **inferior**.

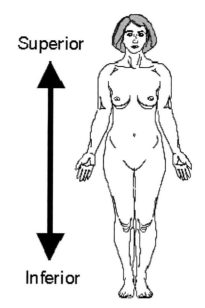

A body part nearer to the imaginary **midline** is said to be **medial**. Moving away from the midline the part is said to be **lateral**. These terms may also be used when the midline marks the centre line of an organ rather than the whole body.

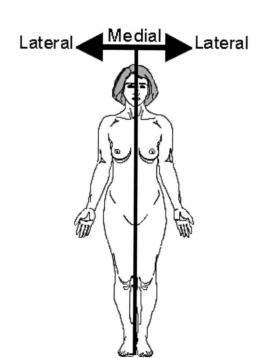

The final two positional terms are **proximal** and **distal**. They are used to describe the location of body parts within a **limb**. The location is described in relation to where the limb attaches to the trunk of the body. A part comparatively **closer** to where the limb **attaches** to the trunk is described as **proximal**. A part comparatively **further** away from the point of attachment is **distal** (Memory Hint: If there is more DISTance from the trunk, it is DISTal).

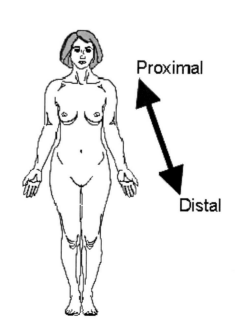

As you study anatomy, you will also see parts of the body described as **superficial** or **deep**. **Superficial** simply means "located on or near the **surface** of the body". This may also be described as **external**. **Deep** just means "**away from** the **surface** of the body". This may also be described as **internal**.

You will also see references to the body relative to **planes**. A plane is an imaginary flat surface that passes through the body or an organ so you can see a **cross section**. Imagine a rectangular piece of glass slicing the body in two, so allowing you to view the parts of the structure through which it passes. We'll look at 3 common planes or sections.

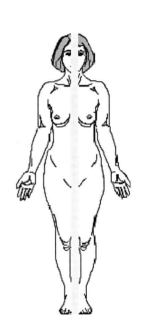

The **sagittal** plane sections the body or an organ **vertically** into **left** and **right** sides.

A sagittal plane does not have to split the body or organ into equal parts, but if the plane is down the midline, creating equal left and right sides, it is call a **midsagittal** plane. If the sides are unequal, it is called a **parasagittal** plane.

The sagittal plane, when applied to the whole body as shown here, creates a **longitudinal** section. Longitudinal literally means running **lengthwise**. However, be careful. The shape of the body part determines which way a longitudinal section would go. For example, on a rib, a longitudinal section would run from medial to lateral, lengthwise along the bone.

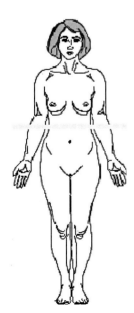

The **transverse** plane sections the body or an organ **horizontally** into **superior** (top) and **inferior** (bottom) sections.

The **frontal** plane sections the body or an organ into **anterior** (front) and **posterior** (back) sections.

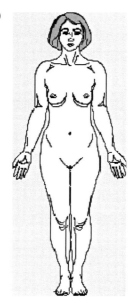

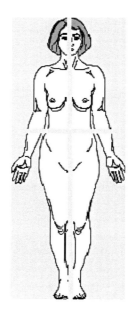

When you study a part of the body, you will often see it in section - sagittal (left/right), transverse (superior/inferior) or frontal (anterior/posterior).

Remember that with any section you are looking at only **one flat surface** of a three-dimensional structure.

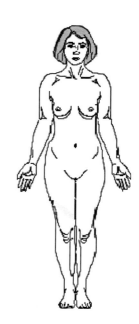

There is one other plane you may occasionally come across. It is called the **oblique** plane. An oblique plane passes through the body or organ at an **angle** (as shown here on the thigh).

Like any subject, becoming familiar and comfortable with the language is always a step in the right direction. In anatomy and physiology you are probably halfway there because you may already be familiar with the layman's terms for many body parts. However, you will have to get to grips with the more technical references.

You may be surprised how many words you already know. Just for fun, a number of commonly used anatomical words are shown below. See how many you already recognise. You can add your own terms here too.

Term:	Refers to:
Axillary	Armpit
Brachial	Arm
Carpal	Wrist
Cephalic	Head
Cervical	Neck
Cranial	Skull
Digital	Fingers/Toes
Femoral	Thigh
Inguinal	Groin
Lumbar	Loin
Nasal	Nose
Oral	Mouth
Orbital	Eye
Otic	Ear
Tarsal	Ankle
Thoracic	Chest

There are of course **new terms** that you will have to learn. These terms are **important**. They help you immediately know what part of the body is being referred to. For example, if you knew that calcaneal related to the heel, it would come as no surprise to find out that the Achilles tendon is called the calcaneal tendon, and the bone at the heel is called the calcaneus! See the connections you can make from nomenclature?

There are some useful terms for you on the next page.

Term	Pertains to:	Term	Pertains to:
Buccal	Mouth	Palmar	Hand
Calcaneal	Heel	Parietal	Outer wall of a body cavity
Cardiac	Heart	Patellar	Front of knee
Celiac / Coeliac	Belly or intestines	Pectoral	Chest or breast
Costal	Rib	Pedal	Foot
Crural	Leg	Perineal	Pelvic floor
Cubital	Forearm	Popliteal	Back of knee
Cutaneous	Skin	Plantar	Foot
Gluteal	Buttock	Sacral	Base of spine
Mammary	Breast	Umbilical	Navel
Ophthalmic	Eye	Visceral	Organ or its covering

Before we move on to look at homeostasis, here's a **summary** of anatomical position:

➢ The body is split into 6 main regions, head, neck, chest (thorax), abdomen, pelvis and limbs.

➢ The anatomical position assumes that the body is in the upright position, facing the observer, feet flat on the floor, arms at the sides, with the palms of the hands turned forward.

➢ Anterior - nearer to the front of the body.

➢ Posterior - nearer to the rear of the body.

➢ Superior - towards the head or upper part of the body

➢ Inferior - away from the head, towards the lower part of the body.

➢ Lateral - further from the midline of the body or structure.

➢ Medial - nearer to the midline of the body or structure

➢ Proximal - nearer to the attachment of a limb to the trunk of the body.

➢ Distal - further from the attachment of a limb to the trunk of the body.

➢ The sagittal plane divides the body or organ into left and right sides.

➢ The frontal plane divides the body or organ into anterior and posterior sections.

➢ The transverse plane divides the body or organ into superior and inferior sections.

➢ An oblique plane passes through the body or organ at an angle.

Homeostasis

The human body is a highly specialized **living** structure. Living beings are distinguished from non-living entities by a number of **life processes**:

1. Metabolism
Chemical processes occur in a living being. All these chemical processes are referred to as metabolism.

2. Responsiveness
Living beings can detect and respond to changes in the internal and external environments.

3. Movement
There is movement in a living body, from single cells, tissues, individual organs and body systems to the whole structure.

4. Growth
The living body grows. It increases in both size and complexity.

5. Differentiation
Cells in the living body develop specialized functions. Specialized cells have structural and functional characteristics that differentiate them from their unspecialized ancestors.

6. Reproduction
The living body can reproduce new cells (for replacement and growth) and totally new individuals.

To **maintain** life (characterized by metabolism, responsiveness, movement, growth, differentiation and reproduction), the body needs a **stable internal environment**. The internal environment is generally defined as the **fluid that surrounds the cells**.

The maintenance of a stable internal environment is called **homeostasis**, literally meaning same/still (homeo/stasis).

For the cells to function efficiently, the composition of the surrounding fluids must be precisely **maintained** at all times. An organism is said to be in **homeostasis** when the internal environment:

✓ contains the optimum concentration of **gases**, **nutrients**, **ions** and **water**
✓ is at the optimum **temperature**
✓ has an optimum **volume** for the health of the cells

Many **external** factors can affect homeostasis and create an **imbalance**. For example, extremes of temperature or lack of oxygen can disturb the internal environment. Any factor that causes an imbalance is referred to as **stress**.

Stress may also originate **internally**. For example a low blood-sugar level, pain or unpleasant thoughts can all affect homeostasis.

When homeostasis is disrupted **illness** may occur. If homeostasis isn't restored, the imbalance may eventually result in **death**. It is clearly important that the body is capable of maintaining a state of homeostasis by **rectifying imbalances** quickly should they occur.

The body's homeostatic responses are regulated by the **nervous system** – in particular the **hypothalamus** - and the **endocrine system**. These systems detect imbalances and then work to return the body to a state of homeostasis as soon as possible. The body works to maintain homeostasis using **feedback systems**.

The nervous system **detects** the state of the internal environment and **feeds back** the information to a **control centre**. The control centre compares the information received to the norm and decides what action, if any, is required. If action is required, the control centre **sends information** to the part of the body that needs to **respond**. An endocrine gland may be instructed to secrete a hormone to help restore balance, or the nervous system may directly trigger the response. The nervous system then analyses the internal environment again, feeds back, and so the **cyclical process** goes on.

Many body conditions are regulated by feedback systems, e.g. heart rate, breathing rate, blood pressure, blood-sugar level, pH and temperature. In most cases, the response is required to **reverse** the situation. For example, if the blood pressure is detected as being too **high**, the feedback system responds by bringing about the necessary changes to **reduce** it. When the response reverses the original stimulus, the system is known as a **negative feedback** system. Negative feedback systems tend to regulate conditions that require frequent monitoring and adjustment.

Sometimes the feedback system **increases** the original stimulus. This is called a **positive feedback** system, but there are fewer examples.

One example of a positive feedback system is the control of contractions during labour. When labour begins, the stretching of the uterus causes the hormone oxytocin to be released into the blood. The oxytocin causes the uterus to contract, which pushes the baby further down the birth canal. This stretches the uterus further and consequently more oxytocin is secreted causing even stronger contractions.

Here's a **summary** of homeostasis:

➢ Living beings are characterized by metabolism, responsiveness, movement, growth, differentiation and reproduction.

➢ Living cells require a stable internal environment to function efficiently.

➢ The maintenance of a stable internal environment is called homeostasis.

➢ Homeostasis exists when the internal environment; 1) contains the optimum concentration of gases, nutrients, ions and water, 2) is at the optimum temperature and 3) has an optimum volume for the health of the cells.

➢ External and internal stress cause imbalance.

➢ Homeostatic responses are responsible for regulating many vital levels such as blood-sugar, blood pressure, heart rate, breathing rate, temperature and pH.

➢ The body works to maintain homeostasis using feedback systems. The nervous system reports to the control centre. The control centre triggers any necessary response, which may include the secretion of a hormone.

➢ When the response reverses the original stimulus, the system is known as a negative feedback system.

➢ Positive feedback systems are less common than negative feedback systems and increase the original stimulus.

Temperature Control

One of the requirements of homeostasis is for the internal environment to maintain the **optimum temperature**. This is no simple task, but even in extremes of external temperature the body is usually able to maintain an internal body temperature of about **37** degrees Celsius. The body is clearly able to cope with the stress of extreme temperatures.
Let's see how…

To control the internal temperature the body has to be able to both **produce** and **lose** heat.

Most of the heat **produced** by the body comes from the **digestion** of food. Catabolic reactions break down the food and **energy** is released. Some of the energy released during digestion is used to form **adenosine triphosphate** (ATP), the energy carrying molecule, used in every cell to capture and store energy. The rest is released as **heat**.

The rate at which **heat** is produced during the breakdown of nutrients is called the **metabolic rate**. The metabolic rate measured under normal conditions is called the **basal metabolic rate** (BMR). The BMR measures the rate at which the quiet, resting, fasting body breaks down nutrients to release energy. This is effectively the minimum of energy expenditure required to maintain the vital processes.

The metabolic rate is **increased** when food is **ingested**, producing more **heat**. Remember that most of the body's heat is produced during the digestion of food. The other main factors that affect the metabolic rate - and therefore heat production - are listed below:

Exercise
The metabolic rate increases during exercise, so increasing the body temperature. The chemical reactions that occur in the skeletal muscles during exercise are responsible for producing a great deal of heat.

Nervous System
When stressed the nerves release the hormonal neurotransmitter noradrenaline, which increases the metabolic rate.

Hormones
Hormones excreted from the thyroid during stressful situations cause an increase in the metabolic rate, as does the release of adrenaline and noradrenaline from the adrenal glands. Testosterone (a male sex hormone produced in the testes) and growth hormone (produced and released by the pituitary gland) also increase the metabolic rate.

External Temperature

A high external temperature increases the internal body temperature. The higher the internal body temperature, the higher the metabolic rate.

Age

A child's metabolic rate is approximately double that of an elderly person. This is due to the higher number of reactions taking place to facilitate growth.

The heat **produced** in the body must be continuously **removed**. If it isn't, the internal body temperature will increase and homeostasis will be lost. Heat is lost from the body in a number of ways:

1. Radiation

Heat is transferred as infra-red rays from the warmer body to a cooler object (e.g. ceiling, wall or floor), **without physical contact**.

2. Conduction

Heat is lost by conduction when the warmer body comes into **physical contact** with a cooler object (e.g. chair, clothing or air).

3. Convection

Heat is lost by convection when the warmer body comes into contact with a liquid or gas. The substance gets heated by conduction, expands and becomes less dense. The warmed substance then rises and is replaced. The transfer of heat in this way by a moving substance is called convection.

4. Evaporation

Water evaporating from the skin takes much heat with it. Perspiring therefore helps to cool the body.

Ideally, heat produced by the body should **equal** the heat lost. This keeps the body at a **constant** temperature. If more heat is produced than can be lost, the body temperature will rise. Likewise, if more heat is lost than is being produced, the body temperature will fall. Both situations can be harmful.

Homeostatic mechanisms attempt to regulate body temperature, keeping a balance between heat production and heat loss.

The **hypothalamus**, an endocrine gland situated at the base of the brain, is the **control centre** for temperature regulation. It receives information from the **heat receptors**. If the body temperature is too low or too high, nerve **impulses** are sent from the hypothalamus to trigger **responses** that will help to return the body temperature back to normal. Temperature control is a **negative** feedback system.

Physiological responses that may be triggered by the hypothalamus when the body temperature is detected as being too low include:

✓ **Constriction** of the **blood vessels** (vasoconstriction) in the skin. This decreases the flow of warm blood to the skin so reducing heat loss.

✓ **Erection** of the **hairs** on the skin. This traps air that acts as an insulating layer.

✓ Stimulation of the **adrenal glands** to secrete **adrenaline** and **noradrenaline**. These hormones increase the metabolic rate, which consequently increases body temperature.

✓ Increased **muscle tone**. This instigates **shivering**, which increases body heat production.

✓ Stimulation of an increased production of **thyroid hormones**. Thyroid hormones increase the metabolic rate, so raising body temperature.

When the body temperature is too **high**, the hypothalamus triggers responses to increase heat loss. **Blood vessels** in the skin are **dilated** (vasodilation) and the **metabolic rate** and **shivering** are **decreased**. The **sweat glands** are stimulated to produce **perspiration** to increase the amount of heat lost by evaporation.

Here's a **summary** on temperature control:

➢ Maintaining an optimum temperature is a requirement of homeostasis.

➢ To control the internal temperature, the body has to be able to both produce and lose heat.

➢ Most of the heat produced by the body comes from the digestion of food.

➢ The rate at which heat is produced during the breakdown of nutrients is called the metabolic rate.

➢ The metabolic rate measured under normal conditions is called the basal metabolic rate (BMR).

➢ The metabolic rate directly affects temperature. Temperature increases with the metabolic rate.

➢ The main factors that affect the metabolic rate - and therefore heat production – are eating, exercise, age and the release of hormones that affect the metabolic rate.

➢ Ideally, the amount of heat produced by the body should equal the amount of heat lost.

➢ Heat is lost from the body by radiation, conduction, convection and evaporation.

➢ A homeostatic negative feedback system regulates body temperature, keeping a balance between heat production and heat loss.

➢ The hypothalamus is the control centre for temperature regulation.

➢ When the body temperature is too low, the blood vessels of the skin contract, hairs rise, hormones are secreted to increase the metabolic rate, and shivering is induced.

➢ When the body temperature is too high, the blood vessels are dilated, the metabolic rate is decreased and the sweat glands produce perspiration.

Questions (Answers: Page 385)

1. What is the lowest level of structural organization?

2. What term is given to all the chemical reactions that occur in the human body?

3. What is another name for the cell membrane?

4. Fill in the missing word:

    Semi-fluid within the cell membrane that surrounds the organelles is called _____.

5. What name is given to the central part of the cell that contains the chromosomes?

6. What organelle is responsible for producing the majority of the cell's energy-carrying molecule, adenosine triphosphate (ATP)?

    a. mitochondrion
    b. golgi-body
    c. lysosome
    d. ribosome

7. What name is given to the part of the nucleus that functions in the synthesis and storage of ribonucleic acid?

8. How is endoplasmic reticulum described when there are no attached ribosomes?

9. What word is missing from the equation of aerobic cellular respiration?

    Glucose + ? = Energy + Carbon Dioxide + Water

10. True or False?

    The semi-permeable cell membrane allows any substance to freely pass through it.

11. What is defined as the process in which water passes passively through a semi-permeable membrane from the side of low chemical concentration to the side of high chemical concentration?

12.   True or False?

Filtration is not a passive process.

13.   In which of the following processes is extracellular fluid taken into the cell?

        a. phagocytosis
        b. pinocytosis

14.   True or False?

Meiosis produces two identical cells.

15.   How many cells are produced during mitosis?

        a. 1
        b. 2
        c. 3
        d. 4

16.   What happens to the chromosomes prior to mitosis?

        a. they divide into two
        b. they cease to function
        c. they replicate
        d. they align down the centre of the cell

17.   What name is given to the first phase of mitosis?

18.   The second phase of mitosis is metaphase. What happens to the chromosomes during metaphase?

        a. they replicate again
        b. they move to opposite ends of the cell
        c. they align down the centre of the cell
        d. they are divided into two cells

19.   Yes or No?

During anaphase, the third phase of mitosis, the chromatids move to opposite ends of the cell. At this point do the two groups contain identical genetic information?

20. Fill in the missing word:

   During telophase, the _____ membrane forms around each group of chromosomes.

21. Which membrane indents until it finally divides the cytoplasm?

22. What is formed when cells of the same type combine?

23. Which type of epithelium is comprised of only one layer?

   a. simple
   b. compound

24. What type of simple epithelium is shown here?

   a. simple squamous
   b. simple cuboidal
   c. simple ciliated columnar
   d. compound cuboidal

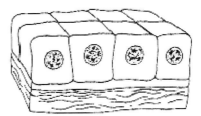

25. Which type of simple epithelium is the thinnest?

   a. squamous
   b. cuboidal
   c. columnar
   d. ciliated columnar
   e. columnar with microvilli

26. Which type of cells found in columnar epithelium secrete mucus?

27. Which type of compound epithelium lines the urinary bladder?

28. Which diagram shows compound stratified squamous epithelium?

A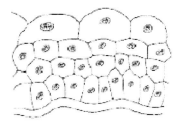

B

C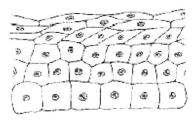

D

29. Which type of epithelium may be ciliated?

    a. squamous
    b. cuboidal
    c. columnar

30. Which type of connective tissue contains cells that are specialized for storing fat?

    a. areolar
    b. adipose
    c. white fibrous
    d. yellow elastic
    e. lymphoid
    f. blood
    g. bone
    h. cartilage

31. Which connective tissue surrounds blood vessels, nerves and muscles and connects the skin to the underlying tissues and muscles?

32. True or False?

Yellow elastic connective tissue is found in tendons and ligaments.

33. Which type of connective tissue contains cells called lymphocytes?

34. Which is the most common type of cartilage?

    a. hyaline
    b. white fibrous
    c. yellow elastic

35. True or False?

    Intervertebral discs are made up of white fibrous cartilage.

36. Which type of membrane does not contain epithelium?

    a. mucous
    b. serous
    c. synovial

37. Which type of membrane lines body cavities that do not open to the exterior and covers many organs?

38. True or False?

    All types of membrane produce a secretion.

39. What type of tissue forms glands and the outer part of the skin, and lines blood vessels, hollow organs and passages that lead out of the body?

40. What type of tissue contains an extracellular matrix?

41. Which type of tissue consists of elongated cells capable of expanding and contracting?

42. Which of the 4 main tissue types is missing from this list?

    epithelial
    connective
    muscle

43. What term is given to a structure that comprises of more than one tissue type?

44. True or False?

    Several related organs, with a common function, make up an organism.

45.   Which region of the body is also referred to as the thoracic area or thorax?

       a. head
       b. chest
       c. abdomen
       d. pelvis.

46.   Which region of the body is immediately below the diaphragm?

       a. head
       b. chest
       c. abdomen
       d. pelvis.

47.   The head is positioned higher than the pelvis. Which statement is correct?

       a. The head is posterior to the pelvis.
       b. The head is anterior to the pelvis.
       c. The head is superior to the pelvis.
       d. The head is inferior to the pelvis.

48.   The sternum (breast bone) runs down the midline of the body. The scapula (shoulder blade) is positioned further away from the midline. Is the scapula lateral or medial to the sternum?

49.   Fill in the missing word:

       The wrist is _____ to the shoulder.

50.   Match the plane with the sections it creates.

       Transverse   Left/Right
       Frontal   Anterior/Posterior
       Sagittal   Superior/Inferior

51.   True or False?

       Homeostasis is maintained by ensuring that the external environment remains constant.

52.   Which two body systems are involved in homeostatic responses?

53. Which feedback system reverses the original stimulus?

    a. negative
    b. positive

54. How is the majority of body heat produced?

55. True or False?

    During the digestion of food, catabolic reactions take place in which the large, complex molecules are broken down. The resulting energy is all released as heat.

56. Fill in the missing word:

    The rate at which heat is produced during the breakdown of nutrients is called the _____ rate.

57. What is defined as "the metabolic rate measured under normal conditions"?

58. True or False?

    Factors that increase the metabolic rate will increase body temperature.

59. Which endocrine gland, situated at the base of the brain, is the control centre for temperature regulation?

60. When does vasodilation within the skin take place?

    a. When the body is too cold.
    b. When the body is too warm.

61. When the body is too cold, which glands are triggered to produce adrenaline and noradrenaline?

This page has intentionally been left blank.

Skeletal System

45

This page has intentionally been left blank.

46

The human skeletal system consists of **206 bones**, **cartilage**, **bone marrow** and the **periosteum** (the membrane around the bones).

Bone is formed by a process called **ossification**. Ossification begins around the 6th week of embryonic life and continues throughout adulthood. The embryonic skeletal framework consists of fibrous connective tissue. The ossification process creates spaces in this tissue and then deposits **calcium** and other **mineral salts**.

The skeleton is divided into the **axial skeleton**, consisting of the skull, spine, ribcage and the sternum (breast bone), and the **appendicular skeleton**, consisting of the shoulders, arms, hands, pelvis, hips, legs and feet.

The skeleton has a number of functions:

✓ It **supports** and **shapes** the body (we would be very floppy without it).

✓ It provides **fixation points** for the muscles and tendons to facilitate **movement**.

✓ It **protects** internal organs and delicate tissues.

✓ The **red marrow** in the bones produces **new blood cells**.

✓ The **yellow marrow** in the bones consists of fat, which is used as an **energy store**.

✓ The bones **store minerals** – especially calcium and phosphorous - that can be released when required.

We'll take a quick look now at the anterior and posterior views of the skeleton. We will be looking at various parts of the skeleton in detail later, but the next two pages allow you to preview the skeletal structure.

Anterior View of Skeleton

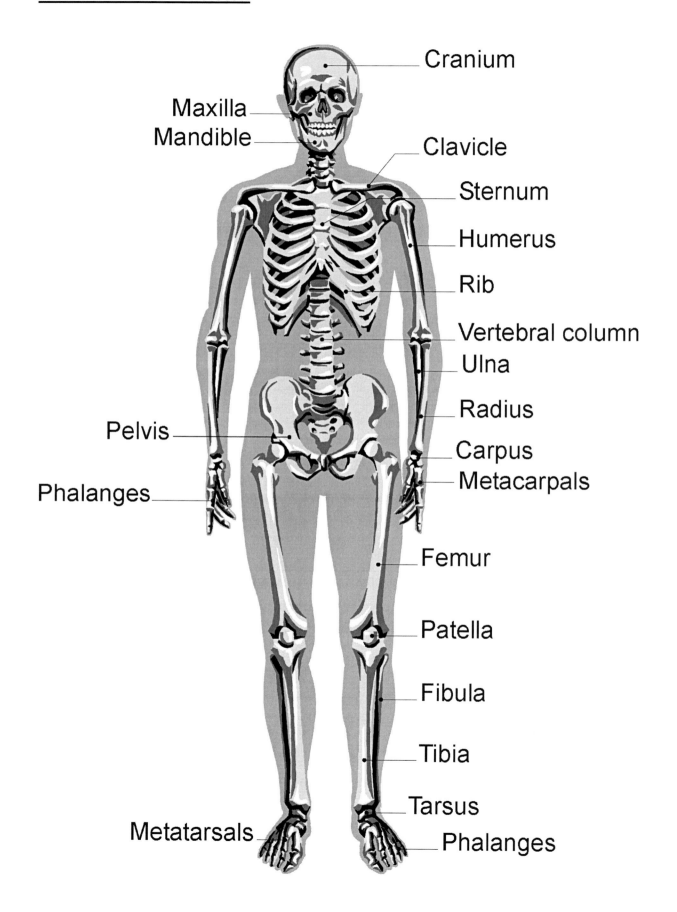

Cranium

Maxilla

Mandible

Clavicle

Sternum

Humerus

Rib

Vertebral column

Ulna

Radius

Pelvis

Carpus

Metacarpals

Phalanges

Femur

Patella

Fibula

Tibia

Tarsus

Metatarsals

Phalanges

Posterior View of Skeleton

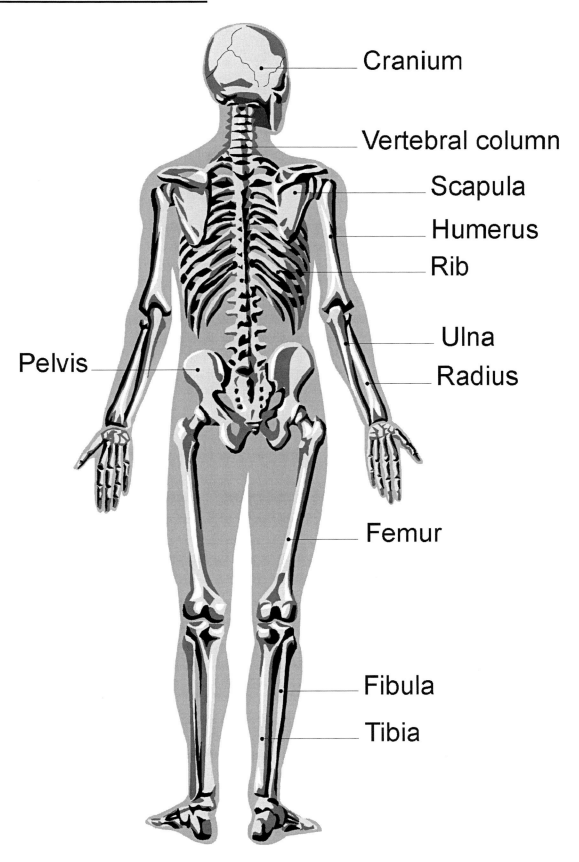

Cranium

Vertebral column

Scapula

Humerus

Rib

Ulna

Radius

Pelvis

Femur

Fibula

Tibia

For the skeletal structure to be able to support the body and facilitate movement, the bones in the body have to be **attached**. The point at which two or more bones articulate (meet) is called a **joint**. Muscles, tendons and ligaments all have a part to play in enabling the joints to be strong and moveable.

The impetus for any movement is derived from the **contraction** of a **muscle**. However muscles rarely connect directly to the bones – most muscles are connected to the bones by **tendons**. Tendons are comprised of strong, almost inelastic **white fibrous connective** tissue and vary in length and thickness. When a muscle contracts it pulls on its tendon. The tendon then pulls on the bone to which it is attached to cause the bone to move at the joint.

Ligaments are also made of **white fibrous connective** tissue and are **silvery** in appearance. They join bone to bone to **strengthen**, **support** and **protect joints**. They hold the bones together to prevent dislocation but stretch slightly to allow movement. Ligaments are thicker at the joints that require the most strength and support (e.g. the hip) but are thinner and less abundant in joints that require a lot of movement (e.g. the shoulder).

Before we look at individual bones and joints, let's look at the **general structure** of a typical bone and the **components** of bone tissue.

Bone Structure

To describe the general structure of a bone, we'll look at the humerus (shown here). The humerus connects the shoulder to the elbow.

Bones are categorized according to their shape (see Classification of Bones). The humerus is defined as a **long bone** because its length is greater than its width. Let's take a look at the structure of a long bone.

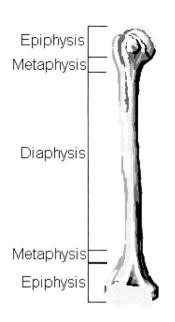

Epiphysis
Metaphysis
Diaphysis
Metaphysis
Epiphysis

The main parts of the long bone are labelled.

Before we go any further, notice that all the main parts of the bone shown here finish with the letters '**physis**', meaning **growth**. Remember this and the terms will not seem so unfriendly and the spelling becomes easier.

The main **shaft** of the bone is the **diaphysis** (dia- = through). There is a tunnel that runs through the diaphysis called the **medullary** or **marrow cavity**. This contains fatty **yellow** bone marrow.

The lining of the medullary cavity is called the **endosteum**.

The area at each **end** of the bone is called the **epiphysis** (epi- = above).

The diaphysis and the epiphyses are joined by an area of bone called the **metaphysis** (meta- = behind). This is the growing area of the bone.

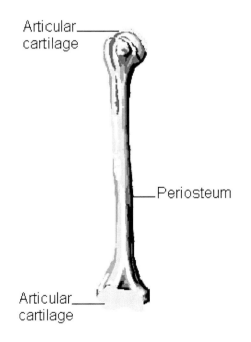

Articular cartilage
Periosteum
Articular cartilage

The epiphyses are covered by **articular (hyaline) cartilage**. Articular cartilage is a **gristly** connective tissue. It is composed of chondrocytes (cartilage cells) and a dense network of fibrous collagen and elastic fibres in a jelly-like substance. This cartilage **reduces friction** and acts as a **shock absorber**.

The outer membrane of the bone is called the **periosteum**. The periosteum surrounds the outside surface of the bone that is not covered by cartilage. It is composed of **fibrous** connective tissue and contains **blood** vessels, **lymphatic** vessels and **nerves**.

The vessels and nerves pass into the bone through holes called **Volkmann's (or perforating) canals**. The periosteum is essential for bone **growth**, **repair** and **nutrition**. It is also the part of the bone to which muscles, ligaments and tendons **attach**.

Bone Tissue

Bone is a **connective tissue**. It consists of widely **separated cells** within a **matrix**. The matrix consists of approximately 25% **water**, 25% **protein** and 50% **mineral salts**.

The mineral salts **crystallize** in the collagen (a protein) fibres of the matrix, hardening the tissue. This process is called **calcification**. The hardness of the bone depends on this, but the presence of the collagen fibres allows the bone to be pliable and prevents it from being too brittle.

There are 4 types of bone cell within the matrix:

1. Osteoprogenitors

These cells are **unspecialized**. They can divide mitotically to develop into **osteoblasts**. Osteoprogenitor cells are found in the inner portion of the periosteum, endosteum and in the canals in the bone that contain blood vessels.

2. Osteoblasts

These are the cells that **form bone**. They **secrete** collagen and other organic components needed to build it. They are located on the surface of bone. As they surround themselves with matrix materials they become osteocytes.

3. Osteocytes

These are the **principal bone cells**, derived from osteoblasts. Osteocytes do not secrete matrix materials. They maintain the **cellular activities** of the bone tissue.

4. Osteoclasts

It is believed that osteoclasts develop from **monocytes**, a type of white blood cell (see Cardiovascular System). Osteoclasts play a part in the **re-absorption** of bone. This is a necessary function for growth and repair.

Bone Types

There are two types of bone tissue, compact and spongy. Let's look at them now.

Compact Bone

As the name suggests, **compact** bone tissue contains **few spaces**. It forms the **external** layer of all bones in the body and the **diaphysis** (shaft) of long bones. Compact bone tissue is strong, providing **protection** and **support**.

In compact bone tissue, canals run **longitudinally** through the bone. These are called **Haversian (or central) canals**. Blood vessels run through the Haversian canals, connecting with those that penetrate the bone laterally through the Volkmann's canals.

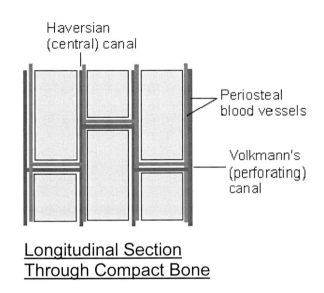

Longitudinal Section
Through Compact Bone

Hard, calcified matrix called **lamellae** form concentric circles around the Haversian canals. Between the lamellae there are spaces called **lacunae**. These contain **osteocytes**. Minute canals called **canaliculi**, filled with extracellular fluid, radiate from the lacunae. The canaliculi contain finger-like projections from the osteocytes. Each Haversian canal with its lamellae, lacunae, osteocytes and canaliculi forms an **osteon**. Osteons are characteristic of adult compact bone.

Cross-Section
Through An Osteon

The vast network of longitudinal and lateral canals that runs through compact bone provides the vascular route for nutrients and oxygen to reach the osteocytes and wastes to be removed.

Spongy Bone

Spongy bone is also called **cancellous** bone. During the ossification process, spongy bone is the **forerunner** of most **compact** bone.

In long bones, spongy bone forms the **epiphyses** and **metaphyses**. It is also the main component of **short** bones, **flat** bones, **irregularly shaped** bones and **sesamoid** bones (see Classification of Bone).

Spongy bone does not contain osteons. Its structure is more **irregular**. The bone tissue is arranged in an **interlacing network**. This network consists of **plates** of lamellae, lacunae and canaliculi called **trabeculae**. In some bones, **red bone marrow** is located in the spaces formed by the meshwork.

Spongy bone does not have the extensive vascular network present in compact bone. Like compact bone, the **osteocytes** are located in the **lacunae**. However, as they are not so deeply buried in spongy bone, they receive their nutrients directly from the blood circulating through the medullary (or marrow) cavities.

Bone Growth

Bone growth is vital to development and repair. Bone grows both in length and in diameter but growth is usually complete by about the age of 25. We'll look at the longitudinal growth of bone first.

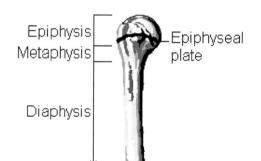

During times of bone growth four layers of tissue, collectively called the **epiphyseal plate**, run across the epiphysis.

The activities of the epiphyseal plate enable the bone to extend in length.

The **cartilage** cells on the **epiphyseal side** of the epiphyseal plate divide **mitotically**. These chondrocytes **mature** and **calcify**. Calcified cartilage forms the layer of the epiphyseal plate on the diaphysis side.

Under the influence of osteoclasts and osteoblasts, the calcified cartilage is replaced by bone in the **metaphysis**. The metaphysis is therefore the growing area of the bone. The bone produced is initially spongy but later the outer regions are **reorganized** into **compact** bone.

The mitotic division of cartilage cells, to **replace** those that are forming bone, maintains the thickness of the epiphyseal plate. When the cartilage cells stop dividing, bone growth stops. All the cartilage cells of the epiphyseal plate are replaced by bone and the remaining structure is called the **epiphyseal line**.

Bones increase in **diameter** as they extend in length. **Osteoclasts destroy** the bone on the **inside** of the medullary cavity. At the same time, **osteoblasts** from the periosteum **add** new bone to the **outer** surface of the bone.

Some skeletal characteristics are **inherited** but **diet** plays a part in maintaining healthy bones. A balanced diet containing minerals such as calcium and phosphorous promotes strong bones, and Vitamin D is required for calcium to be successfully absorbed from the blood and stored in the bones. Growth and development are also affected by **hormones** - see Endocrine System.

Classification of Bone

As we mentioned earlier, bones are classified by shape. So far we have concentrated on the long bone but there are 5 main bone types - long, short, flat, irregular and sesamoid.

Long Bones
Long bones have a greater length than width and have a shaft. They are slightly curved and consist mostly of compact bone.

For example: the femur (thigh bone), tibia and fibula (bones in the lower leg), humerus (bone in the upper arm), ulna and radius (bones of the forearm) and the phalanges (fingers and toes).

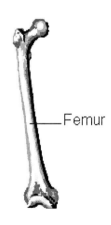
Femur

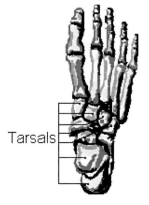
Tarsals

Short Bones
Short bones are nearly equal in length and width. They consist of spongy bone except for the thin outer layer of compact bone.

For example: carpals (bones of the wrist) and tarsals (bones of the ankle).

Flat Bones

As the name suggests, these are flat. They are composed of 2 layers of compact bone sandwiching a layer of spongy bone.

For example: cranial bones (bones that make up the skull), sternum (breast bone), ribs and scapula (shoulder blade).

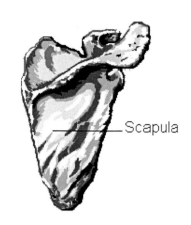
Scapula

Irregular bones

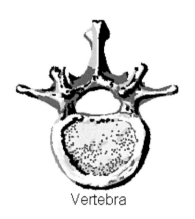
Vertebra

These have complex shapes and vary in the quantities of compact and spongy bone present.

For example: the vertebrae (bones of the vertebral column).

Sesamoid Bones

Sesamoid bones are small rounded bones found in some **tendons** as they cross the joint. They enable the tendon to **move smoothly** over certain bones, so preventing damage.

For example: the patella (knee cap) keeps the tendon of the anterior thigh muscle in place when the knee is bent. Sesamoid bones consist of spongy bone except for the outer layer. They tend to be tiny and are most common in the hands and the feet.

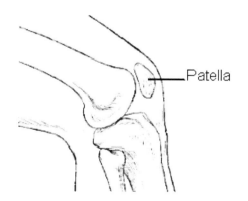
Patella

Before we move on and look at individual bones and consider the types of joint, we'll take a look at the structure that is central to the whole system – the vertebral column.

Vertebral Column

Posterior   Anterior

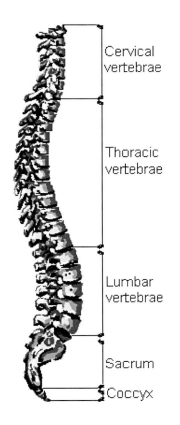

Cervical
vertebrae

Thoracic
vertebrae

Lumbar
vertebrae

Sacrum

Coccyx

The **vertebral column** (spine) runs from the base of the cranium (skull) down through the centre of the skeleton. The vertebral column is strong and yet it can bend forwards, backwards and to either side. It can also rotate. This mobility is possible as the adult vertebral column is made up of a series of **26** individual bones, or **vertebrae**, separated by rings of cartilage called **intervertebral discs**.

The vertebral column has **five** main areas as shown here.

The structure of the vertebrae in each area is slightly different but all have similar features.

Let's look at the structure of a typical vertebra.

This is a superior view of a typical vertebra.

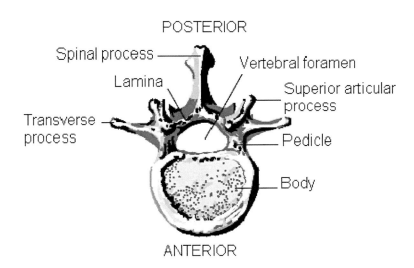

POSTERIOR

Spinal process — Vertebral foramen

Lamina — Superior articular process

Transverse process — Pedicle

— Body

ANTERIOR

The **body** of the vertebra is **thick** and **disc** shaped. The body is the weight bearing part of the vertebra and it **contacts** on either side with **the intervertebral discs**.

The **spinal cord** runs through the **gap** in the center of the vertebra. This gap is called the **vertebral foramen.** The **laminae** and the **pedicles** make up the bony **vertebral arch** that surrounds the spinal cord.

The **spinal process** and the 2 **transverse processes** all provide points of attachment for **muscles**. Each vertebra has 4 **articular processes**, 2 superior and 2 inferior (only visible from an inferior aspect), that form joints with the neighbouring vertebrae. The 4 articulating surfaces are called **facets**.

The vertebral column has 5 main areas:

Cervical Vertebrae:

The **7 cervical** vertebrae are in the **neck**. The top cervical vertebra (C1) is called the **atlas**, which permits the nodding movement. The second (C2) is the **axis**. The joint between the atlas and the axis is a pivot joint, allowing the head to rotate from side to side. The remaining 5 cervical vertebrae (C3 – C7) are typically structured as shown here. Cervical vertebrae are smaller than thoracic vertebrae but their vertebral arches are larger. Each transverse process has a gap called a **transverse foramen** through which the vertebral artery, vein and nerve pass.

Thoracic Vertebrae:

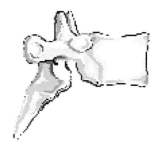
The **12 thoracic** vertebrae (T1 - T12) are located in the **chest area**. They are larger and stronger than the cervical vertebrae and their spinal and transverse processes are longer. Each thoracic vertebra articulates with a pair of **ribs**.

Lumbar Vertebrae:

The **5 lumbar** vertebrae (L1 – L5), located in the **lower back**, are the **largest** and the **strongest**. Their various projections are short and thick. The spinal process is nearly straight.

Sacrum:

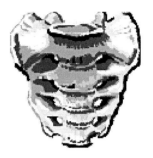

The **sacrum** is a **triangular bone**. It is formed by the **fusion** of **5 sacral** vertebrae (S1 – S5), which gradually occurs usually between the ages of 16 and 25. The sacrum provides a strong base for the vertebral column.

Coccyx:

The **coccyx** is a **triangular bone** at the very **tail** of the vertebral column. It is formed by the fusion of the **4 coccygeal** vertebrae (Co1 – Co4). This fusion usually occurs between the ages of 20 and 30.

The vertebrae, along with other structures such as ligaments, fat and fluid, protect the **spinal cord**.

The spinal cord is a mass of **nerve tissue** from which **31 pairs** of spinal nerves originate and then run to all parts of the body. For more details, see the Nervous System section.

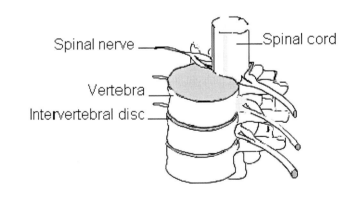

Let's now look at the skeletal structure in more detail.

Skeletal Structure

We will be looking at the following bones in detail:

Area	Bones
Skull and Face	frontal, parietal, temporal, occipital, zygomatic, sphenoid, ethmoid, nasal, maxilla, mandible
Shoulder Girdle	clavicle, scapula
Vertebral Column	cervical, thoracic, lumbar, sacral and coccygeal vertebrae
Thorax	ribs, sternum
Upper Limb	humerus, ulna, radius, carpals, metacarpals, phalanges
Lower Limb	femur, tibia, fibula, patella, tarsals, metatarsals, phalanges 4 arches of the foot.
Pelvic Girdle	ilium, ischium, pubis

Skull and Face

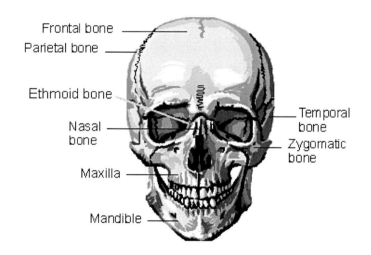

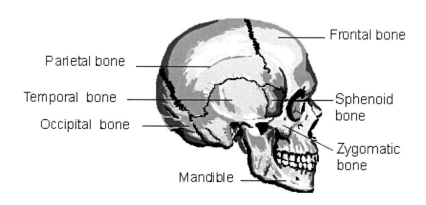

Ethmoid – One light bone located in the anterior part of the cranial floor between the orbits. It is a major supporting bone in the nasal cavity.

Frontal – The one bone that forms the forehead and the upper part of the eye sockets. It contains the two frontal sinuses, one above each eye near the midline.

Mandible – The one bone of the lower jaw. It is the only moveable bone of the skull.

Maxilla – Two fused bones that form the upper jaw and support the teeth. Each contains a maxillary sinus that empties into the nasal cavity.

Nasal bone – Two bones that make up part of the bridge of the nose.

Occipital – One bone that forms the posterior part and base of the cranium.

Parietal – Two bones that form the upper sides and the posterior roof (crown) of the cranial cavity.

Sphenoid – One wedge-shaped bone that lies in the middle part of the base of the skull. It is known as the "keystone" of the cranial floor because it articulates with the other cranial bones.

Temporal – Two bones that form the inferior sides (temples) of the cranium and the cranial floor.

Zygomatic – Two bones that form the cheeks.

Shoulder Girdle

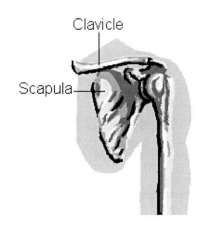 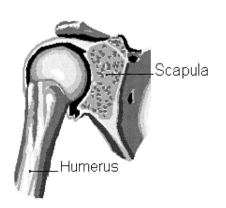

Clavicle – Long bone, commonly called the collar bone. It articulates with the sternum and the scapula.

Humerus – The long bone of the upper arm. It articulates with the scapula at the shoulder and the ulna and radius at the elbow.

Scapula – Large, triangular flat bone, commonly called the shoulder blade. It articulates with the clavicle and the humerus.

Vertebral Column – See Page 57

Thorax

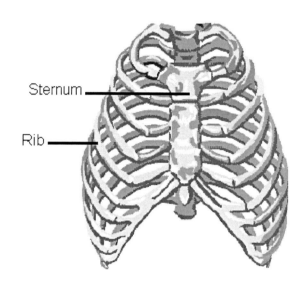

Sternum

Rib

Rib – One of the 12 pairs of bones that make up the thoracic cavity. Each pair articulates posteriorly with the corresponding thoracic vertebra. Anteriorly, the top 7 pairs attach to the sternum and are referred to as "true" ribs. The remaining 5 pairs are called "false" ribs.

The top 3 pairs of false ribs attach indirectly to the sternum via cartilage and rib pair 7. The bottom 2 pairs do not attach to the sternum at all and are called "floating" ribs.

Sternum – Flat bone, commonly called the breast bone. The sternum articulates with the clavicles and the 7 pairs of "true" ribs.

Pelvic Girdle

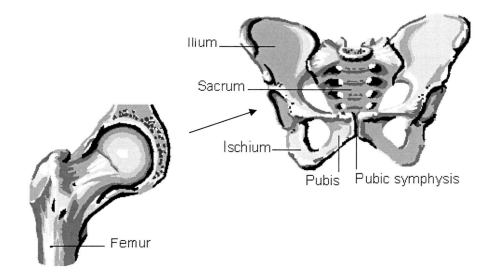

Femur – The longest, heaviest and strongest bone in the body, commonly called the thigh bone. It articulates with the pelvis, tibia and patella.

Ilium – The largest of the 3 main pelvic bones. The ilium, ischium and pubis fuse to form the innominate bone. The 2 innominate bones join anteriorly at the pubic symphysis and posteriorly at the sacrum to form the pelvic girdle.

Ischium – Forms the posterior part of the pelvis.

Pubic symphysis - The slightly moveable cartilaginous joint between the anterior surfaces of the innominate bones.

Pubis – Forms the anterior part of the pelvis.

Sacrum - A triangular bone formed by the fusion of 5 sacral vertebrae (S1 - S5).

Upper Limb - Elbow

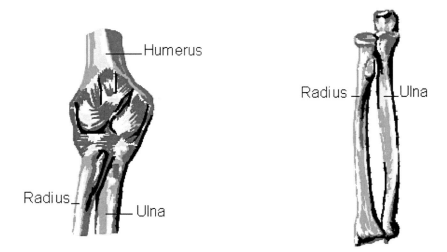

Humerus – The long bone of the upper arm. It articulates with the scapula at the shoulder and the ulna and radius at the elbow.

Radius - Long bone of the forearm that articulates with the wrist on the thumb (lateral) side. It is shorter than the ulna and articulates with the humerus at the elbow.

Ulna – Long bone of the forearm that articulates with the wrist on the little finger (medial) side. It is longer than the radius and articulates with the humerus at the elbow.

Upper Limb – Wrist and Hand

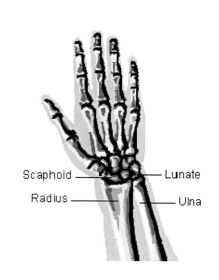
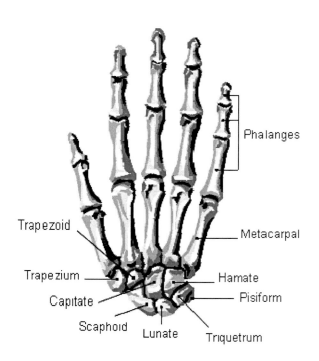

Carpal – One of the 8 small bones (trapezoid, trapezium, capitate, scaphoid, lunate, triquetrum, pisiform and hamate) called the carpals that make up the wrist (carpus).

Metacarpal – One of the 5 long bones that make up the hand. They articulate with the fingers and the wrist.

Phalanges – The 14 bones that make up the fingers and thumb. There are 3 phalanges in each finger and 2 phalanges in the thumb.

Radius - Long bone of the forearm that articulates with the wrist on the thumb (lateral) side. It is shorter than the ulna and articulates with the humerus at the elbow.

Ulna – Long bone of the forearm that articulates with the wrist on the little finger (medial) side. It is longer than the radius and articulates with the humerus at the elbow.

Lower Limb- Knee

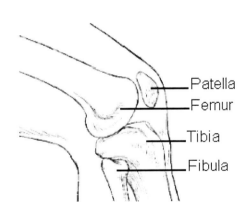
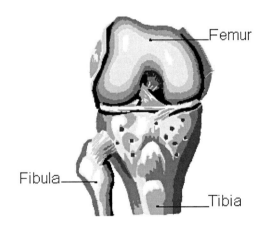

Femur – The longest, heaviest and strongest bone in the body, commonly called the thigh bone. It articulates with the pelvis, tibia and patella.

Fibula – The smaller of the two bones in the lower leg. It is situated on the lateral side of the tibia and articulates with the tibia and the lateral part of the ankle.

Patella – A sesamoid bone, commonly called the knee cap. It stabilizes and protects the knee joint.

Tibia – The larger of the two bones in the lower leg, commonly called the shin. It is the medial bone and bears most of the weight. It articulates with the femur, fibula and the tarsals (bones of the ankle).

Lower Limb – Ankle and Foot

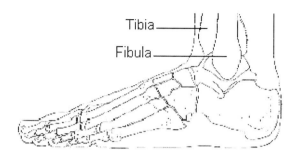

Tibia – The larger of the two bones in the lower leg, commonly called the shin. It is the medial bone and bears most of the weight. It articulates with the femur, fibula and the tarsals (bones of the ankle).

Fibula – The smaller of the two bones in the lower leg. It is situated on the lateral side of the tibia and articulates with the tibia and the lateral part of the ankle.

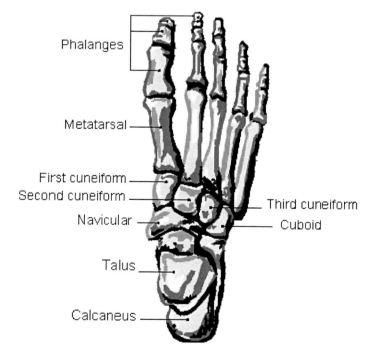

Tarsal - One of the 7 small bones (first cuneiform, second cuneiform, third cuneiform, navicular, talus, calcaneus and cuboid) called the tarsals that make up the ankle (tarsus).

Metatarsal - One of the 5 long bones that make up the foot. They articulate with the toes and the ankle.

Phalanges - The 14 bones that make up the toes. There are 3 phalanges in each toe except for the big toe which has only 2.

Lower Limb – Arches of the Foot

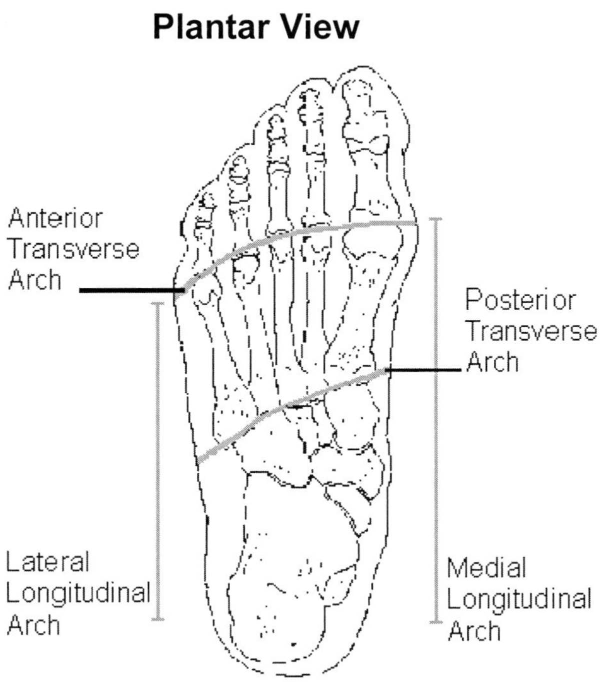

Plantar View

The bones of the foot are arranged into **arches**. These arches enable the foot to be able to **support** the weight of the body, **distribute** the **weight** over the foot, and provide leverage while walking. The arches are maintained by **ligaments** and **muscles**. The four main arches are shown here.

Anterior Transverse Arch

Posterior Transverse Arch

Lateral Longitudinal Arch

Medial Longitudinal Arch

Anterior transverse arch – Runs across the anterior end of the metatarsals.

Lateral longitudinal arch – On the little-toe side of the foot. It runs from the calcaneus to the anterior end of the metatarsals.

Medial longitudinal arch – The highest arch on the big-toe side of the foot. It runs from the calcaneus to the anterior end of the metatarsals.

Posterior transverse arch - Runs across the posterior end of the metatarsals.

Joints

The skeleton provides a strong structure to support the body, but it also facilitates **movement**. The skeleton provides the site of **attachment** for muscles and tendons. The contraction of the muscles is therefore able to create skeletal movement.

Movement occurs at the **joints**. The structure of the joint will determine the movement permitted. The main movements are:

Gliding – the simplest movement where the bones can only move side to side and back and forth (e.g. the movements that occur between the carpals and between the tarsals).

Flexion – when the angle between the articulating bones decreases (e.g. when the elbow is bent to pull the forearm up towards the upper arm).

Extension – when the angle between the articulating bones increases (e.g. when a bent arm is straightened).

Abduction – when the bone is moved away from the midline (e.g. moving the leg out to the side).

Adduction – when the bone is moved towards the midline (e.g. moving a leg that is out to the side back to the normal position).

Rotation – when the bone moves in a single plane around its longitudinal axis (e.g. turning the head from side to side as if indicating "no").

A **combination** of these movements can create others. For example, a combination of flexion, extension, abduction and adduction can create a circular movement. This circular movement is called **circumduction**.

Here are a few more specific terms for movements that the elbow and ankle joints enable:

Supination - a rotational movement of the forearm in which the palm of the hand is moved to face the anterior (e.g. as in the anatomical position or as when waving) or upward.

Pronation - a rotational movement the forearm to turn the palm of the hand to face the posterior (e.g. a 180 degree anti-clockwise rotation of the right arm from the anatomical position or rotating the forearm in front of the face to look at the palm) or downward.

Eversion - the movement of the sole of the foot outward at the ankle joint.

Inversion - the movement of the sole of the foot inward at the ankle joint.

Dorsiflexion - the movement of the foot in the direction of the upper surface, i.e. pulling the foot up to lessen the angle between the top of the foot and the shin.

Plantar flexion - the movement of the foot in the direction of the plantar surface (sole), i.e. stretching the foot out, increasing the angle between the top of the foot and the shin.

We will be looking at the muscles that enable these movements in the Muscular System.

Classification of Joints

There are many different types of joint in the body. Joints can be classified either by their **structure** or by the type of **movement** they allow.

Structurally a joint can be classified as:

1. Fibrous, when there is no cavity between the bones and the bones are held together by fibrous connective tissue.

2. Cartilaginous, when there is no cavity between the bones and the bones are held together by cartilage.

3. Synovial, when there is a joint cavity and the bones are surrounded by a fluid-filled capsule.

Functionally, there are again 3 classifications of joint - **immovable**, **slightly movable** and **freely movable**.

We'll look at some examples of joints under these functional headings, but we'll also give you their structural classification.

1. Immovable Joints

As the name suggests, there is no freedom of movement between bones at an immovable joint.

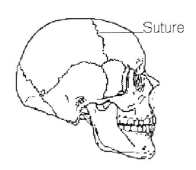

Fibrous, immovable joints exist between the bones of the **cranium**. Here the irregular bones are held together by fibrous connective tissue. The interlocking of the bones strengthens the joints. These joints are also called **sutures**.

2. Slightly Movable Joints

There are 2 types of slightly movable joint:

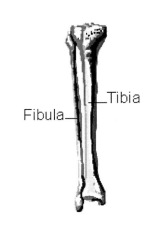

Syndesmosis
A syndesmosis is a **fibrous** joint that has more connective tissue than in an immovable joint to allow a **little** movement. An example of a syndesmosis is the distal joint between the tibia and fibula, the two long bones in the lower leg.

Symphysis

A symphysis is a **cartilaginous** joint, for example the intervertebral joints (between the vertebrae). A symphysis also exists in the pelvis. The joint is called the pubic symphysis.

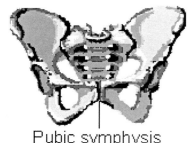

Pubic symphysis

3. Freely Movable Joints

This last functional classification of joints encompasses a **variety** of joints that give the skeleton considerable **flexibility** but they all have some similar features.

The shoulder, shown here, is an example of a freely movable joint. We'll look at it to illustrate the general characteristics of this joint type.

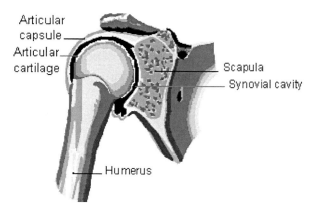

Freely movable joints are characterized by having a **space** between the bones. The bone ends are protected by **articular (hyaline) cartilage** and the bone ends are **surrounded** and held together by the **articular capsule**. The space within this capsule is called the **synovial cavity**. The synovial cavity is filled with a lubricating fluid called **synovial fluid**. Structurally, therefore, all freely movable joints are **synovial joints**.

The articular capsule consists of 2 layers. The inner layer is called the **synovial membrane**, which secretes the nourishing and lubricating **synovial fluid**.

The outer layer of the articular capsule is **fibrous**. This fibrous layer has to be flexible enough to allow the movement, but strong enough to resist dislocation. In some joints this layer consists of bundles of dense, parallel fibres called **ligaments**. Ligaments add strength to the joints.

Although called freely movable joints there are **limits** to the possible movement. The most obvious limitation is that other body parts can get in the way! For example you cannot over bend your elbow as your hand hits your shoulder. Structurally, the shapes of the articulating bones and how they fit together, the strength of the joint ligaments and the tension of the surrounding muscle are all limiting factors. Hormones can also affect joint flexibility.

There are 6 types of freely movable joint:

1. Gliding (or plane) joint
2. Hinge joint
3. Pivot joint
4. Ellipsoidal (or condyloid) joint
5. Saddle joint
6. Ball and socket joint

We'll look at each in turn.

1. Gliding (Plane) Joint

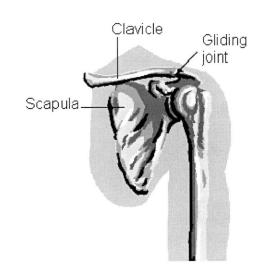

This is the simplest of the freely movable joints. The articulating surfaces of bones at a gliding joint are usually **flat**. Only **side to side** and **back and forth** movements are permitted.

An example of a gliding joint is the joint between the clavicle (collar bone) and the scapula (shoulder blade).

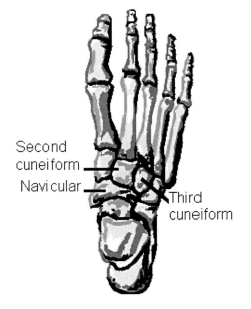

Gliding joints also exist between the navicular and second and third cuneiforms of the tarsus in the foot (shown here) and in some intercarpal joints.

2. Hinge Joint

In a hinge joint, the **convex** surface of one bone fits into the **concave** surface of another. Hinge joints work like a hinge on a door in that the movement is restricted to a **single direction**.

Examples of hinge joints include the knee, elbow and ankle. They allow **flexion** and **extension**.

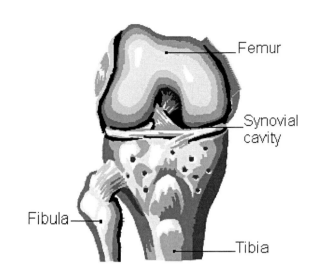

3. Pivot joint

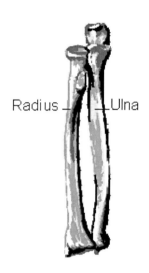

A pivot joint is like a **peg** in a **hole**. A rounded or pointed surface of one bone articulates with a ring formed by another bone and partly by a ligament. The main movement allowed is **rotation**.

A pivot joint exists at the proximal ends of the radius and the ulna. This joint allows the palms to be turned upward or downward. The joint between atlas and the axis is also a pivot joint.

4. Ellipsoidal (Condyloid) Joint

In an ellipsoidal joint, also called a condyloid joint, the oval end of one bone fits into another. It allows **flexion, extension, abduction, adduction** and **circumduction**.

An ellipsoidal joint exists between the radius and the scaphoid and lunate bones of the carpus.

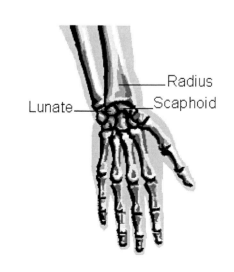

5. Saddle Joint

In a saddle joint, one bone sits over another like a rider in a saddle. Movement is **side to side** and **back and forth** but is freer that in the ellipsoidal joint. **Flexion, extension, abduction, adduction** and **cicumduction** are allowed.

An example is the joint between the trapezium and the metacarpal of the thumb.

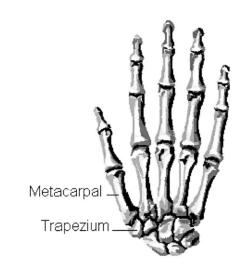

6. Ball and Socket Joint

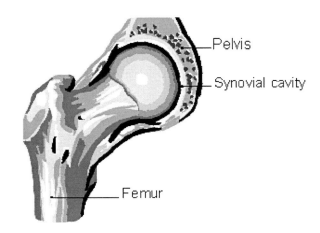

The **hip** (shown here) and the **shoulder** are the only ball and socket joints in the body. They consist of the **ball-shaped end** of one bone fitting into a **cup-shaped depression** of another.

Ball and socket joints give **maximum** movement. They allow **flexion, extension, abduction, adduction** and **rotation**.

Summary

➤ The human skeletal system consists of 206 bones, cartilage, bone marrow and the periosteum (the membrane around the bones).

➤ The skeleton supports, shapes, protects, provides fixation points for the muscles and tendons, produces new blood cells, provides an energy store and stores minerals.

➤ The ends of a long bone are called the epiphyses. The shaft is called the diaphysis. The metaphyses separate the diaphysis from each epiphysis.

➤ Bone consists of osteoprogenitors, osteoblasts, osteocytes and osteoclasts within a water (25%), protein (25%) and mineral salt (50%) matrix.

➤ Compact bone, characterized by osteons, makes up the external layers of all bones and the diaphysis of the long bones.

➤ Spongy (cancellous) bone is the forerunner to compact bone. Spongy bone tissue is arranged in an interlacing network with red bone marrow in the spaces. It is the major component of short, flat and irregularly shaped bones.

➤ The epiphyseal plate is responsible for bone growth. Cartilage cells mature, calcify and are then replaced by bone in the metaphyses.

➤ Bones are classified according to their shape, i.e. long, short, flat, irregular and sesamoid.

➤ The main bones of the skull and face are the frontal, parietal, temporal, occipital, zygomatic, nasal, sphenoid, ethmoid, maxillae and mandible.

➤ The shoulder girdle comprises of the clavicle and scapula.

➤ The vertebral column consists of 7 cervical vertebrae in the neck, 12 thoracic vertebrae in the chest, 5 lumbar vertebrae in the lower back, the sacrum and the coccyx.

➤ The thorax consists of 12 pairs of ribs and the sternum.

➤ The humerus, ulna, radius, carpals, metacarpals and phalanges make up the upper limb.

➢ The femur, tibia, fibula, patella, tarsals, metatarsals and phalanges form the lower limb.

➢ The pelvic girdle is made up of two innominate bones formed by the fusion of the ilium, ischium and pubis. The 2 innominate bones join anteriorly at the pubic symphysis and posteriorly at the sacrum to form the pelvic girdle.

➢ Joints can be classified either according to structure, i.e. fibrous, cartilaginous and synovial, or according to function, i.e. immovable, slightly movable and freely movable.

➢ Freely movable joints are characterized by an articular capsule and a synovial cavity.

➢ Freely movable joints can be gliding (plane), hinge, pivot, ellipsoidal (condyloid), saddle or ball and socket.

Questions (Answers: Page 386)

1.   How many bones are there in the human body?

   a. 106
   b. 206
   c. 306
   d. 406

2.   Which mineral salt has the largest role to play in the process of ossification?

   a. phosphorous
   b. potassium
   c. sodium
   d. calcium

3.   What name is given to the skull, spine, ribcage and sternum?

   a. axial skeleton
   b. appendicular skeleton

4.   Which of the following statements about the functions of the skeletal system is untrue?

   a. The skeleton supports the body and gives it shape.
   b. The skeleton protects internal organs.
   c. The red marrow in the bones consists of fat which is used as an energy store.
   d. The skeleton facilitates movement by providing the fixation point for muscles and tendons.
   e. The bones act as a mineral reservoir.

5.   True or False?

   Tendons attach muscle to bone and ligaments attach bone to bone.

6.   What name is given to the main shaft of the bone?

   a. epiphysis
   b. metaphysis
   c. diaphysis

7.   What is the name of the cavity that runs through the diaphysis?

8.   What name is given to the ends of the bone?

9.   Which area of bone joins the diaphysis to the epiphysis?

10.   What is the name of the connective tissue that covers the epiphyses?

11.   True or False?

The membrane that covers the bone is called the endosteum.

12.   Fill in the missing word:

The blood vessels, lymphatic vessels and nerves in the periosteum enter the bone through _____ canals.

13.   Which of the following makes up about 50% of the matrix of bone tissue?

   a. water
   b. protein
   c. mineral salts

14.   Which are the principal bone cells?

   a. osteoprogenitors
   b. osteoblasts
   c. osteocytes
   d. osteoclasts

15.   From which bone cells are osteocytes derived?

   a. osteoprogenitors
   b. osteoblasts
   c. osteoclasts

16.   Which cells found in bone tissue can re-absorb bone?

   a. osteoprogenitors
   b. osteoblasts
   c. osteocytes
   d. osteoclasts

17.   What name is given to the longitudinal canals that run through compact bone?

   a. Haversian (central) canals
   b. Volkmann's (perforating) canals

18. What is the name of the concentric circles of calcified matrix that form around the Haversian canals?

    a. lamellae
    b. lacunae
    c. canaliculi

19. What type of bone cell is located in the lacunae?

    a. osteoprogenitors
    b. osteoblasts
    c. osteocytes
    d. osteoclasts

20. What is the name of the minute canals that radiate from the lacunae?

21. What name is given to the unit consisting of a Haversian canal with its lamellae, lacunae, osteocytes and canaliculi?

22. What is another name for spongy bone?

23. True or False?

Spongy bone is found in the epiphyses and metaphyses of long bone.

24. What substance fills the spaces between the trabeculae of some spongy bone?

25. Fill in the missing word:

During times of bone growth four layers of tissue, collectively called the epiphyseal _____, run across the epiphysis.

26. True or False?

Cartilage cells on the epiphyseal side of the epiphyseal plate divide mitotically to replace those that form bone on the diaphyseal side of the epiphyseal plate.

27. When mitotic division of the cartilage cells stops, the epiphyseal plate forms bone. What is this structure called?

28.   Which cells destroy the bone that lines the medullary cavity?

      a. osteoprogenitors
      b. osteoblasts
      c. osteocytes
      d. osteoclasts

29.   Which bone type is about equal in length and width?

      a. long
      b. short
      c. flat
      d. irregular
      e. sesamoid

30.   Which bone type is composed of two plates of compact bone with spongy bone in between?

31.   Which bone type is found in tendons?

32.   To which category of bone do vertebrae belong?

33.   What is the name of the main thick, disc shaped, weight-bearing part of a vertebra?

34.   Fill in the missing word:

The laminae and the pedicles form a bony circle called the vertebral _____.

35.   Which bony projection extends to the posterior aspect of the vertebra?

      a. spinal process
      b. transverse process
      c. articular process

36.   Which processes form joints with neighbouring vertebrae?

      a. spinal processes
      b. transverse processes
      c. articular processes

37. Which vertebrae are located in the neck?

    a. cervical
    b. thoracic
    c. lumbar
    d. sacral
    e. coccygeal

38. Where are the 12 thoracic vertebrae located?

    a. lower back
    b. chest
    c. at the base of the vertebral column

39. Which 5 vertebrae are located in the lower back?

40. The area of the vertebral column below the lumbar vertebrae is called the sacrum. How many sacral vertebrae fuse to form this triangular bone?

    a. 2
    b. 3
    c. 4
    d. 5

41. What is the name of the triangular bone that forms the tail of the vertebral column?

42. Which bone is labelled with the letter F?

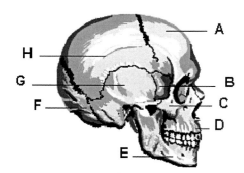

43. Which of the following are all bones of the arm?

    a. femur, tibia, fibula
    b. humerus, tibia, fibula
    c. tibia, ulna, femur
    d. radius, ulna, humerus
    e. ulna, radius, femur

44.   What is the common name for the scapula?

      a. collar bone
      b. thigh
      c. shoulder blade
      d. knee cap
      e. breast bone

45.   How many pairs of ribs are attached either directly or indirectly to the sternum?

      a. 5
      b. 7
      c. 10
      d. 12

46.   Which of the following bones are found in the wrist and hand?

      a. carpals, metacarpals and phalanges
      b. tarsals, metatarsals and phalanges

47.   Which bone of the forearm articulates with the wrist on the lateral (thumb) side?

48.   Which of the following leg bones is located in the thigh?

      a. tibia
      b. fibula
      c. femur

49.   Which arch is labelled with the letter A?

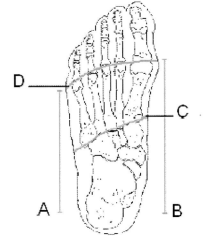

50.   What movement is created when the lower leg is bent up towards the back of the thigh?

51. What movement is created when an arm is moved outwards from the side of the body?

     a. flexion
     b. extension
     c. abduction
     d. adduction
     e. rotation

52. Which type of slightly movable joint is fibrous?

     a. syndesmosis
     b. symphysis

53. What is the name of the capsule that surrounds and binds the ends of the bone at a synovial joint?

54. Which freely movable joints resemble a peg in a hole and allow rotation?

     a. gliding (plane)
     b. hinge
     c. pivot
     d. ellipsoidal (condyloid)
     e. saddle
     f. ball and socket

55. Which is the simplest type of freely movable joint in which the articulating surfaces of the bone are usually flat?

56. Fill in the missing word:

     The elbow, knee and ankle are examples of _____ joints.

57. Name the only two ball and socket joints.

58. Which of these 2 joint types allows the most movement?

     a. ellipsoidal (condyloid)
     b. saddle

Skin, Nails and Hair

This page has intentionally been left blank.

The skin is a part of the **integumentary** system. The integumentary system comprises of the skin and its associated components such as the nails and hair. The skin is one of the largest **organs** of the body, covering the majority of the outside area of the individual. It has many functions. The skin:

✓ provides a **protective barrier** between the inner body and the external environment. It offers the first level of non-specific resistance.

✓ **regulates temperature**. Sweating and increasing the blood flow to the skin cools the body. Decreasing the blood flow to the skin, and raising the hair on the surface of the skin, insulates it. (For more information see Temperature Control.)

✓ provides **sensitivity** via the skin's sensory nerve endings and receptors so that temperature, pressure and pain can be detected. (For more information see Touch.)

✓ allows the **excretion** of water, heat, some toxic waste and small amounts of salt.

✓ allows the **secretion** of sebum

✓ provides a **reservoir of blood** that can be used elsewhere if required.

✓ synthesizes **vitamin D** when stimulated by ultra-violet light.

✓ allows the **absorption** of certain substances, although it is generally impermeable.

The skin is made up of three main layers. The **top** layer of the skin is the **epidermis** (epi- = above, dermis = skin). Under the epidermis is the **dermis**. The deepest part of the skin is the **subcutaneous layer** (sub- = under, cutaneous = pertaining to the skin).

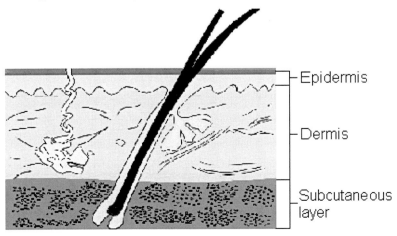

Epidermis

Dermis

Subcutaneous layer

We'll look at each of the layers of the skin, starting with the epidermis.

Epidermis

The epidermis offers the body a **waterproof protective** coating. There are no blood vessels or nerve endings.

The epidermis is composed of **4** types of **cells** and has **5 layers**. This complex cellular structure allows new cells to be continually **produced** to **replace** those that get **worn away** and facilitates the **healing** of damaged skin.

The **new cells** are produced in the **deepest** epidermal layer and then **push up** to the surface. The **top** layer consists of flat, **dead** cells that are continually shed but replaced.

We'll take a look at the 4 cell types first and then discuss the 5 epidermal layers.

The epidermis is composed of **epithelium**. The epidermal cells are **closely packed** and arranged in **layers**. There are 4 types of epidermal cell:

1. Keratinocytes
Keratinocytes make up about **90%** of the epidermis. They produce **keratin**. Keratin is a protein that helps **to waterproof** and **protect** the skin. As cells make their way up through the epidermis, they form more and more keratin. By the time the cells reach the surface of the skin they are completely filled with keratin. This process is called **keratinization**.

2. Melanocytes
Melanocytes make up about **8%** of the epidermis. Melanocytes produce **melanin**. Melanin is a brown-black pigment that contributes to **skin colour**. Melanocytes have long, thin projections that **transfer** granules of **melanin** to the **keratinocytes**.

3. Langerhans cells
Langerhans cells originate in the **bone marrow** and migrate to the epidermis. They play a part in **immune** responses because they have the ability to recognize certain antigens.

4. Merkel cells
Merkel cells are found in the **deepest** layer of the epidermis of **hairless** skin. They make contact with **sensory neurons** and are thought to have a part to play in the sensation of **touch**.

In most areas, the epidermis is about **0.1mm** thick and consists of **4** layers. Where the skin is exposed to the most **friction** (e.g. soles of the feet and palms of the hands) it consists of **5** layers and is **1-2mm** deep.

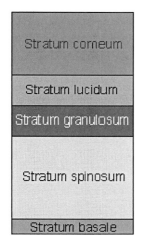

This graphic represents the **5 layers** of the epidermis.

The surface layer is the stratum corneum.

The deepest layer is the stratum basale.

Stratum basale (or stratum germinativum or basal cell layer)
The stratum basale consists of just **1** layer of cells. It contains stem cells, melanocytes and Merkel cells (hairless skin only). The stem cells continually divide to produce **keratinocytes**, which push up towards the surface. Some stem cells migrate into the dermis and form **sweat glands**, **sebaceous glands** and **hair follicles**.

Stratum spinosum (or prickle cell layer)
This layer consists of **8-10** layers of cells, closely packed together. The long, thin projections of **melanocytes** extend among **keratinocytes**. This enables the melanocytes to transfer melanin to the keratinocytes.

Stratum granulosum (or granular layer)
The stratum granulosum consists of **3-5** layers of flattened **keratinocytes**, whose nuclei are in various stages of degeneration. These cells have begun the keratinization process. They contain granules of **keratohyalin**, a compound produced in the first step of keratin formation.

Stratum lucidum (or clear layer)
This layer only exists in places where the skin is **thickest**, such as on the palms of the hands and soles of the feet. It consists of **3-5** rows of clear, flat, dead cells. These cells contain a substance, formed from keratohyalin, which is eventually transformed into keratin.

Stratum corneum (or horny layer)

The top stratum of the epidermis contains **25-30** rows of flat, dead cells. They are completely filled with **keratin**. These cells are continually shed and replaced by cells that are being pushed up from the lower strata. The corneum is a protective barrier against light, heat, bacteria and many chemicals.

<u>Dermis</u>

The **dermis** is the second major layer of the skin. It is situated **under** the epidermis. The dermis is **thicker** than the epidermis, **tough** and **elastic**. It is composed of connective tissue, collagen (a protein) and elastic fibres.

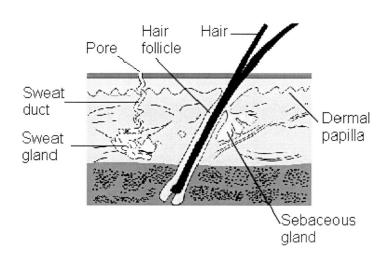

The dermis contains blood vessels, lymph vessels, nerve endings (not shown here), sebaceous (oil) glands, sweat glands and ducts, hair follicles and hairs.

The **upper** portion of the dermis is called the **papillary region**. It consists of connective tissue that contains fine elastic fibres. The papillary region is characterized by small, finger-like projections called **dermal papillae** that indent the epidermis. Dermal papillae can contain loops of **capillaries** and **nerve endings** that are sensitive to touch.

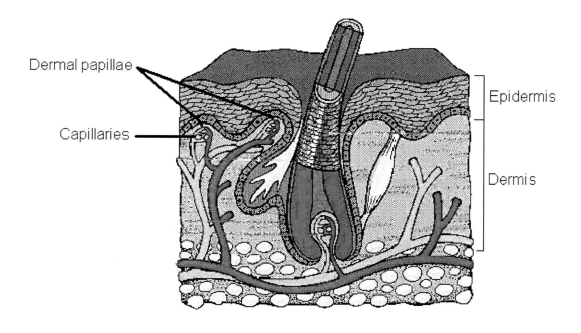

The **lower** portion of the dermis is called the **reticular region**. It contains connective tissue and a network of collagen fibres and coarse elastic fibres. These fibres provide the skin with **strength**, **extensibility** and **elasticity**. The reticular region contains the hair follicles, nerves, sebaceous (oil) glands and ducts, and sweat glands.

Sweat glands play an important role in **temperature control**. They release sweat which removes heat from the body. Sweat, containing a mixture of water, salts, urea, uric acids, amino acids, ammonia, sugar, lactic acid and ascorbic acid, is secreted from the **coiled gland** and travels up the **sweat duct**. When the duct reaches the surface of the epidermis it forms a **pore** from which the sweat is released. There are two types of sweat gland:

Eccrine glands
Most sweat glands are eccrine. Eccrine sweat glands release the sweat **directly** onto the surface of the **skin**. Eccrine sweat glands are distributed throughout the body except for the lips, nail beds and parts of the external genitals. They are most numerous on the palms of the hands, soles of the feet and under the arms.

Apocrine glands
Apocrine glands open onto **hair follicles** and secrete a more viscous secretion than the eccrine glands. They are found mainly under the arms, in the genital areas and on the areolae of the breasts. Apocrine glands begin to function at puberty and are stimulated during emotional stress and sexual excitement.

Subcutaneous Layer

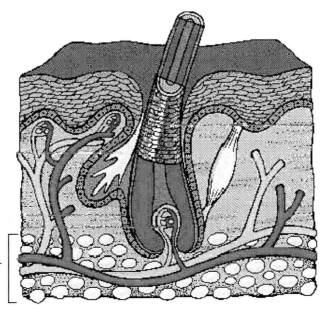

Subcutaneous layer

The **subcutaneous layer** connects the dermis to the underlying tissues (e.g. muscle or bone). It consists mainly of **adipose** and **areolar** tissue. Adipose tissue **insulates**, **protects** and is an **energy store**. Areolar tissue protects, supports and **connects** the skin to the underlying structures.

The subcutaneous layer also contains many **blood vessels**. **Pressure** sensitive **nerve endings** are also located here.

Skin Colour

There are a variety of **skin colours**. Skin colour is affected by the presence of three **pigments** - melanin, carotene and haem.

Melanin is located mostly in the **epidermis**. It varies the skin colour from **pale yellow to black**. The more melanin the melanocytes produce and transfer to the keratinocytes, the darker the skin. Melanin-filled cells can cluster in patches to form **freckles** or, in older people, **liver spots**. Melanin is also a major contributor to the colour of the **hair**.

Melanin absorbs **ultra-violet** (UV) light. When stimulated by UV light, melanin granules in the keratinocytes form **protective shields** over the nuclei, protecting the genetic material from being damaged. Exposure to UV light also **increases melanin production**. This both **darkens** the skin and **further protects** the cells.

Carotene is located mainly in the **dermis**. It is a **yellow-orange** pigment. The less melanin in the epidermis, the more the colour of carotene can be seen.

Haemoglobin is found in red **blood** cells. It contains a **red** pigment called **haem**. As the blood flows through the capillaries in the **dermis**, the red colour can be seen, providing there is not too much melanin in the epidermis.

Skin Health and Ageing

The health and appearance of the skin is affected by diet, lifestyle, environmental factors, skin type and, of course, age.

Diet - A **nutritionally balanced** diet helps the skin to grow and repair and therefore skin condition will be lost if essential nutrients are not available. If the body becomes dehydrated the skin becomes dry and toxins build up and so it is important to drink adequate amounts of **water** and **avoid** the excessive consumption of **alcohol**.

Lifestyle - Like most other parts of the body, the skin will suffer in cases of **sleep** deprivation and excessive **stress**. The skin needs rest to regenerate and excessive tension can cause skin sensitivities and create lines. **Exercise** promotes circulation, increasing the supply of nutrients to the skin. **Smoking** has the opposite effect – it causes vasoconstriction and also releases chemicals that destroy vitamins that are vital to the health of the skin.

Environment - Skin damage can be caused by contact with various **chemicals** (such as detergents). These chemicals can remove the sebum from the skin and so cause dehydration. Skin condition can also be affected by the **climate**, air **pollutants**, and some **medications**. **Ultra-violet radiation** can cause serious skin damage. It can burn, dehydrate and damage the collagen and elastin fibres, resulting in wrinkling and sagging or serious skin conditions including cancer.

Skin Type - The appearance of the skin is affected by the skin type. There are 5 main types:

1. **Dry** - Dry skin is caused by underactive or inactive sebaceous glands. Dry skin usually has a dull appearance and it feels dry and itchy and may also be sensitive.

2. **Oily** - Oily skin is caused by overactive sebaceous glands. The excessive quantity of sebum results in skin that has a greasy, slippery texture. Oily skin appears shiny and frequently has large, clogged pores.

3. **Normal (Balanced)** - In normal, balanced skin, the sebaceous glands produce sebum at a moderate rate, resulting in skin that is not too oily and not too dry. Normal skin looks consistently plump, moist, and vibrant.

4. **Sensitive** - Sensitive skin can be dry, oily or normal. Sensitive skin reacts excessively to environmental conditions and substances that it comes into contact with. When sensitive skin reacts, it becomes sore and may appear flushed.

5. **Combination** - Most people have more than one type skin - even on just one area of the body. Facially, for example, it is quite common to have oily skin around the forehead, nose and chin and normal or dry skin around the cheeks, eyes and mouth.

Age - Sadly, no matter how hard we try, the body shows signs of age and the skin is no exception. Young skin is thicker, smoother, moister and more elastic than mature skin. The skin is constantly ageing, but the effects become more noticeable in the late forties. In older skin, it takes longer for cells to migrate to the surface. Aged skin is less elastic, thinner, drier and is slower to heal. As the skin ages, a number of changes occur:

➤ Collagen fibres decrease in number and elastic fibres lose their elasticity, causing wrinkles and less springy skin.

➤ Langerhans cells decrease in number, reducing immunity.

➤ Sebaceous glands become smaller, leading to drier, broken skin that is more susceptible to infection.

➤ Sweat production decreases, increasing the likelihood of heat stroke.

➤ Melanocytes reduce in number and increase in size, resulting in grey hair and different skin pigmentation.

➤ Subcutaneous fat is lost, causing thinner skin.

➤ Hair and nails grow more slowly.

All good news then!

Nails

Nails are epidermal growths. They are plates of **hard**, **clear**, **keratinized** cells covering and protecting the tips of the fingers and toes. They grow continuously throughout life. As well as **protecting** the digits, they aid **dexterity** by making it easier to handle small objects.

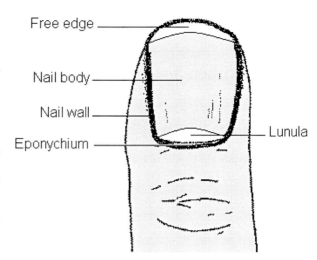

The nail **body** is the portion that is **visible**. Below the nail body is the **nail bed**. The nail bed serves to attach the nail to the underlying tissues.

The **free edge** is the growth that may **extend past** the end of the digit, and the **root** is the part of the nail that is **buried** in the skin.

Skin overlaps at the lateral and proximal edges of the nail to form the **nail walls**. A narrow band of epidermis extends from the proximal nail wall to the base of the nail. This is called the **eponychium**. The eponychium sheds an epidermal layer of skin to the newly formed nail plate. This layer of non-living, almost invisible **stratum corneum** is called the **cuticle**. The eponychium and the cuticle help to prevent harmful substances from getting under the nail. This proximal skin is sometimes called the **mantle**.

The tissue on the lateral sides of the nail is called **paronychium**. This forms the **lateral skin folds**. The longitudinal indentation between the lateral skin folds and the nail forms the lateral **nail grooves** into which the nail appears to be embedded.

The epidermis that is located beneath the nail plate at the junction between the free edge and the skin of the fingertip is called the **hyponychium**.

Most of the nail body appears pink because of the blood following through the capillaries below. There is, however, a whitish semi-circular area called the **lunula**. The lunula appears lighter because the stratum basale under the nail is thicker in this area and blocks the sight of the vascular tissue.

From the diagram on the following page, showing the nail in cross-section, you can see many of the parts of the nail that we have already discussed - free edge, nail body, cuticle and nail root. Notice also the matrix...

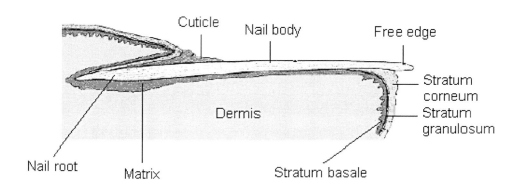

The epithelium under the nail root is the **nail matrix**. Cells undergo **mitosis** in the matrix to create nail **growth**. This area receives a rich blood supply and has nervous connections. The cells created by mitosis differentiate to form nail cells. The cells are pushed forward over the stratum basale. They keratinize and die to form the strong, hard nail.

Nail **growth** is determined by the turnover rate of the **matrix** cells. Nails grow **continually** throughout life but various **factors**, including age (growth slows with age), season (they grow quicker in summer), nutritional state (a poor diet will slow growth), trauma, some medications and various diseases, **affect** the growth **speed**.

The finger itself also affects the nail growth. Generally, the longer the digit the faster the nail grows. The nail on the middle finger therefore grows faster, at about **0.1mm** per day, than the nail on the little finger.

Fingernails grow 3–4 times faster than toenails. It takes about **6 months** for a **fingernail** to grow out, and about **18 months** for a **toenail** to be replaced.

Hair

Hair protrudes from the surface of the **epidermis**. It is an epidermal growth, composed of **dead**, **keratinized** cells.

The primary function of hair - called **pili** - is **protection**. Hair on the head protects the skin from sunlight. Eyebrows and eyelashes protect the eyes, and hair in the nostrils helps to prevent foreign particles from being inhaled. Hair is also **insulating**. When the hairs are raised, more air is trapped providing an insulating layer.

The hair **shaft** is the portion of the hair that **projects** from the skin.

The portion of the hair **below** the skin is called the **root**.

Surrounding the root is the hair **follicle**. The follicle consists of an **external root sheath** and an **internal root sheath**.

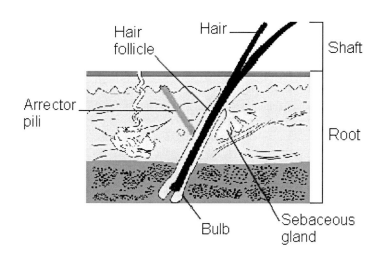

The external root sheath is a downward continuation of the epidermis. The internal root sheath forms a tubular covering between the external root sheath and the hair. The base of each hair follicle is enlarged and layered and is called the **bulb**.

The bulb has an indentation at the bottom called the **papilla** (see graphic below). The papilla contains **areolar** connective tissue. Blood vessels loop into the papilla to supply nutrients to the follicle. The bulb contains a ring of cells called the **matrix**. The cells in the matrix are responsible for the growth of the existing hair and produce new hair by cell division when the older hair is shed. As the cells push up the bulb they quickly fill with **keratin** and die.

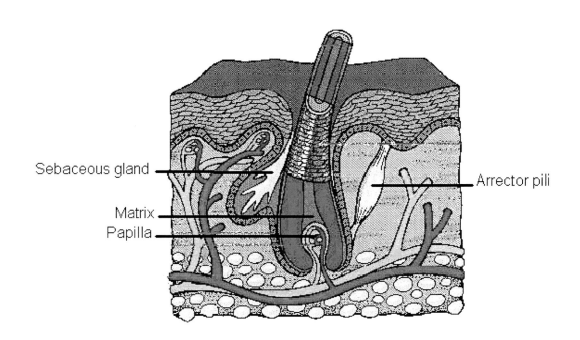

The follicles also have a **nerve** supply. **Root hair plexuses** (see Touch) allow **sensory** information to be received when the hair is moved. Links to the **autonomic nervous system** facilitates the stimulation of the arrector pili muscle by motor neurons. The arrector pili is a **smooth** muscle that attaches to the side of the hair follicle. It contracts when the body is under stress, cold or frightened to pull the hair into an upright position.

A **sebaceous (oil) gland** is also connected to the follicle. The sebaceous glands lie in the dermis and open into the neck of the hair follicles. Sebaceous glands secrete **sebum**. Sebum is a mixture of fats, cholesterol, proteins and inorganic salts that prevent the hair from drying and becoming brittle.

Sebum **moisturises** the skin, **protects** it, **inhibits** the growth of some **bacteria** and **prevents** excessive **evaporation** of water. The vast majority of sebaceous glands are attached to follicles but some secrete directly onto the surface of the skin (e.g. on the lips, the distal end of the penis and the medial pubic labia).

Together, sebum and sweat form a protective barrier referred to as the **acid mantle**.

The **outer** layer of the hair is called the **cuticle**. The cuticle consists of a **single layer** of scale-like heavily keratinized cells that overlap.

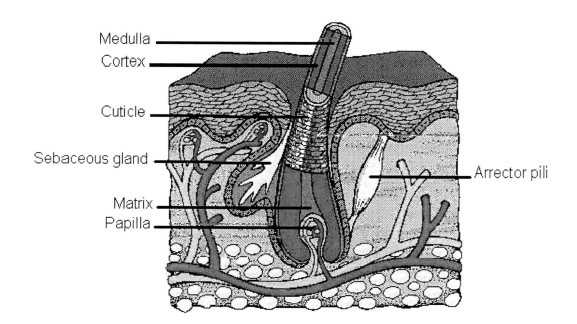

The layer beneath the cuticle is called the **cortex**. The cortex forms the major part of the shaft. The elongated cells contain pigment granules in dark hair but mostly air in white hair.

The **inner** part of the hair is the **medulla**. The medulla consists of loose cells containing pigment granules with much air between the cells. The reflection of light on these air spaces plays a part in determining the colour tone and sheen of the hair. Not all hair contains this inner layer and, when present, it may not run for the full length of the hair.

Hair Types

There are 3 main types of hair:

1. Lanugo

Lanugo hair grows on the body of the developing **foetus**. Lanugo hair is **soft**, **fine** and lacks a medulla. It is usually **shed** about a month before birth, to be replaced by vellus hair.

2. Vellus

Vellus hair is **soft** and **downy**. It covers the **whole body** except for the palms of the hands, soles of the feet, lips and parts of the genitals. Vellus hair tends to **lack pigment** and a **medulla**, has a **shallow follicle** and a bulb that is **not** well **developed**. Hormonal changes can stimulate the development of the follicle and alter the hair produced from the soft, downy vellus to the stronger terminal hair.

3. Terminal

Terminal hair is **longer** and **coarser** than vellus hair and contains **pigmentation**. The follicles are **deeply seated** and the bulb is well **developed**. Terminal hair is found on the scalp, under the arms, in pubic regions, on arms and legs, and makes up the eyebrows and eyelashes. Hormonal influences also cause facial and chest hair in men.

The growth of terminal hair is influenced **hormonally** by **puberty**, which changes hair growth in teenagers, **pregnancy**, during which hair growth may increase on certain areas of the body (particularly the abdomen), and the **menopause**, during which characteristic male hair growth may occur.

As well as hormonal influences, hair growth can also be affected by excessive **stress**, **hereditary factors** (including race), **illness** and some **medications**. Hair loss may take place **topically** (in one place, not generally), due to factors such as skin damage and localised skin conditions.

Although, as we have discussed, the amount of **air spaces** in the hair can affect its colour, **melanin** is primarily responsible for hair colour. It is synthesised by melanocytes in the matrix and is passed to cells in the cortex and medulla. Generally the more melanin the darker the hair, but melanin with more iron and sulphur shows as blond or red hair. As people age, melanin production slows, causing the hair to appear grey. White hair results from the accumulation of air in the medulla.

Hair Growth

It may take a few months to several years for hair to become **fully grown** and then **shed**. Each hair develops at its **own rate** but will be at one of **three stages** of the **hair growth cycle**.

1. Anagen

This is the **active growing** stage. Under **hormonal** stimulation the germinal cells in the **matrix** undergo **mitosis** to create new cells. The cells make their way up the follicle and differentiate to form the hair structure. They also **keratinize** and the hair eventually emerges through the surface of the skin. The anagen stage of growth can last a few months to several years.

2. Catagen

When the hair is fully grown it **no longer requires** its connection to the **papilla** to receive a supply of nutrients. The hair **separates** from the papilla and moves slowly up the follicle. The **follicle shrinks** and some parts of the follicle break down or remain domant until another hair is produced.

3. Telogen

During the final stage of the hair growth cycle, the hair is **shed** from the shortened follicle and the **follicle rests**. This resting stage ends when the follicle is once again activated by hormones, triggering the growth of another hair.

Summary

➢ The skin is one of the largest organs of the body with many functions including protection, sensation and temperature control.

➢ The top layer of the skin is the epidermis.

➢ The epidermis is composed of 4 types of cell - keratinocytes, melanocytes, Langerhans cells and Merkel cells.

➢ The epidermis has 5 strata - basale, spinosum, granulosum, lucidum and corneum.

➢ The middle layer of the skin is the dermis. The upper portion of the dermis is the papillary region. The lower portion is the reticular region.

➢ Eccrine sweat glands secrete sweat through a pore directly onto the surface of the skin. Apocrine sweat glands secrete onto a hair follicle.

➢ The subcutaneous layer joins the dermis to the underlying tissues.

➢ Skin colour is affected by the pigments melanin, carotene and haem.

➢ The health and appearance of the skin is affected by diet, lifestyle, environmental factors, skin type and age.

➢ As skin ages it becomes less elastic, thinner, alters in pigmentation and is slower to heal.

➢ Nails and hair are epidermal growths.

➢ Nails have 3 main areas, the nail body, free edge and root.

➢ Nail cells are created by mitosis in the nail matrix.

➢ Nails grow continually throughout life but the speed of growth is affected by a number of factors such as length of the digit, age, season, nutrition, trauma and disease.

➢ Fingernails grow at about 0.1mm per day.

➢ Fingernails grow 3-4 times faster than toenails.

➢ Hairs grow from follicles.

➢ Follicles indent to form the papilla (the site of vascular connection) and provide the insertion points for the arrector pili muscles.

➢ Sebaceous glands open into the neck of the hair follicles and secrete sebum.

➢ Sebum is a mixture of fats, cholesterol, proteins and inorganic salts that prevent the hair from drying and becoming brittle.

➢ Hairs are comprised of three layers, a cuticle, cortex and (not in all cases) medulla.

➢ The three hairs types are lanugo, vellus and terminal.

➢ The hair growth cycle has three stages - anagen, catagen and telogen.

Questions (Answers: Page 387)

1. True or False?

   The skin is a tissue that covers the majority of the outside area of the individual.

2. Which vitamin is synthesized by the skin?

   a. A
   b. B
   c. C
   d. D

3. True or False?

   The skin has a part to play in protection, sensation and temperature control.

4. What is the top layer of the skin called?

5. Which type of epidermal cell makes up about 90% of the epidermis?

   a. keratinocytes
   b. melanocytes
   c. Langerhans cells
   d. Merkel cells

6. What protein is produced by keratinocytes?

7. Which cells make up about 8% of the epidermis and produce melanin?

8. Where do Langerhans cells originate before they migrate to the epidermis?

9. Which cells are located in the deepest epidermal layer of hairless skin and are thought to function in the sensation of touch?

10. Fill in the missing word:

    The deepest layer of the epidermis is called the stratum _____ .

11.   What type of cell is produced by the stem cells in the stratum basale?

        a. melanocytes
        b. Merkel cells
        c. Langerhans cells
        d. keratinocytes

12.   Which layer of the epidermis contains 8-10 layers of closely packed cells?

        a. stratum corneum (horny layer)
        b. stratum lucidum (clear layer)
        c. stratum granulosum (granular layer)
        d. stratum spinosum (prickle cell layer)
        e. stratum basale (basal cell layer)

13.   In which layer of the epidermis can granules of keratohyalin be seen?

        a. stratum corneum
        b. stratum lucidum
        c. stratum granulosum
        d. stratum spinosum
        e. stratum basale

14.   Which layer of the epidermis only exists where the skin is thick?

        a. stratum corneum
        b. stratum lucidum
        c. stratum granulosum
        d. stratum spinosum
        e. stratum basale

15.   What term is given to the surface layer of the epidermis?

16.   Which part of the dermis has dermal papillae that indent the epidermis?

17.   Which part of the dermis contains a network of collagen and elastic fibres that give the skin its strength, extensibility and elasticity?

18.   Which type of sweat gland releases sweat directly onto the surface of the skin?

19.   Which type of sweat gland begins to function at puberty?

20.   In which homeostatic process do the sweat glands perform a major role?

21. What layer of the skin connects the dermis to the underlying tissues?

22. What name is given to the connective tissue containing fat that makes up the majority of the subcutaneous layer?

23. Which connective tissue found in the subcutaneous layer protects, supports and connects the skin to the underlying structures?

24. Which pigment absorbs ultra-violet light?

25. In which layer of the skin is the majority of melanin found?

     a. epidermis
     b. dermis
     c. subcutaneous layer

26. True or False?

     Exposure to ultra-violet light decreases melanin production.

27. Other than melanin, which two pigments play a part in the colouration of the skin?

28. True or False?

     Promoting the adequate supply of nutrients and avoiding dehydration can improve the health of the skin.

29. Which skin type is caused by underactive sebaceous glands?

     a. dry
     b. oily
     c. normal (balanced)
     d. sensitive
     e. combination

30. Which of these does NOT describe the cells that make up both the hair and the nails?

     a. hard
     b. keratinized
     c. living
     d. protecting

31.   What name is given to the part of the nail that is buried under the skin?

        a. nail wall
        b. lunula
        c. nail root
        d. nail body

32.   What name is given to the epidermis located beneath the nail plate at the junction between the free edge and the skin of the fingertip?

        a. eponychium
        b. paranychium
        c. hyponychium

33.   What name is given to the semi-circular whitish area at the proximal end of the nail?

34.   Which epidermal layer makes up the cuticle?

35.   True or False?

       Nails grow continually throughout life but the speed of their growth is affected by a variety of factors.

36.   Which part of the nail provides the site for mitosis?

37.   What structure is a downward continuation of the epidermis and consists of an external and internal root sheath?

38.   What name is given to the enlarged base of the follicle?

39.   What term is given to the indentation at the bottom of the hair follicle that contains areolar connective tissue?

40.   What name is given to the ring of cells in the bulb that undergo mitosis?

41.   What name is given to the oily secretion produced by the sebaceous glands?

42.   What is the name of the muscle that is attached to the hair follicle?

43. Which layer of the hair comprises of a single layer of flat, keratinized, over-lapping cells?

44. Which layer of the hair forms the majority of the shaft?

45. True or False?

   Not all hair contains a cortex.

46. Which hair type is grown by a foetus but lost before birth?

   a. terminal
   b. vellus
   c. lanugo

47. Which coarse hair type is found on the scalp, under the arms and in pubic regions?

48. Which pigment is primarily responsible for hair colour?

49. Which is the active stage of hair growth?

   a. catagen
   b. anagen
   c. telogen

50. Which is the resting stage of hair growth?

51. During which phase of hair growth does the hair separate from the papilla?

This page has intentionally been left blank.

Respiratory System

This page has intentionally been left blank.

Respiration (breathing) is a vital process to sustain human life. It is concerned with **supplying oxygen** to the cells and **removing** toxic **carbon dioxide** from the body.

During the respiratory process:

- **oxygen** is **inhaled** into the lungs
- the oxygen **diffuses** from the lungs into the **blood**
- **oxygen** is transported in the blood to the **cells**
- oxygen diffuses from the blood into the cells for use in **metabolic reactions**
- the metabolic reactions create **energy** and **carbon dioxide**
- the carbon dioxide diffuses from the cells into the **blood**
- the blood transports the carbon dioxide back to the **lungs**
- the **carbon dioxide** diffuses from the blood into the lungs
- the carbon dioxide is **exhaled** from the lungs

As well as **carbon dioxide** being exhaled from the body, the process of exhalation also expels **heat** and some **moisture**. Respiration therefore contributes to the body's **excretory** processes.

Respiration consists of 3 phases:

1. The inhalation (inspiration) and exhalation (expiration) of air between the atmosphere and the lungs is called **pulmonary ventilation**.

2. The diffusion of gases between the lungs and the blood is called **external respiration**. (Memory Hint: Think of the description 'external' to mean 'outside the cells'.)

3. The diffusion of gases between the blood and the cells is called **internal respiration**.

Before you go any further, it is suggested that you take questions 1 – 5.

As we have seen, respiration is dependent on **two** major systems:

1. The **respiratory system** - provides the mechanics for pulmonary ventilation and the site for external respiration.

2. The **cardiovascular system** - transports the gases between the lungs and the cells to facilitate internal respiration.

We'll look at the structure of the respiratory system next.

The upper respiratory system starts at the **nose**, through which air is taken into the **nasal cavity**. The **mucus** and the **cilia** (tiny hairs that line the nasal passages) **trap dust** particles. As the air passes through the nasal cavity, it is **warmed** and **moistened** by mucus droplets.

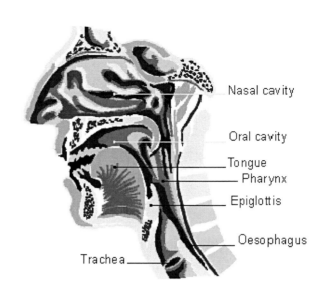

The warmed, moistened air then travels from the **nasal cavity** into the **pharynx** (throat). The pharynx connects the mouth and the nasal passage to the **oesophagus** and the **trachea**.

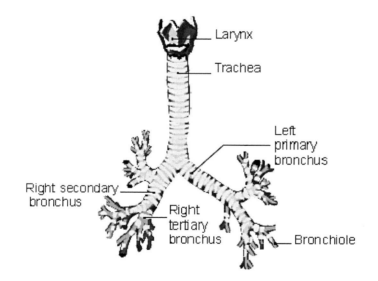

At the top of the trachea is the **larynx**, or voice box. The vocal cords are folds in its lining. The larynx contains cartilage which keeps the trachea open to air. The trachea is closed off by the epiglottis during swallowing. This ensures that any food travels down the oesophagus and not the trachea.

The trachea extends down to the level of the **5th thoracic** vertebra. The trachea then divides into the **left primary bronchus** and **right primary bronchus**, which descend into the left lung and right lung respectively. The bronchi continue to divide until, after branching into **secondary** and **tertiary** bronchi, they become **bronchioles**.

The finest bronchioles terminate in little **air sacs** called **alveoli**. It has been estimated that there are about 300 million of them in the lungs. Alveoli are moist and surrounded by a network of **capillaries**. It is here that **external respiration** takes place. Oxygen diffuses from the alveoli into the blood and carbon dioxide diffuses from the blood into the alveoli.

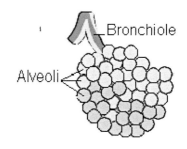

In order for external respiration to take place, 'new' air needs to be drawn into the lungs and the 'old' air expelled. Pulmonary ventilation is made possible by the physical structure and location of the lungs.

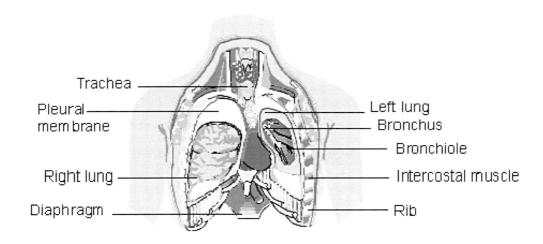

The **lungs** are located in the **upper thorax**. The right lung has three main lobes and the left lung has two. A double **pleural membrane** covers each lung, and the lungs are further protected by the **ribcage**. The **intercostal muscles** and the **diaphragm** provide a muscular setting in which the lungs can **expand** and **relax** – a vital feature of respiration.

Note:
You need to understand the actions of the **external** and **internal intercostal muscles** and the **diaphragm**. Only continue with this section now if you have an understanding of these muscles. If not, please go to the Muscular System Page 243.

For air to be taken **into** the lungs, the **air pressure** in the lungs has to be **less** than the external air pressure. This is achieved by making the lungs **bigger**.

For air to be **expelled** from the lungs, the air pressure in the lungs has to be **greater** than the external air pressure. This is achieved by making the lungs **smaller**.

The **muscular** movement of the **diaphragm** and the **intercostal muscles** is involved in increasing or decreasing the lung capacity.

During **inspiration**, the **diaphragm contracts**, causing it to flatten. This **expands** the chest, drawing the lungs out, so **increasing** the size of the lungs. The **external intercostal** muscles also **contract** to **elevate** the **ribs** so **increasing** the size of the thorax. These actions **decrease** the **pressure** in the lungs and allow air to be **inhaled**.

During **expiration**, the **diaphragm relaxes**, causing it to rise, and the **external intercostal** muscles **relax** causing the ribs to fall. This **decreases** the size of the chest, pulling the lungs in, so **reducing** the size of the lungs. These actions **increase** the **pressure** in the lungs and allow the air to be **exhaled**. When expiration is **forced**, the **internal** intercostals draw adjacent ribs together to **decrease** the size of the thorax even more.

The normal breathing rate is **10-12** breaths per minute, although this increases during exercise and stress, and decreases during sleep. Each breath contains approximately **500ml** of air.

Pulmonary ventilation takes place **rhythmically**. Usually **inspiration** lasts for about **2 seconds** and **expiration** takes approximately **3 seconds**. This is the basic rhythm.

The rhythm of pulmonary ventilation is **controlled** by areas in the **pons** and **medulla oblongata** of the **brain** (see Nervous System). These respiratory control areas contain both inspiratory and expiratory neurons (nerve cells).

After the 3 seconds of expiration, the **inspiratory** neurons become active. The inspiratory nerve impulses last for about **2 seconds**. These impulses reach the **diaphragm** and the **external intercostal muscles** causing them to **contract**. This expands the chest and increases the size of the lungs. The pressure in the lungs therefore decreases and **air** is **drawn in**.

During normal, quiet respiration, **expiration** occurs **passively**. After the 2 seconds of inspiration, the inspiratory impulses cease. Then, in the absence of nervous stimulation, the diaphragm and external intercostal muscles relax. The chest **naturally** reduces in size, increasing the air pressure in the lungs, and the air is exhaled.

It is believed that the expiratory neurons function only during **high levels** of respiration. The expiratory neurons cause various muscles to decrease the size of the chest to **force** expiration.

As we have said, the respiratory centres in the brain control the basic rhythm of pulmonary ventilation, with the fundamental objective to maintain **optimum** levels of carbon dioxide and oxygen in the blood. This is essential for the health of the cells.

The basic rhythm of respiration adequately maintains **optimum** levels of carbon dioxide and oxygen in the blood during the normal **resting** state. However, when the body is under stress, the metabolic rate increases and **more oxygen** is required. The increased metabolic rate also produces more carbon dioxide that has to be expelled from the body. To provide the necessary oxygen and to remove the excess carbon dioxide, the rate of respiration has to **increase**.

The body is able to **alter** the rate of respiration according to the metabolic needs. When the metabolic rate increases (e.g. during exercise) the level of carbon dioxide in the blood rises. This is detected by **chemoreceptors**. Chemoreceptors transmit this information to **strongly** stimulate the inspiratory control areas. Consequently, nerve impulses are sent to contract the diaphragm and the external intercostal muscles. This results in faster and deeper breathing. The increased respiratory rate leads to more oxygen being supplied to the cells and the elimination of the excess carbon dioxide.

It is not only the metabolic rate that can affect pulmonary ventilation. The rate of respiration is also affected by:

- **Blood pressure:** An increase in blood pressure, detected by baroreceptors, causes a decrease in the respiratory rate. A decrease in blood pressure increases the respiratory rate.

- **Temperature:** An increase in body temperature, detected by thermoreceptors, increases the rate of respiration. A decrease in temperature results in a decrease in respiration.

- **Pain:** Sudden pain can bring about the temporary cessation of breathing. However, prolonged pain can increase the respiratory rate.

- **Irritation of airways:** Mechanical or chemical irritation of the airways causes breathing to cease, followed by coughing or sneezing.

- **Stretching of the anal sphincter:** This increases the respiratory rate.

The **cerebral cortex** has connections with the respiratory control centres. This allows the respiratory rhythm to be **voluntarily** altered. However, the ability to voluntarily alter respiration is limited...

When respiration is voluntarily reduced or stopped, the level of **carbon dioxide** in the blood **builds up**. As we have seen, an increased level of carbon dioxide strongly stimulates the inspiratory control area. Inspiration is stimulated and breathing resumes. It is therefore impossible for people to kill themselves by holding their breath! The breathing rate would resume even upon fainting.

So, to recap, the respiratory system provides the mechanics for pulmonary ventilation and the site for external respiration. The cardiovascular system transports the gases in the blood between the lungs and the cells to facilitate internal respiration.

A major part in facilitating internal respiration is supplying the heart with newly oxygenated blood. The heart can then pump it, via the vascular network, to all the body tissues. Deoxygenated blood, received back in the heart from the tissues, is then returned to the lungs. This process is called **pulmonary circulation**.

The blood vessels involved in transporting gases to and from the lungs are the **pulmonary arteries** and the **pulmonary veins**.

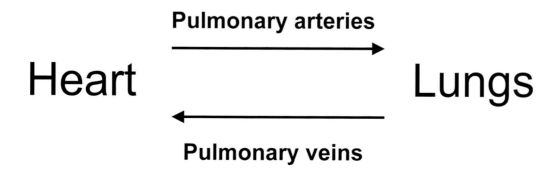

The **pulmonary arteries supply** blood to the lungs. They run from the right ventricle of the heart and contain **deoxygenated** blood (without oxygen). The blood releases its carbon dioxide and becomes oxygenated in the lungs.

The **oxygenated** blood is then **carried away** from the lungs in the **pulmonary veins**. The pulmonary veins take the oxygenated blood to the left atrium of the heart. It passes into the left ventricle from which it is **circulated** around the body.

During **internal respiration** the blood loses its oxygen and gains carbon dioxide. Deoxygenated blood then arrives back in the right atrium and is passed to the right ventricle for the cycle to repeat.

Summary

➤ Respiration is concerned with supplying oxygen to the cells and removing toxic carbon dioxide from the body.

➤ The respiratory system has an excretory function as it removes carbon dioxide, heat and moisture from the body.

➤ The inhalation (inspiration) and exhalation (expiration) of air between the atmosphere and the lungs is called pulmonary ventilation.

➤ The diffusion of gases between the lungs and the blood is called external respiration.

➤ The diffusion of gases between the blood and the cells is called internal respiration.

➤ Air, containing oxygen, is inhaled through the nose. It travels into the pharynx and down into the trachea.

➤ The trachea divides into the left primary bronchus and right primary bronchus, which descend into the left lung and right lung respectively.

➤ The primary bronchi divide to form secondary bronchi. The secondary bronchi divide to form tertiary bronchi. The tertiary bronchi divide to form bronchioles.

➤ The finest bronchioles terminate in little air sacs called alveoli. Alveoli are surrounded by a network of capillaries and provide the site for external respiration.

➤ In the alveoli, oxygen diffuses into the blood and carbon dioxide diffuses from the blood.

➤ The carbon dioxide is expelled from the lungs during exhalation.

➤ The oxygenated blood is taken to the heart in the pulmonary veins.

➤ The oxygenated blood is then pumped from the heart and circulated around the body.

➤ During internal respiration, the blood loses its oxygen and gains carbon dioxide. It is then returned to the heart.

➢ The pulmonary arteries take the deoxygenated blood from the heart to the lungs. In the lungs, oxygen diffuses into the blood and the cycle continues.

➢ The flow of deoxygenated blood from the right ventricle to the lungs and the return of oxygenated blood from the lungs to the left atrium is called pulmonary circulation.

➢ The rhythm of pulmonary ventilation is controlled by respiratory areas in the pons and medulla oblongata of the brain.

➢ Usually inspiration lasts for about 2 seconds and expiration takes about 3 seconds.

➢ Inspiratory nerve impulses cause the diaphragm and the external intercostal muscles to contract. This expands the chest and increases the size of the lungs. The pressure in the lungs therefore decreases and air is drawn in.

➢ Expiration usually occurs passively. Without inspiratory nervous stimulation, the diaphragm and external intercostal muscles relax. The chest naturally reduces in size, increasing the air pressure in the lungs, and the air is exhaled. Only during high levels of respiration do the expiratory neurons function.

➢ The rate of respiration is affected by the metabolic rate. The level of carbon dioxide in the blood is monitored by chemoreceptors and the respiratory rate altered accordingly.

➢ Other factors that affect the respiratory rate include body temperature, blood pressure, pain, irritation of the air passages and stretching of the anal sphincter.

Questions (Answers: Page 388)

1.   Which phase of respiration is this?

   ➤ Oxygen is inhaled into the lungs.

   a. pulmonary ventilation
   b. external respiration
   c. internal respiration

2.   Which phase of respiration is this?

   ➤ The oxygen diffuses from the lungs into the blood.

   a. pulmonary ventilation
   b. external respiration
   c. internal respiration

3.   Which phase of respiration is this?

   ➤ The oxygen diffuses from the blood into the cells for use in metabolic reactions. The metabolic reactions create carbon dioxide, which diffuses into the blood.

   a. pulmonary ventilation
   b. external respiration
   c. internal respiration

4.   Which phase of respiration is this?

   ➤ The carbon dioxide diffuses from the blood into the lungs.

   a. pulmonary ventilation
   b. external respiration
   c. internal respiration

5.   Which phase of respiration is this?

   ➤ The carbon dioxide is exhaled from the lungs.

   a. pulmonary ventilation
   b. external respiration
   c. internal respiration

6.   Respiration is concerned with supplying oxygen to the cells. What gas, produced by metabolic reactions in the cells, is removed during this process?

7.	Oxygen is inhaled via the nasal cavity. Into which passage does the oxygen then travel?

	a. trachea
	b. larynx
	c. bronchus
	d. pharynx

8.	The pharynx connects to the oesophagus and the trachea. Into which of these passages does oxygen pass?

	a. oesophagus
	b. trachea

9.	The trachea extends to the level of the 5th thoracic vertebra. It then divides to extend into either lung. What are these two passages called?

	a. primary bronchi
	b. secondary bronchi
	c. tertiary bronchi

10.	The tertiary bronchi continue to divide to form the smallest air passages in the lungs. What are these smallest air passages called?

11.	What is the name of the little air sacs at the end of each bronchiole?

	a. cilia
	b. alveoli
	c. capillaries

12.	Which gas diffuses from the alveoli into the blood during external respiration?

13.	Which gas diffuses from the blood into the alveoli during external respiration?

14.	What membrane covers each lung?

	a. nuclear membrane
	b. pleural membrane
	c. synovial membrane
	d. cell membrane

15.	Which dome-shaped muscular structure contracts to draw air into the lungs, and relaxes to allow air to be expelled?

16. Which intercostals muscles contract to increase the size of the thorax, so aiding inspiration?

        a. internal intercostals
        b. external intercostals

17. What organ of the nervous system controls the rhythm of pulmonary ventilation?

18. What stage of pulmonary ventilation lasts the longest?

        a. inspiration
        b. expiration

19. True or False?

The inspiratory nerve impulses last for about 2 seconds and cause the diaphragm and the external intercostal muscles to contract.

20. Which stage of pulmonary ventilation is usually passive?

21. Which receptors detect changes in the level of carbon dioxide in the blood?

        a. chemoreceptors
        b. baroreceptors
        c. thermoreceptors

22. True or False?

When the chemoreceptors detect an increase in the level of carbon dioxide, they strongly stimulate the inspiratory control centres. Consequently, nerve impulses are sent to contract the diaphragm and the external intercostal muscles, resulting in faster and deeper breathing.

23. Fill in the missing word:

An increase in blood pressure or a decrease in body temperature will _____ the rate of respiration.

24. What blood vessels supply blood from the right ventricle of the heart to the lungs?

25. Which blood vessels transport the newly oxygenated blood from the lungs to the heart, for circulation around the body?

Senses

This page has intentionally been left blank.

Our senses exist to **provide information** about the environment.

The body receives various stimuli from the **external** environment, e.g. sight, sound, taste, touch and smell. Due to the presence of **sensory receptors**, either on the surface of the relevant organ or within its tissues, these stimuli can be received and translated into meaningful information. The body can then respond accordingly.

The body can also pick up stimuli originating in the body, such as changes in the organs or blood flow and the presence of pain or congestion. We are, however, often unaware of many **internal** changes that take place to keep the body in balance (see Homeostasis).

We will concentrate on the external senses.

Sight

The **eyes** are the organs that allow **visual** information to be received.

Each eye is a **spherical** organ, encased in a **bony cavity** on the anterior surface of the face. It is held in place by six **muscles** that allow the eye to perform many thousands of movements per day. The **retinal** arteries and veins provide the blood supply. Let's take a look at the anatomy of the eye.

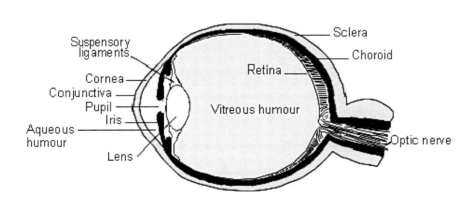

The wall of the eye consists of three layers. The **outside** layer is the **sclera**. This is tough and fibrous. The sclera is white, except at the **front** where there is a transparent area called the **cornea**. The cornea allows light into the eye and is covered by the **conjunctiva**.

The **middle** layer is the **choroid**, which contains many **blood vessels**. At the **front** of the eye the choroid forms the **iris**. The iris contains **pigment** that gives the eye its colour. The iris contains bands of **muscle**. The contraction and relaxation of these muscles causes the **pupil** to **dilate** and **constrict** respectively to regulate the amount of light that can enter the eye.

The **inner** layer of the eye is the **retina**. The retina contains the **light receptors**. At the back of the eye, **sensory neurons** emerge from the retina as the **optic nerve**. The optic nerve transmits impulses generated in the retina to the **brain**. The impulses are interpreted as vision in the **occipital lobes** of the cerebrum.

The eye is filled by **aqueous** and **vitreous humour**. Aqueous humour is watery and fills the anterior cavity. Vitreous humour is jelly-like and fills the posterior cavity. Both of these semi-fluids support the eye and give the eye its shape. The **lens**, held in place by the **suspensory ligaments**, is suspended in the aqueous humour at the front of the eye.

As **light** enters the eye, it is **refracted** (bent) by the cornea, the front surface of the lens and the back surface of the lens, before it is **converged** on the **retina**. If this takes place successfully, the light is brought to a **point** on the retina. This allows the brain to create a **focused** and clear image from the visual stimulus.

Summary

➢ Visual stimuli are received by the eyes.

➢ The tough outer layer of the eye is the sclera.

➢ The middle, vascular layer is the choroid.

➢ The eye is supported internally by the aqueous and vitreous humour.

➢ The amount of light allowed to enter the eye is governed by the iris. The iris controls the size of the pupil and gives the eye its colour.

➢ Light entering the eye passes through the conjunctiva and the cornea.

➢ Light is refracted (bent) by the cornea and then passed through the lens. It is refracted again by the front and back surfaces of the lens, before it is converged on the retina.

➢ The retina is the inner layer of the eye. It contains the light receptors. Sensory neurons lead from the retina to the optic nerve.

➢ The optic nerve transmits the nerve impulses generated in the retina to the brain for interpretation as vision in the occipital lobes of the cerebrum.

Questions – Sight (Answers: Page 389)

1.   Which is the tough, fibrous, outer layer of the eye?

         a. sclera
         b. choroid
         c. retina

2.   Which is the middle layer of the eye that contains the blood vessels?

         a. sclera
         b. choroid
         c. retina

3.   What part of the eye contracts and relaxes to cause the pupil to dilate and constrict?

4.   What is the name of the inner layer of the eye?

5.   What structure, held in place by the suspensory ligaments and suspended in the aqueous humour, refracts the light so that it is brought to a point on the retina?

6.   What nerve transmits impulses generated by the retina to the brain?

Sound

The **ears** are the organs that allow **sound** to be received. They are capable of hearing even the faintest sounds and can deal with many different stimuli at the same time.

There are **three** main parts to the ear. Only the outer part of the ear can be seen. The other two parts are buried deep within the skull. The **outer ear** is responsible for **trapping** the **sound** and passing it to the middle ear. The **middle ear** converts the sound into **mechanical vibrations**. In the **inner ear**, these mechanical vibrations **generate nerve impulses** that are transmitted to the **brain**.

Let's look at the anatomy of the ear.

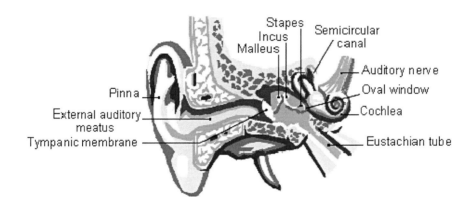

The **outer ear** consists of an external flap of skin and cartilage called the **pinna**. The pinna traps and directs the sound into the **external auditory meatus**. At the end of this passage is the **tympanic membrane** (ear-drum).

The middle ear is connected to the pharynx by the **eustachian tube**. This allows the **air pressure** on either side of the tympanic membrane to be **equalised**. The middle ear is bridged by three small bones, the malleus, incus and stapes, collectively called **ossicles**.

Sound entering the ear causes the tympanic membrane to vibrate. The tympanic membrane then vibrates the ossicles. The innermost ossicle is connected to another membrane called the **oval window**. The oval window transmits the vibrations to the inner ear.

The **inner ear** consists of a complicated series of **fluid filled canals**. The **cochlea** contains the receptors for hearing. Vibrations from the oval window cause pressure waves in the fluid of the cochlea. This causes membranes within the inner ear to vibrate, ultimately resulting in **sensory hairs** within the cochlea being moved. This stimulation of the hair cells generates **nerve impulses** that are transmitted to the **brain** via the **cochlear branch** of the **vestibulocochlear (VIII)** (auditory) **nerve**. The brain then interprets these impulses as sound.

The inner ear is also responsible for **balance**. This role belongs to the three **semicircular canals**. The semicircular canals contain **lymph** and **sensory hairs**. As the head moves, the lymph drags the sensory hairs, stimulating sensory neurons. The nerve impulses are then passed to the brain via the **vestibular branch** of the **vestibulocochlear (VIII)** nerve to give information about the orientation of the head. This information is then used by the brain to co-ordinate movement and posture.

Summary

➢ Sound is trapped by the external flap of the outer ear called the pinna.

➢ The sound is directed into the external auditory meatus. The tympanic membrane is at the end of this passage. The sound causes the tympanic membrane to vibrate.

➢ The tympanic membrane causes the ossicles (three bones) of the middle ear to vibrate. The ossicles transmit the vibrations across the middle ear to the oval window.

➢ The oval window transmits the vibrations to the inner ear.

➢ The inner ear consists of a complicated series of fluid filled canals.

➢ The cochlea of the inner ear contains the receptors for hearing. Vibrations from the oval window ultimately cause sensory hairs in the cochlea to move.

➢ The stimulation of these hair cells generates nerve impulses which are transmitted to the brain via the cochlear branch of the vestibulocochlear (VIII) (auditory) nerve. The brain then interprets these impulses as sound.

➢ The semicircular canals of the inner ear are responsible for balance. As the head moves, the sensory hairs are dragged by the fluid in the canals. The resulting nerve impulses are passed via the vestibular branch of the vestibulocochlear (VIII) (auditory) nerve to the brain.

Questions – Sound (Answers: Page 389)

1. Which part of the ear traps and directs sound into the external auditory meatus?

    a. outer ear
    b. middle ear
    c. inner ear

2. What is the common name for the tympanic membrane?

3. The three bones in the middle ear are called the malleus, incus and stapes. What collective name is given to these bones?

    a. semicircular canals
    b. cochlea
    c. ossicles

4. The innermost ossicle is connected to another membrane. What is this membrane called?

    a. triangular window
    b. square window
    c. oval window

5. The inner ear consists of a complicated series of fluid filled canals. What part of this structure contains the receptors for hearing?

    a. semicircular canals
    b. cochlea

6. The stimulation of the hair cells in the cochlea generates nerve impulses. Which nerve transmits these impulses to the brain?

7. What is the main function of the semicircular canals?

Taste

Taste is otherwise known as **gustatory sensation**. Gustatory sensation is a **chemical** sense and so the substance needs to be dissolved before it can be tasted.

The **tongue** is the muscular organ of **taste**. It is anchored to the back of the mouth. It contains four **taste zones**, enabling the detection of **sweet**, **salty**, **sour** and **bitter** tastes. All other tastes are a combination of these four. The **tip** of the tongue reacts to all four tastes, but is very sensitive to **sweet** and **salty** substances. The **posterior** part of the tongue is highly sensitive to **bitter** substances and the **lateral** edges are more sensitive to **sour** substances.

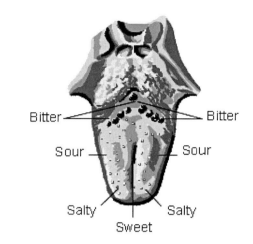

The **receptors** for taste are located in about 10,000 **taste buds**. Taste buds are mainly on the tongue, but some are also found on the roof of the back of the mouth, the larynx and pharynx.

Each taste bud is an **oval** structure consisting of epithelial cells of which about 50 are **gustatory receptor cells**. Each gustatory receptor cell has a hair-like projection. The **gustatory hair** of each cell projects through an opening in the taste bud called the **taste pore**.

The gustatory hairs make contact with the food and initiate the nerve impulses that will ultimately be perceived as taste. Taste impulses are conducted from the taste buds along **3 cranial nerves** (VII, IX and X – see Cranial Nerves) to the **medulla oblongata**. From the medulla, some taste fibres go via the **thalamus** to the **primary gustatory area** in the **parietal lobe** of the cerebrum, where the information is perceived as taste.

Much of what we think we taste we actually smell. Food odours pass into the nasal cavity and stimulate the olfactory receptors (see Smell). Substances stimulate the sense of smell thousands of times more strongly than the sense of taste. Sufferers of colds or allergies sometimes complain that they cannot taste their food. In these circumstances it is common that the sense of taste is functioning normally, but the olfactory system (responsible for the sense of smell) is not.

Summary

➢ Taste is known as gustatory sensation.

➢ The tongue contains 4 taste zones, enabling the detection of sweet, salty, sour and bitter tastes.

➢ Taste buds contain the gustatory receptor cells.

➢ Each gustatory receptor cell has a gustatory hair, capable of initiating a nerve impulse.

➢ The nerve impulse is perceived as taste in the primary gustatory area of the parietal lobe of the cerebrum.

Questions – Taste (Answers: Page 389)

1.   How many main tastes can be perceived?

2.   Which area of the tongue is highly sensitive to bitter substances?

        a. tip
        b. lateral edges
        c. posterior

3.   Fill in the missing word:

        Each taste bud contains about 50 _____ receptor cells.

4.   What is the name of the opening in the taste bud through which the gustatory hairs protrude?

Smell

The sense of smell is the most **immediate** of the senses and the least understood.

The sense of smell **tires**. On first exposure to an aroma the perception of it is quick and sharp. After a fairly short period of time the ability to perceive it fades. This is called **anosmia**.

Smell, like taste, is a **chemical sense**. It is detected by the **olfactory system**. The olfactory system is capable of building a library of more than 10,000 odours, many of which may be linked to a **memory** of a person, place or event.

There are tens of millions of **olfactory receptors**. They are positioned in the **nasal epithelium** at the back of the nasal cavity. Olfactory receptors are **neurons** (see Nervous System). Each neuron has several cilia, called **olfactory hairs**, protruding from the dendrites. These hairs are positioned in the **mucous** membrane covering the nasal epithelium. The olfactory hairs respond to chemical stimuli.

The **nasal cavity** is divided into **left** and **right** cavities by the **nasal septum**, and it receives a rich blood supply.

As the air is inhaled into the nasal cavities, it is **warmed** and **moistened** by **mucus** and dust particles are trapped by the **cilia** and so filtered out.

The air passes to the **back** of the nasal cavities where the odorant molecules pass over the **olfactory receptors**.

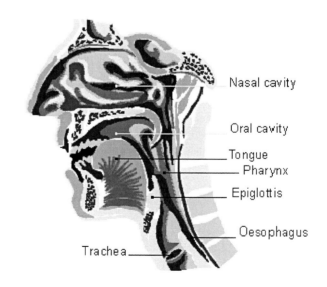

Nasal cavity

Oral cavity

Tongue
Pharynx

Epiglottis

Oesophagus

Trachea

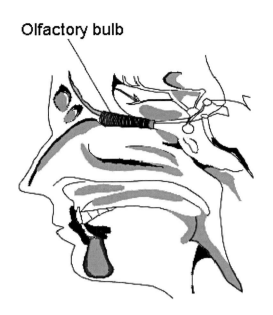

Olfactory bulb

When stimulated, the olfactory receptors transmit the impulse along the **axon**. The axons of olfactory receptors **unite** to form the **olfactory nerves**.

The olfactory nerves run to a pair of **olfactory bulbs**. Olfactory bulbs are composed of **grey matter** and are positioned beneath the **frontal lobes** of the cerebrum.

Nerve impulses leave the olfactory bulbs by way of the **olfactory tract**. The olfactory tract splits into **two** pathways. One pathway goes to the **olfactory portion** of the **cerebral cortex** where the nerve impulse is perceived as smell.

The other olfactory tract pathway goes to the inferior surface of the brain and extends to the **limbic system**. This connection with the limbic system may account for the ability of the perception of smell to induce memories and emotional responses.

Summary

➤ The olfactory system is concerned with the sense of smell.

➤ Olfactory receptors are neurons, which are positioned in the nasal epithelium at the back of the nasal cavity.

➤ Each olfactory receptor has olfactory hairs capable of responding to chemical stimuli.

➤ The axons of olfactory receptors unite to form the olfactory nerves.

➤ The olfactory nerves run to the olfactory bulbs, positioned beneath the frontal lobes of the cerebrum.

➤ Nerve impulses leave the olfactory bulbs by way of the olfactory tract.

➤ One pathway of the olfactory tract goes to the olfactory portion of the cerebral cortex, where the nerve impulse is perceived as smell.

➤ The other olfactory tract pathway goes to the inferior surface of the brain and extends to the limbic system.

<u>Questions – Smell (Answers: Page 389)</u>

1.   What system is concerned with the perception of odours?

2.   Which parts of the olfactory receptors are located in the mucous membrane at the back of the nasal cavity?

3.   Fill in the missing word:

Axons of olfactory neurons unite to form the _____ nerves.

4.   Under which lobes of the cerebrum are the olfactory bulbs located?

        a. frontal
        b. parietal
        c. occipital
        d. temporal

5.   In which part of the brain are nerve impulses from the olfactory receptors perceived as smell?

        a. cerebellum
        b. limbic system
        c. mid brain
        d. cerebral cortex
        e. pons
        f. medulla oblongata

6.   In which part of the brain can nerve impulses from the olfactory receptors trigger emotional responses?

Touch

The sense of touch is provided by the **nervous system** and allows a variety of different sensations to be perceived. The sense of touch plays a protective role in maintaining awareness of the perimeters of the body and allows the early detection of invasion.

The sense of touch becomes of particular importance in providing information about the environment when other senses fail. However, over recent years, the realization of the importance of touch in maintaining health has grown. Research has shown that the sense of touch plays a significant role in promoting healing, good health and recovery from illness.

The sensory receptors of touch are in the **skin**. They are called **cutaneous receptors**.

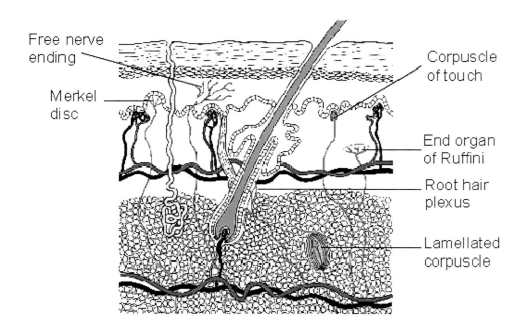

Cutaneous receptors allow **tactile** sensations (touch, pressure, vibration), **thermal** sensations (hot and cold) and **pain** to be detected. The more receptors present in an area of skin, the more sensitive that area of skin will be. Cutaneous receptors consist of the **dendrites** of **sensory neurons** (see Nervous System).

In their simplest form, cutaneous receptors are **unspecialized** and are called **free nerve endings**. Pain and temperature are detected by free nerve endings. Other receptors are more **specialized**. For example, in root hair plexuses (which detect movement of the hair shaft) the dendrites are arranged in networks around the hair follicle. On stimulation, cutaneous receptors generate **nerve impulses**. These nerve impulses are transmitted along **sensory** (afferent) neurons in the **spinal** and **cranial** nerves, through the **thalamus**, to the **parietal lobes** of the cerebrum where they are interpreted as touch. We'll look at the cutaneous receptors that allow sensations of:

- Touch
- Pressure
- Vibration
- Temperature
- Pain

It is advised that you take the Skin section before you go any further.

Touch

There are 2 types of touch. **Discriminative touch** is when the exact point of contact is known. **Crude touch** is when there is an awareness that the body has been touched, but the exact location of the contact is unknown.

Touch is detected by **tactile receptors** in the skin or in the tissues immediately below the skin. Tactile receptors include:

Corpuscles of touch - egg-shaped receptors for discriminative touch. The dendrites are encapsulated by connective tissues and are located in the dermal papillae. They transmit impulses rapidly and are most abundant in the fingertips, palms of the hands and soles of the feet.

Root hair plexuses - dendrites arranged in networks around the hair follicles. The movement of the hair stimulates the dendrites. This allows the detection of movement on the surface of the skin when the hair is disturbed.

Merkel discs - flattened portions of dendrites that make contact with Merkel cells in the deepest layer of the epidermis. They function in discriminative touch.

End organs of Ruffini - dendrites located deep in the dermis and in deeper tissues of the body. They detect heavy and continuous touch sensations.

Pressure

Pressure is a **sustained** sensation, felt over a **larger area** than touch. Pressure sensations are generally created by the stimulation of receptors in the **deeper** tissues.

The pressure receptors are:

End organs of Ruffini - dendrites located deep in the dermis and in the deeper tissues of the body.

Lamellated corpuscles - dendrites enclosed in an oval, layered capsule composed of connective tissue. They are located in the subcutaneous layer of the skin, under mucous membranes, around joints, tendons and muscles, in the mammary glands and in certain organs.

Vibration

The sensation of vibration arises from rapid, repetitive, sensory impulses from the receptors. The receptors for vibration are:

Corpuscles of touch - detect low-frequency vibrations.

Lamellated corpuscles - detect high-frequency vibrations.

Temperature

The thermal sensations are hot and cold. The receptors of temperature are called **thermoreceptors** and are simply **free nerve endings**. Thermoreceptors are **selective** - some respond to hot and some respond to cold.

Pain

The receptors for pain are called **nociceptors**. As for temperature, the receptors for pain are simply **free nerve endings** and are found in almost every tissue of the body. Nociceptors will respond to any stimulus if it is causing tissue damage.

Summary

➤ Sensory receptors in the skin are called cutaneous receptors.

➤ Cutaneous receptors consist of the dendrites of sensory neurons and allow tactile sensations (touch, pressure, vibration), thermal sensations (hot and cold) and pain to be detected.

➤ The touch receptors include corpuscles of touch, root hair plexuses, Merkel discs and end organs of Ruffini.

➤ Pressure is detected by end organs of Ruffini and lamellated corpuscles.

➤ Vibration is detected by corpuscles of touch (low-frequency) and lamellated corpuscles (high-frequency).

➤ Temperature and pain are detected by selective free nerve endings. Thermoreceptors detect temperature, nociceptors detect pain.

Questions – Touch (Answers: Page 389)

1.   Which part of the sensory neuron form cutaneous receptors?

2.   Which receptors are unspecialized dendrites capable of detecting heat and pain?

3.   Which lobes of the cerebrum interpret nerve impulses generated as a result of touch?

   a. frontal
   b. occipital
   c. temporal
   d. parietal

4.   True or False?

   When the tactile receptors are unable to detect the exact point of contact, the touch is described as discriminative.

5.   Which tactile receptors are located in the dermal papillae?

   a. corpuscles of touch
   b. root hair plexuses
   c. Merkel discs
   d. end organs of Ruffini

6.   Which touch receptors are located around the hair follicles?

7.   Fill in the missing word:

   Merkel _____ are flattened portions of dendrites that make contact with Merkel cells in the deepest layer of the epidermis.

8.   Which touch receptors, located deep in the dermis and in the deeper tissues of the body, detect heavy and continuous touch sensations?

   a. end organs of Rufus
   b. end tissues of Rufus
   c. end organs of Ruffini
   d. end tissues of Ruffini

9.   Which receptors are capable of detecting both pressure and high-frequency vibrations?

       a. corpuscles of touch
       b. lamellated corpuscles
       c. end organs of Ruffini

10. Which receptors are capable of detecting low-frequency vibrations?

       a. corpuscles of touch
       b. lamellated corpuscles
       c. end organs of Ruffini

11. True or False?

     A thermoreceptor is a free nerve ending capable of detecting both hot and cold.

12. What term is given to free nerve endings that can detect pain?

This page has intentionally been left blank.

Urinary System

This page has intentionally been left blank.

The body produces waste materials –

➤ Carbon dioxide, excess water, heat, and toxic wastes such as ammonia and urea are produced by the **metabolic reactions** that take place in the cells.

➤ The digestive system does not absorb all that we **ingest** and so the residue is waste.

➤ Some essential ions, for example sodium, chloride, phosphate and nitrogen, build up to **excessive levels** and are no longer required.

It is essential for the health of the body that waste matter is quickly and successfully **excreted** because its build up would quickly lead to ill health.

The urinary system plays a major excretory role. It is responsible for removing **excess water** and **unwanted substances** from the **blood** and expelling them from the body as urine. It is not, however, the only body system involved in excretion...

The large intestine of the **digestive** system prepares faeces for expulsion and eliminates it from the body. The **respiratory** system expels carbon dioxide, heat and some moisture during exhalation, and the sweat glands of the **skin** excrete water, heat, and small amount of salts and urea in sweat. More details on these excretory roles can be found in the appropriate sections.

So, we have mentioned, the urinary system is primarily responsible for **eliminating urine** from the body. Urine consists of **waste** material produced as a by-product of metabolism. It is a pale yellow fluid which is 95% water. The remaining 5% is made up of solutes derived from cellular metabolism and outside sources (e.g. drugs). These components include urea, uric acid, ammonia, sodium, potassium, calcium, chloride and bicarbonate.

The components of the urinary system are the same in the male and female. The constituents that make up urine are absorbed from the blood by the **kidneys**. The urine passes from the kidneys, down the **ureters** to the **bladder**. The bladder is a muscular sac, which temporarily stores urine. When the volume of urine in the bladder exceeds 200-400ml, **stretch receptors** in the bladder trigger urination. The urine leaves the body via the **urethra**.

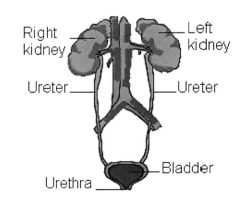

The act of expelling urine from the bladder is commonly called urination, but the physiological term is **micturition**. Micturition is a **reflex** over which there is (luckily!) some **voluntary** control.

When the volume of urine in the bladder causes it to expand, the **stretch receptors** in the bladder wall are stimulated. The stretch receptors then transmit nerve impulses to the lower portion of the **spinal cord**.

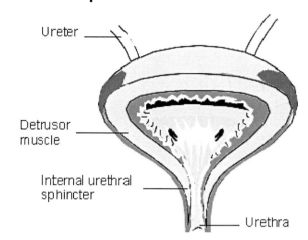

On receiving nerve impulses from the stretch receptors, the urinary control centre in the sacral spinal cord triggers the **micturition reflex**. The micturition reflex causes the **detrusor** muscle in the **wall** of the **bladder** to contract and the **internal urethral sphincter** to relax.

The spinal cord also communicates with the **cerebral cortex** to initiate the **conscious** desire to expel urine. The cerebral cortex permits the **voluntary** relaxation of the **external urethral sphincter**, located in the skeletal muscle that surrounds the urethra.

The combination of **both** the micturition reflex and voluntary control allows urination to take place.

The main function of the urinary system is to control the **composition**, **volume** and **pressure** of the **blood**. The kidneys are vital to this as they filter the blood by **absorbing waste** and excessive **water**. This forms urine that can be excreted from the body.

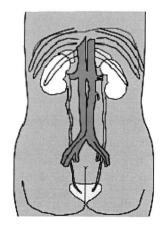

The kidneys are bean-shaped, reddish organs. They are located just **above** the **waist** at the **rear** of the abdomen.

The right kidney is located slightly lower than the left.

The kidneys receive their blood supply from the **renal arteries**. The **renal veins** drain the filtered blood away from the kidneys.

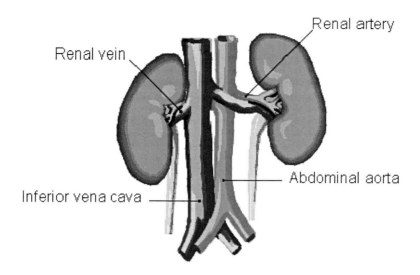

We'll look at the structure of the kidney next.

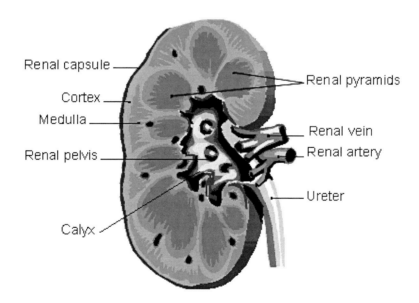

Within the **renal capsule** is the smooth, outer region of the kidney called the **cortex**. The cortex surrounds the darker **medulla**.

The cone-shaped structures in the medulla are called **renal pyramids**. The cortex and the renal pyramids make up the functional part of the kidney, consisting of about 1 million microscopic nephrons. We'll look at nephrons in detail a little later. There is a large cavity in the centre of the kidney called the **renal pelvis**. The renal pelvis has cup-shaped extensions called **calyces**. Each calyx receives urine from the collecting ducts of one renal pyramid. The urine then drains from the calyx into the renal pelvis. The **peristaltic** action of the renal pelvis encourages the urine to drain into the **ureter**.

In order for the kidneys to perform their vital blood filtration processes, they have a vast **capillary network**. Situated within this network of blood vessels are numerous microscopic tubules called **nephrons**.

Nephrons are the functional units of the kidney. They extend from the renal capsule, through the cortex and medulla, to the cup-shaped extensions of the renal pelvis, absorbing excessive and unwanted substances from the blood.

Nephrons are **2-4cm long**. The cup-shaped **Bowman's capsule** encloses a small group of capillaries called the **glomerus**. It is across the walls of the Bowman's capsule that **water** and **waste** are filtered from the blood.

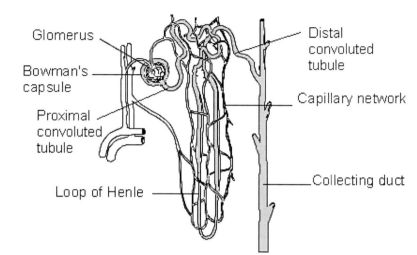

The blood pressure is very **high** in the glomerus because the **efferent** arteriole is **smaller** in diameter than the **afferent** arteriole, creating a **high resistance** to blood flow. This high pressure increases **filtration** of substances in the blood through the capillary walls and into the Bowman's capsule.

As the filtered substances pass through the **proximal convoluted tubule**, **Loop of Henle** and the **distal convoluted tubule**, some useful substances (e.g. water, amino acids, glucose and ions such as sodium, potassium, and calcium) are **selectively reabsorbed** back into the blood. The remainder passes into the **collecting duct**. It is then expelled from the kidney as urine via the renal pelvis and ureter.

The amount of **water** that is **reabsorbed** into the blood is controlled by **antidiuretic hormone** (ADH). Antidiuretic hormone is produced by the hypothalamus but is stored and released into the blood by the posterior lobe of the pituitary gland (see Endocrine System).

The release of ADH is triggered by **dehydration**. The hypothalamus detects when the **water** concentration of the blood is **low** and triggers the release of this hormone. An **increase** in the level of antidiuretic hormone **increases** the amount of **water** that is reabsorbed from the nephron **back** into the **blood**. This reabsorption takes place as the waste substances (filtered from the blood in the Bowman's capsule) travel through the **tubule** of the **nephron**.

The reabsorption of water from the waste substances **decreases** the volume of **urine** that is expelled from the kidneys. In decreasing the amount of urine produced, the **hydration** level of the **blood** is **increased**. This is a negative feedback system (see Homeostasis).

Other factors that affect urination include:

Weather - in hot weather the body can become dehydrated, so causing less urine production. In cold weather, the bladder may be triggered for a more frequent urination.

Activity - movement may trigger the bladder but high levels of activity may cause the body to become dehydrated, so reducing urine production.

Stress - high stress levels may cause more frequent urination.

Water consumption - needless to say what goes in largely comes out! A high intake of water will naturally increase urine production.

Kidney Functions

As we have seen, the primary functions of the kidneys are to **filter** unwanted substances from the **blood** and **regulate** the **fluid balance** but the kidneys perform other important roles.

The kidneys **maintain sodium** and **potassium** levels. If the levels are too high, the excess ions will be filtered out by the kidneys and eliminated in the urine. If, however, the levels are low, these ions are selectively reabsorbed back into the blood. This homeostatic function is partially controlled by the hormone **aldosterone**.

Hydrogen ions, formed by the disassociation of acids (see Chemistry), are excreted by the kidneys. If the hydrogen ions were not eliminated the body would become too **acidic**. This plays a part in **maintaining** the body's **pH**.

The kidneys also:

- secrete an enzyme called **renin** that helps to **regulate blood pressure**

- play a part in the **synthesis** of an active form of **Vitamin** D

- and stimulate the **production** of **red blood cells**.

Summary

➢ Along with the digestive system, respiratory system and the skin, the urinary system plays an excretory role.

➢ The urinary system is responsible for eliminating urine from the body.

➢ The physiological term for urination is micturition.

➢ Urine consists of water, urea and small amounts of sodium, potassium, calcium, chloride and bicarbonate.

➢ The components that make up urine are absorbed from the blood by the kidneys.

➢ The urine passes from the kidneys, down the ureters to the bladder.

➢ A combination of the micturition reflex and voluntary control allows urination to take place.

➢ On urinating, urine leaves the body via the urethra.

➢ Nephrons are the functional units of the kidney.

➢ Waste is filtered from the blood across the walls of the Bowman's capsule.

➢ As the waste passes through the tubule, useful substances are selectively reabsorbed. The remainder passes into the collecting duct.

➢ The urine is collected in the central part of the kidney called the renal pelvis, and drained into the ureter.

➢ Antidiuretic hormone increases the amount of water reabsorbed into the blood, so decreasing urine production.

➢ The kidneys filter the blood, regulate the fluid balance and maintain the sodium and potassium balance, and play a part in maintaining pH, regulating blood pressure, synthesizing an active form of vitamin D and producing red blood cells.

Questions (Answers: Page 390)

1. What is the name of the tube that transports urine from a kidney to the bladder?

2. Fill in the missing word:

    The physiological process of urination is referred to as _____ .

3. Which muscle is voluntarily relaxed to allow micturition?

    a. detrusor
    b. internal urethral sphincter
    c. external urethral sphincter

4. True or False?

    The micturition reflex causes the detrusor muscle in the wall of the bladder to contract and the internal urethral sphincter to relax.

5. Which kidney is slightly lower than the other?

6. Which vessels drain the filtered blood away from the kidneys?

    a. hepatic arteries
    b. hepatic veins
    c. renal arteries
    d. renal veins

7. What is the dark region of the kidney called that contains the renal pyramids?

    a. renal capsule
    b. cortex
    c. medulla

8. What is the name of the large cavity in the centre of the kidney, involved in collecting urine and draining it into the ureter?

9. What is the name of the microscopic functional units of the kidney, that absorb excessive and unwanted substances from the blood?

    a. neurons
    b. nephrons
    c. neutrons

10.   Which part of the nephron encases a small group of capillaries called the glomerus?

       a. Bowman's capsule
       b. loop of Henle
       c. collecting duct

11.   True or False?

Once water and waste have been filtered from the blood into the nephron, these substances can never return to the blood. They are all transported through the loop of Henle, passed into the collecting duct, and expelled as urine.

12.   When is antidiuretic hormone (ADH) released?

       a. when the water concentration in the blood is high
       b. when the water concentration in the blood is low

13.   Fill in the missing word:

An increase in the level of antidiuretic hormone will increase the amount of water reabsorbed into the blood, so _____ urine production.

Reproductive System

155

This page has intentionally been left blank.

Reproduction is the process by which new individuals are produced and the genetic information passed from generation to generation.

The male and female reproductive systems have different structures and functions to reflect their varying roles. However, there are similarities, particularly in terminology. The primary sex organs in both the male and female are called **gonads**. These are the **testes** in the male and the **ovaries** in the female. The gonads secrete **hormones**, a feature that classifies them as **endocrine** glands (see Endocrine System). The gonads produce **gametes**. These are the **sperm cells** in the male and the **ova** (eggs) in the female.

Male Reproductive System

The two main functions of the male reproductive system are to **produce sperm** and **impregnate** the female.

The **testes** are the principal structures. They descend from the abdomen into two pouches of skin called **scrotal sacs**. The testes are supported by the **spermatic cords** which encase the **vas deferens**, testicular blood vessels, nerves, lymph vessels, and the **cremaster muscle**.

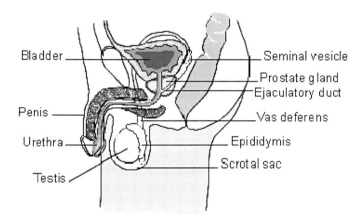

The testes are comprised of thousands of fine, coiled tubes called **seminiferous tubules**. It is in these tubules that the **sperm** are produced in a process called **spermatogenesis**. We'll look at spermatogenesis later.

The tubules in the testis are continuous with the **epididymis**, where the sperm mature, and the **vas deferens**. The vas deferens transports the sperm from the testis and joins the **urethra** just below the bladder. During ejaculation, the muscular movement of the vas deferens and the **ejaculatory duct** aid the ejection of the sperm.

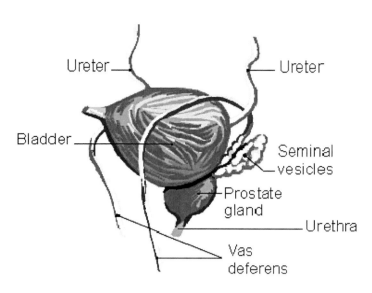

The **seminal vesicles** and the **prostate gland** secrete **fluids** during ejaculation. These fluids and the sperm make up the **semen** that is released via the penis.

The seminal fluids perform many functions including improving the mobility of the sperm, neutralizing acidity in the female reproductive tract and causing the coagulation of the semen after ejaculation.

The development of the reproductive system is triggered during puberty by the levels of **testosterone** (see Endocrine System).

At about the age of 55, there is a **decline** in the **testosterone** level. This leads to fewer viable sperm and a decrease in sexual desire. However, a healthy man can often retain the ability to successfully reproduce well into his 80's or even 90's.

Female Reproductive System

The female reproductive system performs four main functions, **ovulation**, **menstruation**, **pregnancy** and **birth**.

The **ovaries** are the principal structures of the **female** reproductive system. They resemble unshelled almonds in size and shape.The ovaries are suspended by ligaments in the upper pelvic cavity, one either side of the **uterus**.

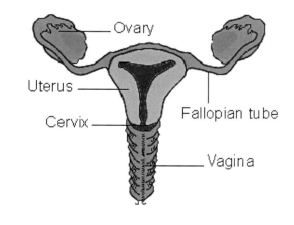

Each ovary contains over 200,000 **immature ova** at birth. Each immature ovum is encased in a sac and the whole structure is called a **follicle**. The follicles progressively develop, usually one at a time, in response to the various sex **hormones** until they become **primary follicles**. Once the primary follicle has matured **ovulation** takes place. A potential ovum (it is not officially called an ovum until fertilization takes place) breaks free and enters the fallopian tube.

We'll look at oogenesis, the process in which ova are produced, in more detail later.

The two **fallopian tubes** (or uterine tubes) connect the ovaries to the uterus. Each fallopian tube resembles a long, thin funnel that is wider at the ovary and narrower at the uterus. At the ovary end, the fallopian tube has finger-like projections called **fimbriae**. The fimbriae encourage the potential ovum to enter the fallopian tube. If fertilization occurs, it usually takes place in the wider part of the fallopian tube. The fertilized ovum, now called a **zygote**, arrives in the uterus about 7 days after ovulation.

The **uterus** is suspended by broad ligaments and is situated between the bladder and the rectum. It is a tough, muscular sac with a rich blood supply. It serves as the pathway for sperm to enter the fallopian tubes. If fertilization occurs, the uterus provides a source of **attachment** and **nourishment** for the zygote, and later expands to facilitate the developing foetus. If fertilization does not occur, the uterus lining, which thickens in preparation for the implantation of the ovum, breaks down during **menstruation**.

The female reproductive system also includes the **vulva** (the collective name given to all the **external genitalia**). The vulva is located inside a diamond-shaped area between the thighs and the buttocks that contains the external genitals and the anus. This diamond-shaped area is called the **perineum**.

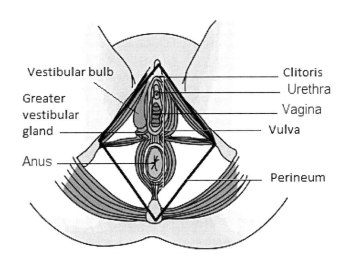

There are two folds of skin that run from the anterior to the posterior on either side of the perineum called **labia**. They are folded back in the illustration shown above and so are not shown.

The outermost labia are called **labia majora**. They have pubic hair, contain adipose tissue and sebaceous and sweat glands. The smaller inner folds are called **labia minora**. These have no hair or fat but do contain many sebaceous glands.

There is a small, cylindrical mass of erectile tissue and nerves at the anterior junction of the labia minora. This is called the **clitoris**. Like the penis in the male, the clitoris is capable of enlargement upon tactile stimulation and has a role in sexual excitement.

The space between the left and right labia minora is called the **vestibule**. The **vaginal** and **urethra** orifices are in the vestibule. There are also two elongated masses of erectile tissue on either side of the vaginal orifice, called **vestibular bulbs**. They become gorged with **blood** during sexual arousal, narrowing the vaginal orifice and putting pressure on the penis during intercourse. **Greater vestibular glands** are also situated either side of the vaginal orifice. These release a **mucus** secretion through their ducts to supplement lubrication during intercourse.

The development of the female reproductive system is triggered by hormones during puberty (see Endocrine System).

The female reproductive system has a more limited timetable for reproduction than the male system because its ability to reproduce is governed by the **menstrual cycle** and ends with the **menopause**. We'll look at both of these next.

Menstrual Cycle.

Menstruation is controlled by hormones. The **menstrual cycle** is usually a 28 day process with four stages:

Menstrual Phase (Days 1-5)
A reduction in oestrogens and progesterone causes the breakdown of the uterine lining, resulting in the discharge of 25-65ml of blood, tissue fluid, mucus and uterine epithelial cells. This is called menstruation or menses. At this stage a mature follicle is being prepared.

Pre-Ovulatory Phase (Days 6-13)
Follicle stimulating hormone and luteinizing hormone stimulate the ovaries to produce more oestrogens. This encourages the re-build of the uterine lining. By the end of this phase a mature follicle is ready for ovulation. This is sometimes referred to as the follicular phase.

Ovulation (Day 14)
The matured ovum is released into the fallopian tube.

Post-Ovulatory Phase (Days 15-28)
This is the time between ovulation and the period of menstrual discharge. Progesterone production by the ovaries is stimulated by luteinizing hormone to prepare the uterus to receive the fertilized ovum. If fertilization and implantation does not occur, hormonal changes initiate the breakdown of the uterine lining and the cycle continues. This is sometimes referred to as the luteal phase.

Menopause

The cessation of the menstrual cycle is called **menopause**.

Menopause occurs usually between the ages of 40 and 50. The **ovaries** become **less responsive** to follicle stimulating hormone and luteinizing hormone. Consequently, the production of oestrogens and progesterone reduces and the follicles do not develop.

During the menopause, some women experience hot flushes, sweating, headaches, hair loss (although an increase in androgens may cause an increase in facial hair), muscular pains, vaginal dryness, insomnia, depression, weight gain and mood swings. There is some decrease in the size of the ovaries, uterine tubes, uterus, vagina, external genitalia and breasts. Osteoporosis (decreased bone mass) may also occur as a result of the reduced level of oestrogens.

Breast Tissue

Until the onset of puberty, breasts are much the same in the male and female. Basically they are made up of **glandular tissue** surrounded by **fat**. The glandular tissue comprises of **lobes** and **ducts** that empty into the **nipple**. These glands are modified sudoriferous (sweat) glands capable of producing **milk**.

In the female the release of **oestrogen** and **progesterone** during puberty causes the breast tissue to develop. Developed breasts in the female is a **secondary sexual characteristic** having the primary function of **lactation** - the synthesis, secretion and ejection of milk. In the male, breasts remain rudimentary.

The breasts are positioned mostly anterior to the upper thorax. Each breast extends from 2nd to the 6th rib vertically and from the side of the sternum to the mid-axillary line horizontally.

The size of the breasts depends upon many factors including the volume of breast tissue, fluid retention, family history, age, weight, history of pregnancies and lactation, the menstrual cycle and the menopause.

Externally the breast appears as a rounded, soft mound of tissue. A **nipple** projects from the surface of the breast. This is the point at which the ducts converge.

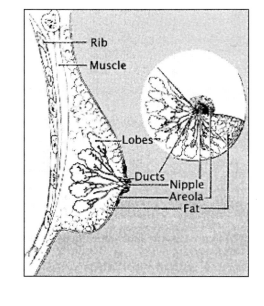

A slightly raised pink or brown pigmented area surrounds the nipple. This is called the **areola**. The nipple and the areola contain specialised **muscle fibres** that respond to stimulation to make the nipple erect. The areola appears rough because it contains sudoriferous (sweat) glands and sebaceous (oil) glands. The secretion from the sebaceous glands helps to protect and lubricate the areola during lactation.

Internally the breast is a mass of **glandular**, **fatty** and **fibrous** tissues. Each breast consists of **15-20 lobes** separated by fatty adipose tissue. Each lobe contains smaller compartments called **lobules**.

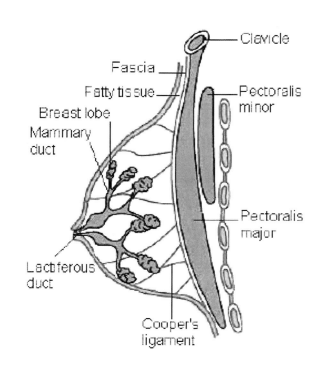

The lobules are made up of connective tissue in which clusters of **milk-secreting** glands called **alveoli** are embedded. (Note: alveoli is also the name given to a cluster of air sacs in the lungs.)

Milk (when it is being produced by the alveoli) first passes into **secondary tubules** (not shown here) and then into the larger **mammary ducts**.

As the mammary ducts approach the nipple they expand and continue as the **lactiferous ducts**.

Fibrous strands of connective tissue called **Cooper's ligaments** run between the **skin** and the deep **fascia** to **support** the breast. The fascia attaches the breast to the underlying muscle. The breast lies mainly on the large **pectoralis major** muscle, which assists in arm movement.

Cooper's ligaments may become **irreparably stretched** when the breasts grow heavy or if they are **unsupported** during exercise, causing the breasts to sag. Exercising the pectoral muscles can however help to increase the strength of the ligaments and maintain uplift if performed without undue strain.

Blood is supplied to the breasts by branches of the **axillary artery**, the **internal thoracic** artery and some **intercostals** arteries. The corresponding veins return the blood to the heart. The breasts contain many lymphatic vessels. Lymphatic drainage is very extensive, with the **axillary nodes** receiving more than **75%** of breast lymph.

The breasts are responsive to **hormonal** levels. They therefore undergo monthly changes and alter during the normal life span. During the **menstrual cycle** when progesterone is preparing for pregnancy, the breasts feel lumpy and tender and increase in size. The blood supply increases and the breasts **retain** more **fluid**. The use of the contraceptive pill may also increase fluid retention in the breasts and cause tenderness.

During **pregnancy**, the lobules multiply increasing significantly the size of the breasts. The areolae darken and the nipples enlarge as do the blood vessels. By the end of pregnancy the breasts become almost entirely **glandular**.

During **menopause** the breasts become less glandular but may feel tender and lumpy, sometimes forming cysts. The glandular tissue is initially replaced with **fat** but then the fatty tissue may decrease causing the breasts to lose their firmness. The elasticity of the Cooper's ligaments decreases causing the breasts to increase in size and sag.

Note: Information on the hormones involved in puberty, menstruation, pregnancy, lactation and the menopause is covered in the Endocrine System.

Creation of Gametes

The objective of reproduction is to produce another individual. This individual will **inherit** genetic information from **both** parents. Half of the necessary genetic complement will come from the father and the other half from the mother.

For reproduction to take place, both parents must be able to create cells with **half** of their normal genetic complement. These cells are called **gametes** and are the **sperm** in the male and the **ova** in the female.

Cells (other than gametes) contain **23 pairs** of chromosomes, **46 chromosomes** in total. The 2 chromosomes that make up the pair are called **homologous chromosomes**. Generally, homologous chromosomes contain similar genes in a similar order. A cell containing **23 pairs** of chromosomes is called a **diploid** cell.

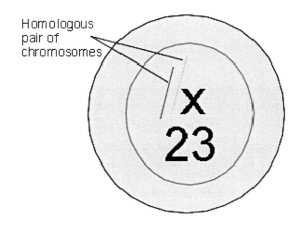

Diploid Cell

Gametes have just **half** the normal genetic complement.

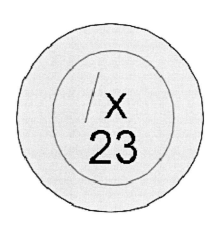

A gamete has **23** chromosomes - just **one** chromosome **from each homologous pair**. A cell containing half the normal genetic complement is called **haploid** (Memory Hint: **H**aploid = **H**alf).

Haploid Cell

When the male and female gametes unite, the new individual produced inherits **one** chromosome of each homologous pair **from each** parent, making up the 23 pairs.

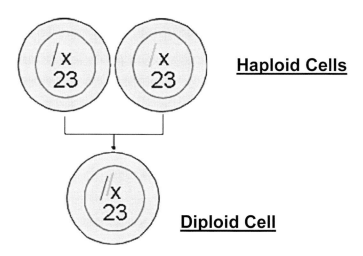

Haploid Cells

Diploid Cell

Sex Chromosomes

One of the 23 **pairs** of homologous chromosomes in each cell is responsible for **determining** the **sex** of the individual. These **sex chromosomes** are referred to as the **X** and **Y** chromosomes.

Diploid cells in a **female** have two X chromosomes (**XX**) and in a **male** have one X chromosome and one slightly smaller Y chromosome (**XY**).

When the cells divide to form gametes, all **female** gametes (ova) will contain **one X** chromosome. In the **male**, **half** the gametes (sperm) will contain **one X** chromosome and the other **half** will contain **one Y** chromosome. When the ova and sperm unite, there is a **50-50** chance of the individual being XX (female) or XY (male).

Sex is therefore determined at **fertilization**, but both female and male embryos develop identically until about 7 weeks after fertilization. The presence of the Y chromosome is then needed to initiate male development.

For haploid cells to be produced, cell division occurs. Cell division consists of **nuclear division** (division of the nucleus) and **cytoplasmic division** (division of the cytoplasm and organelles). The nucleus and cytoplasm **divide** to produce new cells.

There are two main types of nuclear division:

1. Mitosis
The cell divides to produce **two identical** cells. Mitosis ensures that the new cells have the same number and kind of chromosome as the parent. It is an ongoing process that replaces dead or injured cells and adds new cells for growth.

2. Meiosis
The cell divides to produce **four** cells, each with **half** the genetic complement of the parent cell. Meiosis is the process by which the gametes are produced.

Meiosis is a common feature of **spermatogenesis** (the production of sperm) and **oogenesis** (the production of ova). We'll look at meiosis in detail first, and then move on to look at spermatogenesis and oogenesis individually.

Note: Before you continue with this topic we **strongly** advise that, if you have not already done so, you take the topic on Cell Division. If you took Cell Division some time ago, a recap may also be beneficial.

Meiosis

The process of meiosis consists of **2 nuclear divisions**. Each division consists of **prophase**, **metaphase**, **anaphase** and **telophase** – terms you will be familiar with from your study of mitosis.

To aid our explanation of meiosis, we'll use plenty of graphics. However, as it is not practical to show 23 pairs of chromosomes, we'll just show **2 pairs**. The principle is the same.

Prior to meiosis the chromosomes **replicate**. Each chromosome is then made up of 2 identical chromatids, joined at the centromere.

 **Replication**

The **first** meiotic nuclear division, **meiosis I**, produces **2** cells. One chromosome from each homologous pair ends up in each cell. Each cell therefore has just **half** of the genetic information of the parent cell.

The **second** nuclear division, **meiosis II**, is very similar to **mitosis**. The **chromatids** separate to produce 2 cells. The 2 haploid cells produced by the first stage of nuclear division therefore divide to produce a total of **4 haploid** cells.

 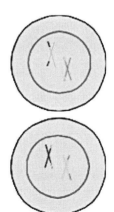 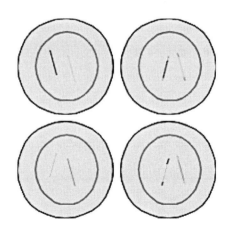

Meiosis I   **Meiosis II**

Let's look at meiosis in more detail.

As we have already said, the process of meiosis begins by the chromosomes in the nucleus **replicating**. Each chromosome is then made up of **2 identical chromatids**, joined at the centromere.

 **Replication**

The 4 phases of **meiosis I** then occur. They are:

1. **Prophase I:** The chromosomes (consisting of 2 identical chromatids) appear to shorten and thicken and the nuclear membrane disintegrates. The chromosomes arrange themselves into their homologous pairs. This pairing is called a **synapsis**. Portions of the 4 chromatids may **crossover** one another, allowing portions of genetic material to be exchanged. This results in 4 chromatids that are **no longer identical** and ultimately gives rise to daughter cells that are not identical to the parent.

Shortening and thickening   **Crossing over**

2. **Metaphase I:** The homologous **pairs align** down the centre of the cell.

3. **Anaphase I:** The homologous chromosomes **split** into two groups. Each group contains **one** chromosome **from each pair**. The groups migrate to opposite ends of the cell.

4. **Telophase I:** A nuclear membrane forms around each group of chromosomes, and the cytoplasm is eventually **divided** by the cell membrane. You may recall this is called cytokinesis. This produces **2 haploid** cells. Each cell contains only one member of the original homologous chromosomes from the parent cell.

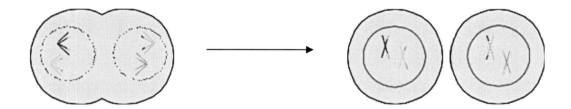

We strongly recommend you take questions 15-25 to reinforce your understanding, before continuing with meiosis II.

Meiosis II is very similar to **mitosis**. Both haploid cells go through this second phase, creating **4 haploid** cells.

Remember, the chromosomes replicated before the first nuclear division, so each chromosome already consists of 2 chromatids.

Let's look at the 4 phases of meiosis II. Remember we begin meiosis II with the 2 haploid cells produced as a result of meiosis I.

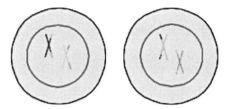

The 4 phases of **meiosis II** are:

1. **Prophase II:** The chromosomes appear to shorten and thicken. The nuclear membrane disintegrates.

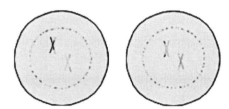

2. **Metaphase II:** The chromosomes align down the centre of the cell.

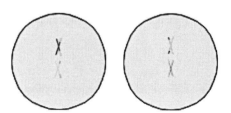

3. Anaphase II: The chromatids split into two groups and move to opposite ends of the cell.

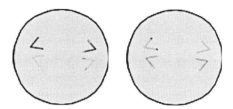

4. Telophase II: A nuclear membrane forms around each group of chromosomes. Later, the cytoplasm is divided by the cell membrane to produce 2 new haploid cells.

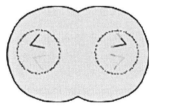 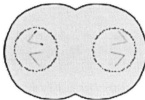

The end result of meiosis is therefore 4 non-identical cells, each with half the genetic complement of the parent cell.

Meiosis, in halving the genetic complement of the cells, creates both sperm and ova. We'll look at both of these processes, starting with spermatogenesis.

Spermatogenesis

Spermatogenesis is the process by which the seminiferous tubules of the testes produce spermatozoa (sperm). In humans, this process takes about **74 days**.

The **seminiferous tubules** are lined with immature stem cells called **spermatogonia**. Spermatogonia are **diploid** cells.

When spermatogonia divide by **mitosis**, some of the resultant cells remain undifferentiated. These new undifferentiated cells continue to serve as stem cells. Other resultant cells undergo changes and differentiate into **primary spermatocytes**.

Each primary spermatocyte divides by meiosis. After **meiosis I**, the 2 resulting haploid cells are called **secondary spermatocytes**.

The secondary spermatocytes undergo **meiosis II** and each produce 2 **spermatids**. Each spermatid develops a **head** and a **tail** and matures into a **spermatozoon** (a sperm cell).

Sperm enter the lumen (cavity) of the seminiferous tubule and migrate to the epididymis. They complete their maturation there in 10-14 days and become capable of fertilizing an ovum.

Let's take a look at how female gametes are produced during oogenesis. You will see similarities between oogenesis and spermatogenesis. The biggest difference is the time scales...

Oogenesis

Oogenesis produces ova, the female gametes. During **early foetal** development, diploid cells called **oogonia** are produced in the **ovaries**.

The oogonia divide by **mitosis** during the **third month** of foetal development to form **primary oocytes**. The primary oocytes **begin meiosis I** but do not complete it until **after puberty**.

Each primary oocyte is surrounded by a single layer of epithelial cells. This whole structure is called a **primordial follicle**. The primordial follicles do not develop any further until they are stimulated by **follicle stimulating hormone**.

After puberty, several primordial follicles respond **each month** to the rising level of follicle stimulating hormone. They develop to become **primary follicles**. Most primary follicles degenerate, but **one**, influenced by **luteinizing hormone**, completes **meiosis I**.

Meiosis I creates two haploid cells, but they are of unequal size. The **smaller** cell is called the **polar body** and contains discarded nuclear material. It may undergo meiosis II and produce 2 polar bodies, which eventually disintegrate.

The **larger** cell is the **secondary oocyte**. It is surrounded by several layers of epithelial cells. This whole structure is known as the **secondary follicle**.

The **secondary oocyte** begins **meiosis II** but stops at **metaphase II**.

At **ovulation** the secondary oocyte enters the **fallopian tube**. Only if **fertilization** occurs, is meiosis II **completed**. The completion of meiosis II produces 2 cells, again of uneven sizes. The larger cell eventually develops into an **ovum** (mature egg).

The smaller cell produced by meiosis II, is known as the **second polar body** and disintegrates.

Therefore, of the 4 cells produced by meiosis, only 1 can develop into an ovum, the other 3 disintegrate.

Fertilization to Birth

We will now **overview** the main processes involved from fertilization to birth. The hormonal aspects of pregnancy, birth and lactation are covered in the Endocrine System.

Fertilization is the **fusion** of the male and female **gametes**. It occurs when the spermatozoon penetrates and enters the secondary oocyte. Fertilization usually takes place in the **fallopian tube**, 12-24 hours after ovulation.

As we have seen, when a spermatozoon enters the secondary oocyte meiosis II is completed. The completion of this cell division results in the production of the **ovum** and a second polar body. The second polar body disintegrates.

When a spermatozoon has entered the secondary oocyte, the **tail** is **shed** and the nucleus in the **head** develops into a structure called the **male pronucleus**. The ovum develops the **female pronucleus**.

The male pronucleus and the female pronucleus are both haploid. They **fuse** to produce a **segmentation nucleus**. The segmentation nucleus has the genetic information from both the male and the female and so becomes **diploid**.

The fertilized ovum containing the segmentation nucleus is called a **zygote**.

The zygote immediately undergoes **rapid mitotic** cell division. The early cell division of the zygote is called **cleavage**. During the early stages the number of cells increases, but the size of the zygote remains unaltered. The progressively smaller cells produced by cleavage are called **blastomeres**.

Successive cleavages produce a **solid mass** of cells called the **morula**. By the end of the fourth day, the morula moves along the fallopian tube **towards** the **uterine cavity**.

By 4.5 – 5 days, the dense cell mass develops into a **hollow ball** of cells and **enters** the **uterine cavity**. It is now referred to as a **blastocyst**.

Shortly after entering the uterine cavity, the blastocyst **attaches** to the wall of the uterine cavity. The blastocyst secretes enzymes that allow the uterine lining to be penetrated. Eventually the blastocyst becomes buried in the endometrium (the mucous membrane lining the uterus). This process is called **implantation**.

Generally, the first 2 months of development is called the **embryonic period**. During this time the developing human is called an **embryo**. By the end of the embryonic period:

✓ **foundations** are laid for all the principal **organs**.

✓ the **embryonic membranes** are developed. These membranes protect and nourish.

✓ the **placenta** and **umbilical cord** develop. The placenta allows the gases, nutrients and wastes to be exchanged between the mother and the developing embryo. The umbilical cord provides the necessary vascular connection for this.

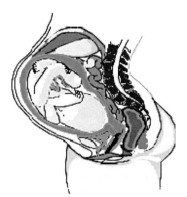

The developmental stage after the embryonic period, is called the **foetal period**. The developing human is called a **foetus**.

During the foetal period, the **organs** established in the embryonic stage **grow** rapidly, and the foetus takes on a **human appearance**.

The time that the zygote, embryo or foetus is carried in the female is called **gestation**. In humans, the gestation period is about **266 days**. The newly formed human is then born. The process of birth is called **parturition**.

During parturition, the foetus is expelled from the uterus. This process is called **labour** and may last for several hours. Strong, rhythmic, muscular contractions of the uterus force the foetus from the uterus into the vagina, and it then leaves the body.

After the delivery of the baby, the placenta is also expelled by powerful uterine contractions.

Summary

➢ Reproduction is the process by which new individuals are produced and the genetic information passed from generation to generation.

➢ The main functions of the male reproductive system are the production of sperm and impregnation.

➢ The testes are the principal structures of the male reproductive system.

➢ Sperm, produced in the testes by a process called spermatogenesis, travel through the seminiferous tubules to the epididymis where they mature.

➢ The vas deferens leads from the epididymis to the urethra.

➢ During ejaculation, the sperm mix with fluids secreted by the seminal vesicles and the prostate gland. The resulting semen is released via the penis.

➢ The main functions of the female reproductive system are ovulation, menstruation, pregnancy and birth.

➢ The ovaries are the principal structures of the female reproductive system.

➢ The ovaries produce ova by a process called oogenesis.

➢ During ovulation, a potential ovum breaks free from the primary follicle and enters the fallopian tube.

➢ The fallopian tube usually provides the site of fertilization.

➢ The fertilized ovum, called a zygote, arrives in the uterus about 7 days after ovulation.

➢ The uterus provides the site of attachment and nourishment for the developing foetus.

➢ The development of the follicles, ovulation, the preparation of the uterus to accept the zygote and the breakdown of the uterine lining if fertilization does not occur, is controlled by hormones.

➢ Diploid cells contain 23 pairs of chromosomes, one pair of which determines sex.

➢ The sex chromosomes are XX in the female and XY in the male.

➢ Meiosis is the process of nuclear division that creates gametes.

➢ Gametes are haploid cells and have 23 chromosomes.

➢ Fertilization, implantation, embryonic and foetal development, and parturition facilitate the delivery of a new human.

Questions (Answers: Page 390)

1.   Which tubule transports sperm from the testis to the urethra?

      a. epididymis
      b. vas deferens
      c. ejaculatory duct

2.   Fill in the missing word:

      The seminal vesicles and the _____ gland secrete fluids during ejaculation.

3.   True or False?

      Every month both ovaries produce and develop an ovum.

4.   What name is given to an immature ovum encased in a sac?

      a. follicle
      b. fimbriae
      c. zygote

5.   In which structure does fertilization normally occur?

      a. ovary
      b. fallopian tube
      c. uterus

6.   A fertilized ovum is called a zygote. To which structure does the zygote attach for nourishment and development?

7.   What collective name is given to the female external genitalia?

      a. vulva
      b. perineum
      c. labia
      d. vestibular glands

8.   Which labia are covered in pubic hair and consist of adipose tissue, sebaceous glands and sweat glands?

      a. labia majora
      b. labia minora

9. Which part of the female genitalia releases mucus during sexual intercourse?

    a. clitoris
    b. vestibular bulbs
    c. greater vestibular glands

10. What causes the breakdown of the uterine lining if the implantation of a zygote does not occur?

    a. reduction in oestrogens and progesterone
    b. increase in oestrogens and progesterone

11. What hormone, secreted by the ovaries, encourages the re-build of the uterine lining?

    a. follicle stimulating hormone
    b. luteinizing hormone
    c. oestrogen

12. What name is given to the slightly raised rough area that surrounds the nipple?

13. How many glandular lobes are present in each breast?

    a. 5-15
    b. 15-20
    c. 20-25
    d. 25-30

14. What are the clusters of milk-secreting glands in the breast called?

    a. lobes
    b. lobules
    c. alveoli
    d. mammary ducts

15. What is the correct order of structures through which milk passes?

    a. mammary duct, secondary tubule, lactiferous duct, nipple
    b. lactiferous duct, secondary tubule, mammary duct, nipple
    c. secondary tubule, lactiferous duct, mammary duct, nipple
    d. secondary tubule, mammary duct, lactiferous duct, nipple

16. True or False?

    Cooper's ligaments run between the skin and the deep fascia.

17.   Which lymphatic nodes receive more than 75% of lymph from the breasts?

18.   How many pairs of chromosomes are contained in a cell (other than a gamete)?

      a. 2
      b. 12
      c. 23
      d. 46

19.   What term is given to cells with just 23 chromosomes - half the normal genetic complement?

      a. diploid
      b. haploid

20.   Which individuals have diploid cells containing two X chromosomes?

      a. males
      b. females

21.   True or False?

All sperm produced contains just one X chromosome.

22.   Which type of nuclear division creates gametes?

      a. mitosis
      b. meiosis

23.   Which of the two nuclear divisions involved in meiosis reduces the genetic complement by half?

      a. meiosis I
      b. meiosis II

24.   What happens to the chromosomes prior to meiosis?

      a. divide into two
      b. cease to function
      c. replicate
      d. align down the centre of the cell

25.   True or False?

       During prophase I, the chromosomes arrange themselves into their homologous pairs.

26.   At which phase of meiosis do the homologous pairs align down the centre of the cell?

       a. prophase I
       b. metaphase I
       c. anaphase I
       d. telophase I

27.   True or False?

       During anaphase I, the chromatids split and migrate to opposite ends of the cell.

28.   What is produced at the end of telophase I?

       a. 1 haploid cell
       b. 2 haploid cells
       c. 4 haploid cells
       d. 2 diploid cells

29.   True or False?

       In meiosis I the homologous chromosomes split into two groups. In meiosis II, the chromatids split into two groups.

30.   What is the name of the immature stem cells that line the seminiferous tubules?

       a. secondary spermatocytes
       b. primary spermatocytes
       c .spermatogonia
       d. spermatids

31.   What nuclear division do spermatogonia undergo to become primary spermatocytes?

       a. mitosis
       b. meiosis I
       c. meiosis II

32.   What is produced when primary spermatocytes undergo meiosis I?

        a. diploid primary spermatocytes
        b. haploid primary spermatocytes
        c. diploid secondary spermatocytes
        d. haploid secondary spermatocytes

33.   What is produced when the secondary spermatocytes undergo meiosis II?

34.   Where do spermatozoa complete their maturation?

35.   Which cells form in the ovaries during early foetal development, and then undergo mitosis during the third month of foetal development to form primary oocytes?

36.   What process begins in the primary oocytes?

        a. mitosis
        b. meiosis I
        c .meiosis II

37.   A single layer of epithelial cells surrounds each primary oocyte. What name is given to this whole structure?

        a. primary follicle
        b. primordial follicle

38.   What do primordial follicles develop into under the influence of follicle stimulating hormone?

        a. primary follicles
        b. polar bodies
        c. secondary oocytes
        d. secondary follicles

39.   When the primary follicle completes meiosis I, two haploid cells are produced. The smaller is the polar body. What name is given to the larger haploid cell?

        a. secondary oocyte
        b. secondary follicle

40.   Fill in the missing word:

       The secondary oocyte begins meiosis II but stops at metaphase II. Meiosis II is not completed until _____ occurs.

41. The completion of meiosis II produces 2 cells of uneven size. Which eventually develops into an ovum?

   a. the largest
   b. the smallest

42. Meiosis produces a total of 4 haploid cells. During oogenesis, how many of these cells can actually give rise to an ovum?

   a. 1
   b. 2
   c. 3
   d. 4

43. Fill in the missing word:

   The male pronucleus and the female pronucleus fuse to form a _____ nucleus.

44. Immediately after fertilization the zygote undergoes rapid cell division. What name is given to the smaller cells that are produced?

   a. blastomeres
   b. morula
   c. blastocytes

45. Fill in the missing word:

   Successive cleavages create a solid cell mass called a _____ .

46. What name is given to the cell mass when it forms a hollow ball of cells and enters the uterine cavity?

   a. blastocyte
   b. blastocyst

47. What stage of development precedes the foetal period?

This page has intentionally been left blank.

Lymphatic System

This page has intentionally been left blank.

Lymph is basically excessive or unwanted **tissue fluid**. It is termed lymph when it drains into the lymphatic vessels. Lymph is a colourless, watery connective tissue. It resembles blood plasma in composition except it contains less plasma proteins (the large molecules do not easily filter out of the blood capillaries) and contains many lymphocytes.

The lymphatic system consists of **lymph**, the network of **vessels** through which it flows, **structures** that contain lymphatic tissue and **bone marrow**.

The lymphatic system has 3 main functions:

1. Drainage of tissues

Waste products produced by the cells get passed into the intercellular fluid. Not all of these waste products can be absorbed into the blood capillaries to be transported away by the cardiovascular system. The lymphatic system supports the cardiovascular system by **removing waste products** which are **not absorbed** into the **blood**, along with any **excessive tissue fluid**. These substances pass into the lymphatic capillaries and form the lymph. The lymph is **filtered** by the lymph nodes and is eventually **drained directly** into the cardiovascular system.

2. Transportation of fats

Fat and **fat soluble vitamins** are passed from the digestive tract into the lymphatic system via lymphatic vessels called **lacteals**. We look at this later in this section.

3. Immunity

The lymphatic system plays a vital role in immunity. It produces white blood cells called lymphocytes which play a part in the body's natural defenses and immunity against disease. Immunity is also covered in detail later.

The bone marrow and lymphatic glands produce lymphocytes (see Cardiovascular System). Lymphocytes are leucocytes (white blood cells) that play a part in the body's natural defenses and immunity against disease.

Let's look at lymphocytes…

There are 2 main types of lymphocyte:

1. **B-cell lymphocytes:** B-cells are responsible for producing **antibodies** (memory hint: **B**-cells = anti**B**odies). They develop into antibody-secreting **plasma cells**. Antibodies are protein molecules formed within the body to **neutralize** the effect of foreign invading substances (antigens). Antibody molecules attach themselves to invading antigen molecules, rendering them inactive.

2. **T-cell lymphocytes:** These have various roles to play in immunity, including **destroying** foreign substances.

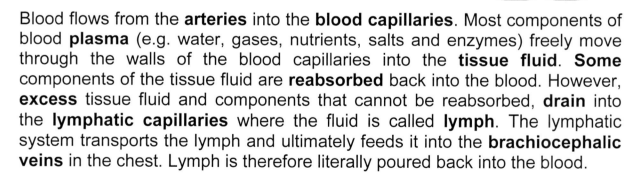

The lymphatic system is similar to the cardiovascular system in as much as it consists of a complete **network** of vessels. However, unlike the cardiovascular system, the lymphatic system **does not** have a **pump**.

The lymph is circulated by the movement of the body's **muscles** and is also assisted by the movements involved in **respiration**. The lymphatic system and the cardiovascular system are interconnected…

Blood flows from the **arteries** into the **blood capillaries**. Most components of blood **plasma** (e.g. water, gases, nutrients, salts and enzymes) freely move through the walls of the blood capillaries into the **tissue fluid**. **Some** components of the tissue fluid are **reabsorbed** back into the blood. However, **excess** tissue fluid and components that cannot be reabsorbed, **drain** into the **lymphatic capillaries** where the fluid is called **lymph**. The lymphatic system transports the lymph and ultimately feeds it into the **brachiocephalic veins** in the chest. Lymph is therefore literally poured back into the blood.

The tubes of the lymphatic system **begin** as **closed-end** lymphatic **capillaries**. Lymphatic capillaries are the smallest of the lymph tubes.

The lymphatic capillaries penetrate the spaces between the cells. They have slightly **larger lumen** than blood capillaries and a unique vessel wall. The wall of the lymph capillaries consists of a single layer of **overlapping endothelial** cells. This overlapping allows the cells to act like **one-way valves, allowing** lymph to **flow into** the capillaries but **not out** of them. The lymphatic capillaries converge to form the larger **lymphatic vessels**. Lymphatic vessels contain **valves** to prevent the back-flow of lymph.

In the intestine, the lymphatic vessels are called **lacteals**.

The lacteals are embedded in the **villi** of the small intestine. **Nutrients** absorbed from the digestive tract into the villi can either pass through the walls of the blood capillaries and enter the blood, or pass through the wall of the lacteal into the lymph. The lacteals absorb **fat** from digested foods, while carbohydrates and proteins are passed into the blood.

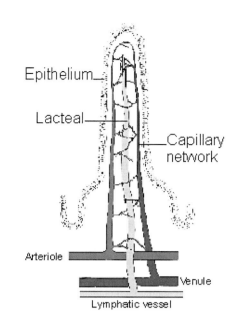

At intervals along the lymphatic vessels, **lymph nodes** occur. These **small**, **oval** or **bean-shaped** bodies are usually found in **clusters**, particularly in the axilla, neck, abdomen and groin. Let's take a look at the structure of a lymph node…

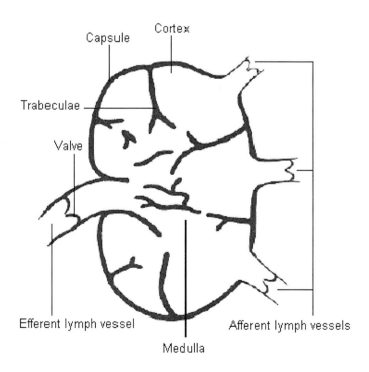

Lymph nodes range from **1 - 25mm** in length. Each node is covered by a **capsule** of dense connective tissue. The capsule extends into the nodes to form **trabeculae**, which partially segment the lymph node into **nodules**.

The lymph is brought to the node in several afferent **vessels**. The afferent vessels have **valves** that only allow the lymph to flow in **one direction**. The lymph flows **slowly** through the node from the **cortex** (outer region) to the medulla (inner region) and then leaves via one or two efferent lymph vessels. Efferent vessels are **wider** than the afferent vessels and their valves open away from the node to encourage the lymph out and prevent back-flow.

As the lymph flows through the node, cell **waste** or **harmful substances** that may cause infection are **trapped** by a network of **fibres**. The trapped substances are then destroyed before the lymph is passed back into the cardiovascular system. The lymph nodes are able to perform this role because they are packed with lymphocytes…

The **cortex** of the lymph nodes contains densely packed **T-cells** and **macrophages**, both capable of **ingesting** and **destroying** foreign particles.

There are B-cells in lymph nodes too. When an immune response is occurring, B-cells produce many **antibody-secreting plasma cells** in the **germinal** centres of the cortex. The medulla also contains macrophages and plasma cells arranged in strands called medullary cords.

Due to the quantity of lymphocytes in the nodes, foreign substances that are transported to the nodes and then filtered out are destroyed by **phagocytosis** or they trigger an **immune response**.

As we have discussed, lymph nodes are often found in clusters and they have a capsule. There is another type of lymphatic tissue, very similar to nodes, called **nodules**. These too are oval shaped but do **not** have a **capsule**. They also tend to be **solitary** rather than being in clusters.

There is an abundance of lymph nodules in the small intestine, particularly in the lower part of the **ileum**. These normally solitary nodules can also be found in **groups** in the ileum. These groups of nodules are referred to as **Peyer's patches**. Their purpose is to prevent bacteria from entering the blood stream.

Let's now take a look at the **location** of the main groups of lymph nodes, firstly in the **whole body** and then specifically in the **head and neck**.

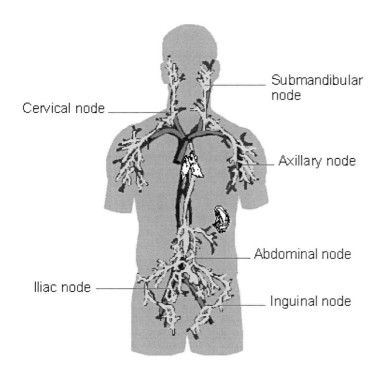

The main lymph nodes in the body are shown here.

There is also a cluster of lymph nodes **behind** the **knees** and behind the **elbows**. These are called the **popliteal** and **supratrochlear** nodes respectively.

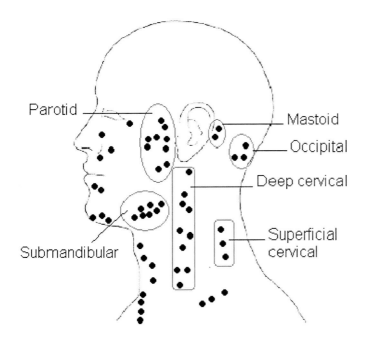

The main lymph node groups in the **head and neck** are shown here.

Deep cervical – deep in the neck, along the path of the large blood vessels.

Mastoid – behind the ear.

Occipital – at the base of the skull.

Parotid – in front of the ear.

Submandibular – under the jaw.

Superficial cervical – at the side of the neck, over the muscle.

Once past the lymph nodes, the lymphatic vessels unite to form **lymph trunks** and then the larger **lymph ducts**.

The lymph ducts join the **cardio- vascular system** and the lymph is drained into the blood.

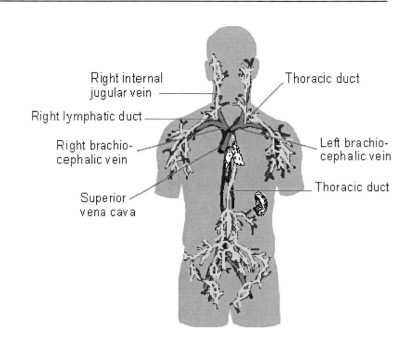

The lymphatic system on the **left** of the body is served by the **thoracic duct** (or left lymphatic duct). The thoracic duct is about 38-45cm long and begins as a dilation called the **cisterna chyli** in front of the second lumber vertebra. The thoracic duct receives lymph from the left side of the head, neck and chest, the left arm and **all** of the lower body. The lymph is then drained into the **left brachiocephalic vein**.

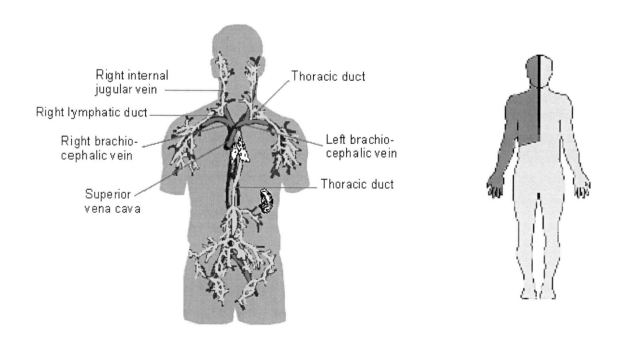

The right of the body is served by the **right lymphatic duct**. This receives lymph from the right side of the head, neck and chest and the right arm. The lymph is then drained into the **right brachiocephalic** vein.

192

The brachiocephalic veins join to form the **superior vena cava**. This major vein carries the blood to the **heart**.

As well as the network of vessels, the lymphatic system also incorporates structures that comprise of **lymphatic tissue**.

The **tonsils**, located at the back of the throat, and the **adenoid** (the nasopharyngeal tonsil), located at the back of the nose, are small bodies of lymphatic tissue embedded in a mucous membrane. They produce lymphocytes and are concerned with defense against bacterial infection. Their location makes them particularly effective in protecting against foreign substances that are inhaled or ingested.

There are also two major lymphatic glands – the **spleen** and the **thymus**.

The **spleen** is the largest mass of **lymphatic tissue** in the body. It produces lymphocytes and is a site at which B-cells develop into plasma cells.

Although the spleen produces lymphocytes, it has no connection to lymphatic vessels and so it is not involved in filtering lymph.

The spleen is an **oval** shaped organ located to the **left** of the abdomen, just **inferior** to the **diaphragm**. It is surrounded by an **elastic capsule**, which allows the spleen to expand and contract. A **membrane** covers the whole structure.

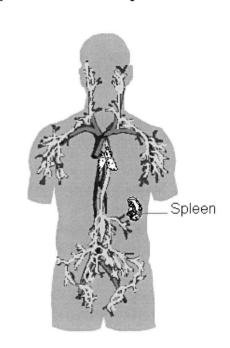
Spleen

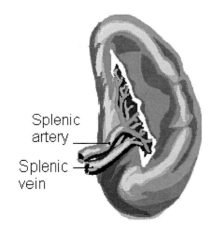
Splenic artery

Splenic vein

The spleen is **highly vascular**. It is connected to the circulatory system by the **splenic artery** and **splenic vein** and has a significant **capillary** network.

The spleen destroys old and worn out **red blood cells** and **platelets**. It also acts as a reservoir for blood. The spleen contains red pulp tissue and white pulp tissue.

The **red pulp** tissue consists of blood-filled sinuses (cavities) and cords of splenic tissue consisting of red blood cells, macrophages, lymphocytes, plasma cells and granular leucocytes. The circulation of the blood through the spleen is slow. Blood can leak out of the sinuses into the lymphatic tissue allowing the phagocytosis of red blood cells, platelets and bacteria.

White pulp is lymphatic tissue, comprising mostly of lymphocytes. White pulp tends to be arranged around the arteries, so allowing the lymphocytes to easily enter the bloodstream.

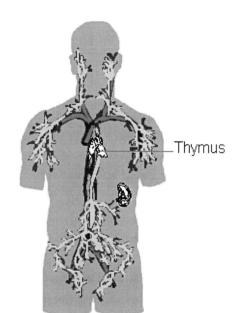
Thymus

The **thymus** consists of two lobes located in the upper chest, between the sternum (breast bone) and the lungs. Connective tissue, encased in a capsule, holds the two lobes together.

Each lobule has an outer layer called the cortex and an inner medulla. The **cortex** is **packed** with **lymphocytes**. **T-cells**, produced in the bone marrow, migrate to the cortex of the thymus for development.

The **medulla** consists of **scattered lymphocytes** within **epithelial** cells. The epithelial cells produce **thymus stimulating hormones** (see Endocrine System), which are thought to help the maturation of the T-cells.

The thymus is large in a child but reduces in size and function for adulthood, when many of its immunity functions are taken over by the spleen.

Immunity

The lymphatic system plays a key role in immunity. Immunity is the ability to resist the activities of **pathogens** (disease-producing organisms).

There are two main types of resistance to disease: non-specific resistance and specific resistance.

1. **Non-specific resistance** includes the defense mechanisms that provide **general** protection against a variety of pathogenic invasions. For example, the skin, in covering the body, provides general protection.

2. **Specific resistance** involves the production of specific antibodies or the activation of T-cells against a particular pathogen.

This chart shows the areas of non-specific and specific resistance that we will cover. You can use it as a recap or to maintain orientation.

IMMUNITY

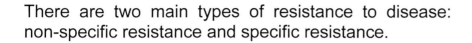

Non-Specific Resistance	Specific Resistance
Skin	Cell-mediated responses
Mucous membranes	Antibody-mediated responses
Anti-microbial substances	Memory cells
Natural killer cells	
Phagocytes	
Inflammation	

Let's take a closer look at non-specific and specific resistance, starting with non-specific resistance.

Non-Specific Resistance

The skin and the mucous membranes are the body's first line of general defense against pathogens. They provide a **mechanical** and a **chemical** barrier.

Skin

The **keratinized** cells of the epidermis provide a **mechanical** barrier to bacteria. The natural **shedding** of the epidermis also helps to remove them. Although bacteria rarely penetrate a healthy epidermis, when it is damaged infection often occurs.

The skin's **chemical** protection arises from the secretion of sebum and perspiration. The sebaceous (oil) glands secrete **sebum**. This forms a protective film over the surface of the skin. Sebum contains fatty acids and lactic acid that inhibit the growth of pathogenic bacteria and fungi. **Perspiration** emitted from the skin flushes bacteria from its surface. It also contains lysozyme, an enzyme capable of breaking down the cell walls of some bacteria.

Mucous Membranes

Mucous membranes consist of an epithelial layer with underlying connective tissue. The epithelial layer secretes **mucus**. Mucus is a **fluid** that prevents cavities from drying out. It is slightly **viscous** so it traps many microbes and other foreign substances. Mucous membranes do not offer the same level of protection as the skin, but they do restrict the penetration of many microbes – mechanically and chemically.

Mechanical protection is provided by **hairs** that project from some mucous membranes. The mucous membrane in the **nasal** cavity has mucus-covered hairs that **trap** microbes, dust and pollutants from inhaled air. The mucous membrane of the upper respiratory tract contains **cilia** (tiny hairs) that play a similar role.

Some mucous membranes are mechanically protected. Preventing damage to the mucous membranes reduces the risk of infection. For example, the secretion of **tears** and the spreading of them over the surface of the **eyeballs** during **blinking**, washes and protects the mucous membrane of the eyes. **Saliva** dilutes the number of micro-organisms and **washes** them from the mucous membranes of the mouth. The mechanical flow of **urine** helps to prevent the build up of microbes in the urethra. **Defecation** and **vomiting**, in response to the irritation of the digestive tract by microbes, are also examples of mechanical protection.

Chemically, the tiny spaces in tissues contain **hyaluronic acid**. Hyaluronic acid is gel-like and **slows** the **spread** of harmful substances in localized infections. Acidic **gastric juices** destroy many bacteria in the stomach. Slightly acidic **vaginal secretions** discourage bacterial growth in the vagina.

Once either the skin or the mucous membranes have been penetrated by pathogens, the next line of defense is provided by **anti-microbial substances**, the **natural killer cells** and the **phagocytes**.

Anti-Microbial Substances

Anti-microbial substances are chemicals that **discourage microbial growth**. Anti-microbial substances are found in the blood and in interstitial fluids.

For example, transferrins (iron-binding proteins) reduce bacterial growth by reducing the amount of available iron.

Natural Killer Cells

Natural killer cells are a type of **lymphocyte**. They have the ability to kill a **wide range** of infectious microbes. Natural killer cells are present in the spleen, lymph nodes, bone marrow and blood. It is not known for certain how natural killer cells actually kill. They may release chemicals or they may cause the fatal damage by direct contact.

Phagocytes

Note: The description of phagocytes requires a knowledge of white blood cells. It is recommended that you have covered the Blood Composition before you go any further.

Phagocytes are leucocytes capable of ingesting (eating) microbes and foreign substances. First they are **chemically attracted** to a particular location. They then **attach** themselves to the surface of the microbe or other foreign substance. The process of **phagocytosis** is complete when the phagocyte extends projections that **engulf** the offending substance.

Once phagocytosis is complete, various **chemicals** are released to **kill** the engulfed microbe. They include:

✓ lysozyme - breaks down the cell walls
✓ digestive enzymes   - break down carbohydrates, proteins, lipids and nucleic acids
✓ oxidants - kill by forcing chemical reactions with oxygen
✓ bactericidal substances - active against bacteria, fungi and viruses

The chemical release is so destructive, a microbe may be destroyed in less than 30 minutes!

The most phagocytic granular leucocytes are the **neutrophils**, but the **eosinophils** have some capability. When an infection occurs, these 2 types of granular leucocyte **migrate** to the infected area. At the same time the **monocytes** (agranular leucocytes) enlarge and develop into **macrophages**. They leave the blood and also migrate to the infected area - they are therefore termed **wandering macrophages**.

The last non-specific resistance to look at is inflammation...

Inflammation
Inflammation occurs when cells are damaged and therefore stressed. Inflammation is characterized by **redness**, **pain**, **heat** and **swelling**.

Inflammation begins with **vasodilation**. This allows more blood to flow through the damaged area. With this, the **blood vessels** become more **permeable** and allow the antibodies, phagocytes and clot-forming factors to enter the injured area. The increased blood flow also enables the removal of the toxic products.

Vasodilation creates **heat** and **redness**. As the temperature rises, the **metabolic rate increases** releasing more heat. The increased **permeability** of the blood vessels creates the **swelling** as more fluid moves from the blood into the tissues. **Pain** may result from the swelling, any nerve damage, or from the toxic chemicals associated with the microbe.

The **neutrophils** arrive within about an **hour** of the beginning of the inflammatory process, but **die** off **quickly**. **Macrophages** arrive later. They are **more phagocytic** and engulf damaged tissue and worn out neutrophils as well as the invading microbes. All phagocytes eventually die. The dead cells and fluid created during the phagocytic process forms **pus**.

Let's move on to specific resistance. To recap, specific resistance involves the production of specific antibodies or the activation of T-cells against a **particular** pathogen.

Specific Resistance

The body is capable of **recognizing** and **remembering** a variety of harmful substances. These identified harmful substances include pathogens, such as bacteria, viruses, toxins and foreign tissues, and are called **antigens**. By definition, an antigen is any chemical substance that is **recognized** as foreign and is capable of **initiating** a **specific immune response**. They are large, complex molecules, usually **proteins**.

The body's reaction against a particular antigen is called **specific immunity**. Specific immune responses are carried out by the **lymphocytes**. Both T-cells and B-cells are involved.

During maturation T-cells and B-cells develop distinctive **surface proteins**. Some of these surface proteins become **antigen receptors**, capable of recognizing specific antigens.

T-cells and B-cells respond to antigens in very different ways. T-cells are involved in cell-mediated immune responses. B-cells are concerned with antibody-mediated immune responses. We'll look at these next…

Cell-Mediated Responses
In cell-mediated immune responses the **T-cells** proliferate into **killer T-cells** that **directly attack** the invading antigen – providing the antigen is a protein.

The process begins by a small number of T-cells **recognizing** the antigen. The T-cells then **proliferate** and **differentiate** to create a group of identical T-cells that all recognize the same antigen. They then all attack in the same way to **eliminate** the antigen.

This '**cell attacking cell**' response is effective against intracellular pathogens, some cancer cells and foreign tissue implants. It works mainly against antigens dissolved in the body fluids and extracellular pathogens.

Antibody-Mediated Responses

In antibody-mediated immune responses, **B-cells** develop into **plasma cells** that secrete **antibodies**.

Antibodies are **proteins** called immunoglobulins. During the immune response, the antibodies **attach** to the specific antigen to render it inactive. The antibody fits to a specific antigen as a key does to a lock.

Memory Cells

A feature of specific immune responses is the body's ability to recognize a subsequent attack by the same antigen. This is due to the creation of **memory cells**.

Antibodies (derived from the B-cells) or the differentiated killer T-cells, both produced in response to a specific antigen, can live for a long time. After the infection has been dealt with they are called memory cells. If the specific antigen that caused the original immune response is encountered again, the immune response is quicker and more intense because some of the necessary cells are already in place to start the specific immune response.

As time progresses, memory cells allow immunity to a variety of antigens to be built up.

Exposure to antigens and the consequent build up of relevant antibodies is called **active immunity**.

Immunity is also gained passively. **Passive immunity** is gained when antibodies are transferred from the mother's blood to the foetus during gestation.

Summary

➢ The lymphatic system consists of lymph, the network of vessels through which it flows, structures that contain lymphatic tissue and bone marrow.

➢ The lymphatic system allows excess fluid, waste materials and bacteria to be drained from the tissues, transports fats and fat soluble vitamins from the digestive tract into the blood, and plays a vital role in immunity.

➢ Lymph is excessive or unwanted tissue fluid.

➢ Bone marrow and lymphatic glands produce lymphocytes, which play a part in the body's natural defenses and immunity.

➢ The lymphatic network consists of lymphatic capillaries, vessels, nodes, trunks and ducts.

➢ Lymph ducts join the cardiovascular system.

➢ The tonsils and adenoid are small bodies of lymphatic tissue that protect primarily against foreign substances that are inhaled or ingested.

➢ The spleen is the largest mass of lymphatic tissue. It produces lymphocytes.

➢ The thymus is the site at which T-cell lymphocytes mature.

➢ Non-specific resistance to disease provides general protection against a variety of pathogenic invasions. Non-specific resistance is provided by the skin, mucous membranes, anti-microbial substances, natural killer cells and phagocytes.

➢ Phagocytosis is the process in which offending substances are engulfed. Chemicals then destroy the substance.

➢ Specific resistance to disease involves the production of specific antibodies or the activation of T-cells against a particular pathogen.

➢ Cell-mediated immune responses involve the T-cells. Killer T-cells attack the invading antigen.

➢ Antibody-mediated immune responses involve the B-cells. The B-cells develop into plasma cells that secrete antibodies. Antibodies attach to the antigen to render it inactive.

➤ Specific immune responses create memory cells.

➤ Active immunity arises from exposure to antigens. Passive immunity is inherited.

Questions (Answers: Page 391)

1. Fill in the missing word:

    Lymph is excessive or unwanted _____ fluid that has drained into the lymphatic system.

2. True or False?

    Lymphocytes are a type of leucocyte. They play a role in immunity.

3. Which type of lymphocyte is responsible for producing antibodies?

4. True or False?

    Excess tissue fluid that is not reabsorbed into the blood drains into the lymphatic capillaries. The lymph is then ultimately returned to the blood.

5. What are the smallest lymph tubes called?

6. Yes or No?

    Can lymph pass from lymphatic capillaries back into the tissue fluid?

7. True or False?

    When lymphatic capillaries converge they form the larger lymphatic vessels.

8. What name is given to the lymphatic vessels embedded in the villi of the small intestine?

9. Which small, round structures, occurring at intervals along lymphatic vessels, are packed with lymphocytes?

10. True or False?

    Lymph nodes filter harmful substances from the lymph and destroy them before the lymph is drained into the blood.

11. Which lymph nodes are found behind the knees?

12.   Which of these lymphatic structures are the largest?

        a. lymph trunks
        b. lymph ducts

13.   True or False?

The left lymphatic duct (thoracic duct) drains lymph from the left side of the body into the left brachiocephalic vein. The right lymphatic duct drains lymph from the right side of the body into the right brachiocephalic vein. The brachiocephalic veins join to form the superior vena cava, which leads to the heart.

14.   Which oval shaped organ is the largest mass of lymphatic tissue in the body?

15.   Which splenic tissue contains closely packed lymphocytes?

        a. red pulp
        b. white pulp

16.   Which part of the thymus is packed with lymphocytes?

        a. cortex
        b. medulla

17.   Which form of resistance to the activities of pathogens provides general protection to a variety of invasions?

        a. non-specific
        b. specific

18.   Do the following non-specific defense mechanisms offer mechanical or chemical protection?

- production of saliva
- hairs on the mucous membranes
- keratinized skin
- shedding of the epidermis
- production of tears

        a. mechanical
        b. chemical

19.   Name one secretion made from the skin that is involved in a non-specific chemical defense mechanism.

20. What is the correct sequence of events during phagocytosis?

    a. attraction, engulfing, attachment
    b. attachment, engulfing, attraction
    c. engulfing, attraction, attachment
    d. attraction, attachment, engulfing

21. Fill in the missing word:

    Once phagocytosis is complete, various _____ are released to kill the engulfed pathogen.

22. Which are the most phagocytic granular leucocytes?

    a. eosinophils
    b. neutrophils
    c. basophils

23. What cells are formed when monocytes enlarge and develop?

24. True or False?

    Inflammation is characterized by redness, pain, heat and swelling.

25. What name is given to a substance (usually a protein) that the body recognizes as being foreign and is capable of initiating a specific immune response?

26. What do T-cells and B-cells develop during maturation?

    a. surface carbohydrates
    b. surface fats
    c. surface proteins
    d. surface acids

27. Which lymphocytes are involved in cell-mediated immune responses?

    a. B-cells
    b. T-cells

28. True or False?

    In cell-mediated responses, the killer T-cells produced are always the same irrespective of the initiating antigen.

29.   Which lymphocytes are involved in antibody-mediated immune responses?

       a. B-cells
       b. T-cells

30.   What cells, produced by the B-cells, secrete antibodies?

31.   True or False?

An antibody can successfully attach to any antigen to render it inactive.

Muscular System

This page has intentionally been left blank.

There are over **600** muscles in the body, accounting for nearly half of the body weight. The muscles:

- ✓ enable **movement**
- ✓ provide a **supportive coverage** for the skeleton
- ✓ give the body **shape** and **contour**
- ✓ provide **strength**
- ✓ help to maintain body **temperature** (70% of the energy generated by the muscles is produced as heat)

Muscle tissue is composed of **75% water**, **20% protein** and **5% mineral salts**, **glycogen** and **fat**. Muscle tissue is characterized by its ability to **contract**. It can also **extend** without damage and its natural **elasticity** allows the muscle to return to its original shape after contraction or extension.

The study of muscles is called myology (my- = muscle, -ology = study of).

Muscles tend to be **narrower** at each **end** than in the middle or 'belly'. They are made up of individual muscle **cells** called **fibres**. Fibres are roughly **cylindrical** and vary in length. A number of fibres are bound together in **bundles**. A collection of bundles is then bound together in a **sheath**. **Nerve impulses**, generated in the brain or spinal column, stimulate their contraction.

The muscles have a **rich blood supply** to deliver the necessary oxygen and nutrients. The venous return drains blood away from the muscles, removing carbon dioxide and wastes.

There are three main types of muscle tissue:

1. **Skeletal (voluntary):** This type is mainly attached to **bones**. The movement of skeletal muscle is under voluntary control.

2. **Smooth (involuntary):** This type is found in the **walls** of **hollow structures** such as blood vessels, the stomach and other internal organs. The movement of smooth muscle is involuntary.

3. **Cardiac (involuntary):** This type of muscle tissue forms most of the **heart**. The movement of cardiac muscle is involuntary.

Let's look at the 3 muscle types in more detail, starting with skeletal.

Skeletal Muscle

As the name suggests, skeletal muscle is mainly attached to **bones**. As the muscle tissue contracts the muscle shortens. This creates a pull on the bone and causes movement. As the muscle tissue relaxes, the **natural elasticity** of the muscle allows it to return to its original size and so the pull on the bone is reduced.

The attachment of the skeletal muscle to the bone is often made using **tendons**. Tendons are made up of non-elastic connective tissue consisting of a mass of parallel white collagen fibres that are continuous with the muscle sheath. The tendons join the muscles to the periosteum of the bone.

When the connective tissues of a tendon extend as a broad, flat layer, the tendon is called an **aponeurosis**. As well as attaching a muscle to the coverings of a bone, an aponeurosis may also attach the muscle to another muscle, or to the skin.

Skeletal muscles can **voluntarily** be made to contract and relax. They are stimulated by **motor neurons**. Motor neurons communicate with each muscle fibre at a chemical synapse called a **neuromuscular junction** (see Nervous System). In most skeletal muscle fibres, there is just one neuromuscular junction. This is located at the **midpoint** of the fibre so that the impulse can spread out from the centre towards both ends.

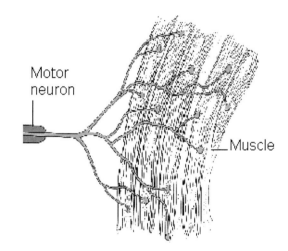

Continued muscular contraction requires much energy in the form of **adenosine triphosphate** (ATP). The muscle therefore needs large amounts of **nutrients** and **oxygen** to produce this energy-carrying molecule during metabolism. The **waste** products produced in this process have to be **removed**. The muscles therefore have a good **blood supply** to deliver the nutrients and oxygen, and to remove the waste products and the heat.

Let's look at the structure of skeletal muscle.

This is a graphical representation of a cross-section through a typical skeletal muscle.

As you can see, the whole muscle is comprised of bundles of muscle fibres. The bundles of muscle fibres are called **fascicles**. The fascicles are **protected** and **supported** by various layers of **connective tissue**.

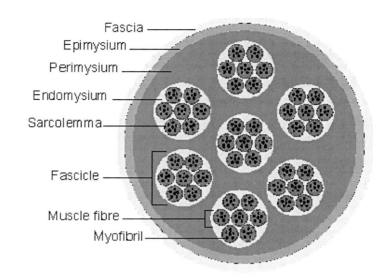

The whole muscle is surrounded by fibrous connective tissue called the **fascia**. The fascia holds the muscle together and segregates one muscle from another, allowing their free movement. It carries nerves, blood vessels and lymphatic vessels, and fills the space between the muscles.

Beneath the fascia is another protective layer called the **epimysium** (epi- = above, my- = muscle). This further protects and strengthens the muscle. The epimysium is continuous with the collagen fibres that connect the muscles to bone or other muscles. These fibres also extend to form the tendons.

The **fascicles** (bundles of muscle fibres) are surrounded by connective tissue called the **perimysium** (peri- = around, my- = muscle). Each fascicle is encased by the **endomysium** (endo- = inside). The endomysium surrounds the individual **muscle fibres**.

At any time, a few muscle fibres are contracting while the others are at rest. These small contractions firm up a muscle without producing movement and are vital for maintaining posture. They also give **firmness**, known as **muscle tone**, to a **relaxed** skeletal muscle.

Muscle fibres are long, cylindrical **cells** that lie parallel to each other. Each muscle fibre is encased in a cell membrane called a **sarcolemma** and contains many **nuclei**. The nuclei are situated on the periphery of the cell, close to the sarcolemma.

In muscle cells, the cytoplasm is called **sarcoplasm**. The sarcoplasm contains many large **mitochondria** necessary for the production of adenosine triphosphate (ATP).

211

The sarcoplasm of the muscle fibre contains many little **threads** called **myofibrils**. Myofibrils run lengthways within the muscle fibre.

The myofibrils contain tiny **filaments**. The filaments **overlap** and do not run the entire length of the myofibril. Cross-partitions called **Z lines** divide the myofibril into **compartments** called **sarcomeres**.

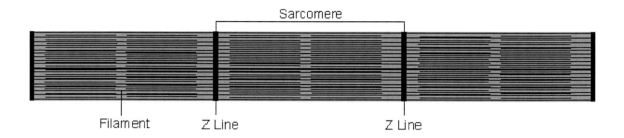

Muscular Contraction

The filaments of the myofibril are composed mainly of two contractile proteins called **actin** and **myosin**. The filaments are responsible for the ability of skeletal muscle to **contract**.

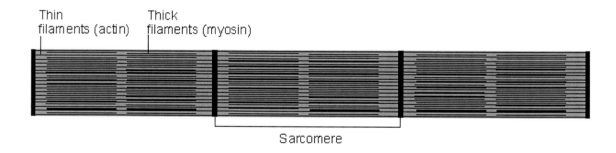

Thin filaments of **actin** project into the sarcomeres from the Z lines. **Thicker** filaments of **myosin** are located between the actin strands. The arrangement of the protein filaments within the sarcomeres gives skeletal muscle its characteristic **striated** (striped) look as the colour alternates between light (actin) and dark (myosin).

During muscular contraction the thin filaments and the thick filaments **slide** past one another. The filaments themselves do **not** alter in size, but their movement pulls the Z lines closer together, shortening the sarcomeres and therefore the whole muscle.

Muscular contraction requires the presence of both **adenosine triphosphate (ATP)** and **calcium**.

The myofibril **filaments contract** when **ATP** is applied to them. However, as ATP is always present in a living cell, an **inhibitor** prevents continuous muscular contraction. The presence of **calcium** ions **neutralizes** the effect of the inhibitor and allows ATP to provide the energy for the muscular contraction.

Calcium is stored in muscle fibres in a system of cisterns called **sarcoplasmic reticulum**. When a muscle fibre is **relaxed** the concentration of calcium ions in the sarcoplasm is **low**. This is because calcium is **actively pumped** from the sarcoplasm into the sarcoplasmic reticulum. When stimulated, calcium is released from the sarcoplasmic reticulum into the sarcoplasm around the filaments. This release of calcium neutralizes the inhibitor so allowing ATP to combine with the protein filaments, triggering muscular contraction.

The ability to remove calcium from the sarcoplasm is very important. If calcium is not removed between contractions, relaxation is either partial or doesn't take place at all.

If a muscle is stimulated at **20-30** times per second, it can only **partially relax** due to the inability to remove the calcium between contractions. This results in a sustained contraction called **incomplete tetanus**.

Should the muscle be stimulated **80-100** times per second, there is **no partial** relaxation. A sustained contraction with no partial relaxation is called **complete tetanus**.

Muscles are never completely relaxed. There is an **involuntary, continuous, partial tension** present known as **muscle tone**. Muscle tone is necessary to keep the body supported – without it we would simply collapse in a heap! Various groups of muscle fibres contract at **different times** to prevent the muscles from becoming fatigued.

Regular **exercise** and **massage** can help to improve the elasticity of the muscle fibres and therefore improve their "tone". Good muscle tone is characterised by firm, rounded muscles. Poor muscle tone shows as floppy, flaccid muscles, whilst over-exercised muscles appear rigid and hard.

Forceful, repetitive muscular activity can result in **muscular hypertrophy**. Muscular hypertrophy is characterised by an **increase** in the **diameter** of **muscle fibres**. This is due to the production of more myofibrils, mitochondria, sarcoplasmic reticulum etc. in the muscle cells. Hypertrophied muscles are capable of stronger contractions.

The opposite to hypertrophy is **muscular atrophy**. This is when the muscles **waste away**. The individual muscle fibres decrease in size due to progressive loss of myofibrils. Muscular atrophy occurs when muscles are not used or if the nerve supply to the muscle is damaged.

Energy Requirements

Muscular contraction requires energy, but there is only enough **ATP** inside the muscle fibres to generate the power to contract the muscle for just a **few seconds**. If activity is to continue, ATP has to be quickly produced. There are a number of ways in which this happens…

Creatine Phosphate
Adenosine triphosphate (tri- = 3) consists of three phosphate groups. It is made when one phosphate group is added to the chemical adenosine diphosphate (di- = 2), ADP.

Muscle fibres contain a unique molecule called **creatine phosphate**. Creatine phosphate can **transfer** its **phosphate** group **to ADP** to form **ATP** and **creatine**. This process is capable of creating enough energy to sustain muscular contraction for about **15 seconds**.

When continued muscle activity uses up the supply of creatine phosphate, **glucose** is **broken down** to generate ATP.

Glucose passes into the muscle fibres from the **blood** and is also produced by the **breakdown** of **glycogen** within the muscle fibres.

Cellular Respiration
The process in which glucose is broken down in the cells to form energy is called **cellular respiration**. Cellular respiration has two phases -

- The **anaerobic** phase breaks down glucose to form some energy in the **absence** of **oxygen**.

- When **oxygen** is available, the **aerobic** phase can take place. In the aerobic phase, further reactions occur in the presence of oxygen to produce greater quantities of ATP.

1. Anaerobic Respiration

During the **anaerobic** phase of cellular respiration, each **glucose** molecule is broken down to produce **two** molecules of **ATP** and **two** molecules of **pyruvic acid**. This occurs in a complex chain of chemical reactions known as **glycolysis**.

When there is **not** sufficient oxygen for the aerobic phase of cellular respiration to take place, the pyruvic acid formed during glycolysis is converted into **lactic acid**. Most of this lactic acid diffuses from the skeletal muscles into the blood. The heart muscle, kidney cells and liver cells can all use lactic acid to **produce ATP**. Liver cells can also **convert back** some of the lactic acid to glucose. Lactic acid that isn't used in these ways remains in the muscle, causing **muscular aches** and adding to **muscle fatigue**, or in the blood until recovery takes place. This anaerobic system can provide enough energy to sustain muscular contraction for about **30 seconds**.

2. Aerobic Respiration

When **oxygen** is present, the **aerobic** phase of cellular respiration occurs.

The pyruvic acid, formed by glycolysis during the anaerobic phase of cellular respiration, enters the **mitochondria**. It is then broken down to produce a **large** amount of **ATP**.

The result of this **aerobic phase** of cellular respiration is that the originating glucose molecule is completely broken down into **carbon dioxide** and **water**, generating **heat** and **large** numbers of **ATP** molecules. Activity that lasts longer than half a minute becomes more and more dependent on **aerobic** reactions.

Oxygen for aerobic cellular respiration in the muscle fibres is obtained from the **blood**. Oxygen is also released from the protein **myoglobin**, found in the sarcoplasm of muscle fibres. Similar to the haemoglobin in the blood, myoglobin in the muscles is oxygen-binding, contains iron and contributes to the red colour.

Aerobic cellular respiration will provide enough ATP as long as there is a **sufficient supply** of **oxygen** and **nutrients**. The body helps to supply these to the muscles during exercise by **dilating** the **blood vessels**.

This system can cope only to a point. When muscular exertion is very great, oxygen cannot be supplied fast enough for cellular respiration to produce sufficient amounts of ATP. The **strength** of the muscular contractions becomes **weaker** and weaker until the muscle **fails** to respond. The inability of the muscle to maintain its strength of contraction is called **muscle fatigue**.

After strenuous exercise, **heavy breathing** continues for some time after the exercise has stopped to recover the oxygen levels.

Recovery from muscle fatigue can be assisted by **resting**. Resting lowers the metabolic rate and therefore lessens the body's need for oxygen. Also, a gentle **massage** of the muscles can promote the blood flow, so increasing the supply of oxygen and glucose and promoting the removal of waste products. This helps the muscles regain their maximum contractile ability.

Muscles work more **effectively** when they are **warm**. An increase in temperature causes **vasodilation** which **increases blood flow**. The chemical reactions that occur in the muscle cells can then take place more **quickly** and so the fibres can contract more easily. However, should the high temperature cause excessive sweating, the loss of sodium from the body in the sweat can cause heat cramps.

When the body is **cold**, the **blood flow** is **reduced** and the chemical reactions in the muscles take place at a **slower** rate. Muscular contractions are therefore slower. The **hypothalamus** may also trigger the muscles to shiver. This involuntary response increases muscular activity and therefore helps to raise the body temperature.

We have completed our look at skeletal muscle. Let's move on to look at the other two muscle types - smooth and cardiac.

Smooth Muscle

Smooth muscle is found in the **walls** of **hollow structures** such as blood vessels, the stomach and other internal organs. It is responsible for regulating the flow of blood in the **arteries**, moving food through the **digestive system** and expelling urine from the **bladder**. Smooth muscle tissue is also responsible for the ability of the **hair** on the skin to stand up.

The **fibres** of smooth muscle are much **smaller** than those found in skeletal muscle. Each fibre has a **single**, central **nucleus**. Smooth muscle is **not striated**. There is no cross-partitioning, and so the thick and thin filaments are not arranged in sarcomeres. Therefore, the fibres do not have the light and dark bands that typify striated muscle.

In smooth muscle, in addition to the thick and thin filaments, there are **intermediate** filaments. Many intermediate filaments **attach** to structures called **dense bodies** that are located in the sarcoplasm. Other intermediate filaments attach to the **sarcolemma**. During contraction, the thick and thin filaments slide, putting tension on the intermediate filaments. This causes a shortening of the muscle fibre.

Contraction in a smooth muscle fibre is **slower** to **start** and **lasts longer** than in skeletal muscles. This is because the **calcium** ions enter and leave the smooth muscle fibres more slowly, so maintaining a continued partial contraction.

There is no conscious, voluntary control over smooth muscles. Their movement is **involuntary**. The **autonomic nervous system** (see Nervous System) governs the contraction and relaxation of smooth muscle.

Smooth muscle can also contract or relax in response to **hormones** or to other factors such as changes in temperature and changes in the chemical composition of the blood.

Cardiac Muscle

The wall of the **heart** (see Cardiovascular System) is made up of cardiac muscle.

Cardiac muscle is **striated** in the same way as skeletal muscle, but its movement is **involuntary**.

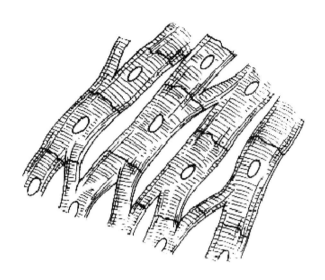

Cardiac muscle has an **inherent** rhythm for alternating between contraction and relaxation, causing the heart to beat about 75 times a minute. To do this, it has no need for nervous or hormonal stimulation. The nervous stimulation received by the cardiac muscle simply increases or decreases the strength of the contractions.

Cardiac muscle fibres interconnect but form **two separate networks**. One network encompasses the **atriums** (upper chambers of the heart) and the other encompasses the **ventricles** (lower chambers). When the fibres of the atriums contract, the blood moves into the ventricles. When the fibres of the ventricles contract, the blood is pumped from the heart into the arteries.

Cardiac muscle fibres have a **single nucleus**. They have **more sarcoplasm** than skeletal muscle fibres and the **mitochondria** are **bigger** and more **numerous**. This is because cardiac muscle is largely dependent on **aerobic** cellular respiration for its ATP production. Cardiac muscle can also use the lactic acid, produced by the skeletal muscles during anaerobic cellular respiration, to make additional ATP.

Movement

One of the principal functions of the muscular system is to facilitate movement.

We have already seen that most of the voluntary, striated **skeletal** muscles are **attached** to the skeleton (usually by a tendon). This skeletal attachment takes place at **both** ends of the muscle. One end of the skeletal muscle is attached to a bone that remains **unmoved**, or fixed, during its contraction. This is called the **origin**. The other end is attached to the bone that the muscle is **intended to move**. This is called the **insertion**.

For example, the **biceps** are the muscles that flex the arm. The biceps are attached by tendons to the scapula (shoulder blade) and the radius (a bone in the forearm). During the contraction of the biceps the scapula remains unmoved. The scapula is therefore the origin. The radius is the bone moved by the biceps. The radius is therefore the insertion.

Skeletal muscles are often arranged in **pairs**. One muscle of the pair opposes the action of the other. As one muscle of the pair contracts, the other relaxes to allow the movement.

The muscle that is contracting to **perform** the **action** is called the **agonist**. The muscle that could oppose the movement but, in relaxing, allows the movement to take place is called the **antagonist**.

For example, when flexing the forearm the biceps contract to cause the movement. The biceps are therefore the agonist. The triceps relax to allow the movement and are called the antagonist.

Some muscles act as **synergists**. Synergists are involved in most movements. They serve to steady the movement created by the agonist. They help to prevent unwanted movement and assist the agonist to make the movement efficient.

Some synergistic muscles function as **fixators**. As the name suggests, these are designed to stabilise the origin of the agonist so that the agonist can move more efficiently. The movement would not be efficient if bone to which the muscle originated could be pulled all over the place! It needs to be fixed so movement is generated at the insertion.

Remember that a muscle may be an agonist, antagonist, synergist or a fixator depending on the movement required.

Muscles are often categorized by the **type** of movement they produce. Most muscular actions can be remembered in **pairs** because one action is the **opposite** of the other. For example:

➢ **Flexors** make a limb bend, **decreasing** the angle at a joint. **Extensors** have the opposite effect. Extensors cause extension, so **increasing** the angle at a joint.

➢ **Abductors** move a bone **away** from the **midline**. **Adductors draw** a bone **closer** to the midline.

➢ **Levators** produce an **upward** movement. **Depressors** produce a **downward** movement.

➢ More specifically, the **supinator** moves the palm **upward** or **anteriorly** and the **pronator** turns the palm **downward** or **posteriorly**.

Muscular actions that do not have an opposing action include **rotators** and **sphincters**. Obviously, rotators allow the bones to rotate. Sphincters control the size of an opening.

Two main types of muscular contraction allow the muscles to perform different actions. They are called isotonic and isometric contractions. We'll look at each…

1. Isotonic Contractions

Isotonic contractions allow the muscle to **shorten** or **lengthen** whilst maintaining a **constant tension**.

For example, when a book is picked up from a table and levered towards the chest, the biceps **shorten** and the angle at the elbow joint decreases. The muscle however maintains the same tension to move the **constant** weight of the book. This is called **concentric contraction**.

When the book is replaced on the table, the biceps lengthen and the angle at the elbow joint increases. However, the muscle still maintains a constant tension. This is called **eccentric contraction**.

2. Isometric Contractions

Isometric contraction occurs when the muscle does **not shorten or lengthen** but **increases** in **tension**.

For example, holding a book out at arm's length does not cause the muscles to alter in length, but the tension applied to them increases. The downward pull of the book continually tries to **stretch** the muscles but this is **opposed** by their **isometric contractions**.

Muscular Structure

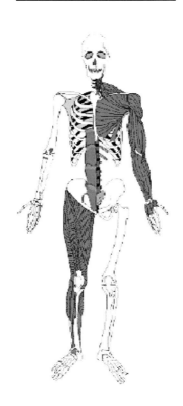

The **muscular structure** of the body is very **complicated**. Muscles are often located on top of one another in **layers** or **overlap** at some point, and their origin and insertion points are usually hidden. Therefore, whole muscles are rarely visible on any diagram.

When studying the muscles, you need to keep a picture of the skeleton in mind as the bones provide the attachment points for the muscles/tendons.

You need to know the **position**, **attachment** (origin and insertion) and **action** of a number of muscles. We will show you as many in-situ as we can but for others we will mark the position of the muscle and tell you if it is positioned deeper or superficial to those shown.

Muscular structure can be difficult to learn and so you need to **revisit** this information and **test** yourself as much as possible.

We'll look at the muscles of the face, head and neck, shoulder, thigh, lower leg, arm and trunk.

Tip: There are a lot of muscles to cover. Don't try to learn them all in one go. Make sure you have mastered one group of muscles before moving onto the next.

Face, Head and Neck

The muscles of the head and face have two main functions; they enable **facial expression** and **mastication** (chewing). The muscles of facial expression differ from muscles in most other parts of the body. Because there is no deep membranous fascia beneath the skin of the head, many of the **thin**, **flat slips** of muscle, **attached** to the **facial skeleton**, **insert directly** into the **skin**.

The three main muscles of facial expression **orbit** the **eyes** (orbicularis oculi) and the **mouth** (orbicularis oris). These are pulled by small straps of muscle that stretch them, so changing the shape/expression of the face. Let's take a look at them…

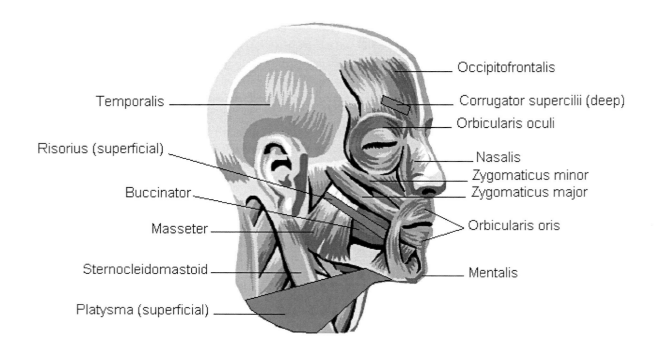

Occipitofrontalis

General: Covers the dome of the skull. (Memory hint: Occipital – to – front)
Attachment: Occipital bone (at the back of the skull) to the muscles and skin at the eyebrows.
Action: The frontal portion draws the scalp forwards, raises the eyebrows and wrinkles the forehead horizontally. The occipital portion draws the scalp backwards.

Corrugator supercilii

General: Medial end of eyebrow, deep into the occipitofrontalis and orbicularis oculi.
Attachment: Medial end of frontal bone to eyebrow.
Action: Draws eyebrow downward. Involved in frowning, producing mainly vertical wrinkles between the eyebrows.

Orbicularis oculi

General: A broad, flat muscle that surrounds the orbit of the eye and extends into the eyelid. (Memory hint: Orbi- = orbit, ocu - = eye)
Attachment: Medial wall of orbit and follows a circular path around it attaching to the skin, subcutaneous tissue of the eyebrow, some adjacent muscles and occasionally to the bone.
Action: Closes the eye. Facial expression including vertical wrinkles above the bridge of the nose.

Nasalis

General: Muscle of the nose. It has two parts; transverse and alar (the wing of the nose that flares to open the nostril).
Attachment: Maxilla to nasal bone.
Action: The transverse part compresses the nasal opening. The alar part widens the nasal opening.

Zygomaticus minor

General: Runs at an angle from the cheek to the mouth, above the zygomaticus major.
Attachment: Zygomatic bone to the muscle of the upper lip.
Action: Elevates the upper lip.

Zygomaticus major

General: Runs at an angle from the cheek to the mouth, below the zygomaticus minor.
Attachment: Zygomatic bone to the orbicularis oris and skin at angle of the mouth.
Action: Draws the angle of the mouth upwards and laterally as when laughing.

Orbicularis oris

General: Muscle, made of four quadrants, that surrounds the mouth. (Memory hint: Orbi- = orbit, or - = oral)
Attachment: Adjacent muscles to the skin of the corner of the mouth.
Action: Closes and protrudes lips and shapes lips during speech. Compresses the lips against the teeth.

Mentalis

General: Located at the front of the chin.
Attachment: Mandible to skin of the chin.
Action: Elevates and protrudes the lower lip and pulls skin of chin up.

Platysma

General: Flat, broad muscle, located superficially to the muscles shown, that extends from the chest to the mandible.
Attachment: Fascia over the deltoid and pectoralis major muscles (in the shoulder and chest) to the mandible, muscles around the angle of the mouth and skin of the lower face.
Action: Draws outer part of lower lip downward and backward.

Sternocleidomastoid

General: Large muscle that runs down the side of the neck.
Attachment: Sternum (breast bone) and clavicle (collar bone) to the temporal bone.
Action: Contraction of the sternocleidomastoid muscles on both sides of the neck causes flexion in the cervical (neck) part of the vertebral column and draws the head forwards. Acting alone, contraction of one muscle rotates the face towards the opposite side.

Masseter

General: Strong muscle that runs down the cheek.
Attachment: Maxilla and zygomatic arch to the mandible.
Action: Elevates the mandible and assists in its side to side movement.

Buccinator

General: Major cheek muscle.
Attachment: Molar area of maxilla and mandible to the orbicularis oris.
Action: Compresses the cheeks against the gums when chewing. Moves cheeks in (as if sucking) and expels air through the lips when the mouth is full of air and the cheeks are distended. (Memory hint: buccinator is Latin for trumpeter)

Risorius

General: Located across cheek, superficially to muscles shown. Size and origins may vary.
Attachment: Include zygomatic arch and fascia over parotid salivary gland, to the skin at the angle of the mouth.
Action: Draws mouth laterally, so involved in grinning and laughing.

Temporalis

General: Temple region to lower jaw. (Memory hint: temp- = temple)
Attachment: Parietal bone to the mandible.
Action: Elevates and retracts mandible. Assists in side to side movement of mandible.

Shoulder – Posterior

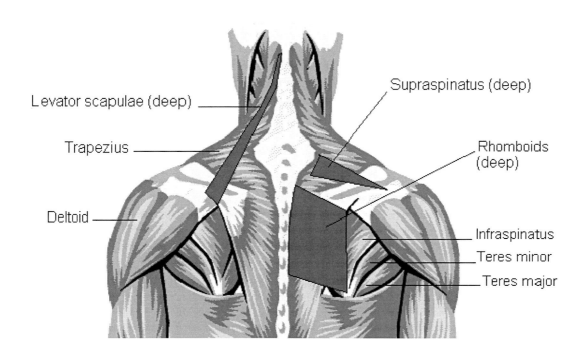

Supraspinatus

General: A thick triangular muscle that runs between the scapula and the humerus. Located deeper than the muscles shown here.
Attachment: Upper part of the scapula to the head of the humerus.
Action: Assists the deltoid muscle to abduct the arm.

Rhomboids

General: Located between the spine and the scapula, deeper than the deltoid but over the infraspinatus, teres minor and teres major muscles. Consist of two parts – rhomboid major and rhomboid minor.
Attachment: Originate from the seventh cervical vertebra to the fifth thoracic vertebra and insert at the medial edge of the scapula.
Action: Adducts the scapula and slightly rotates it downwards.

Infraspinatus

General: A thick triangular muscle that runs between the scapula and the humerus.
Attachment: Scapula to humerus.
Action: Rotates the arm laterally and adducts the arm.

Teres minor

General: Narrow muscle running between the scapula and humerus.
Attachment: Scapula to humerus.
Action: Rotates the arm laterally and adducts the arm.

Teres major

General: A thick, flat muscle running between the scapula and humerus.
Attachment: Scapula to humerus.
Action: Extends arm, assists in adduction and medial rotation of arm.

Deltoid

General: Triangular muscle covering the shoulder.
Attachment: Clavicle and scapula to the humerus.
Action: Abducts the humerus, is involved in the rotation of the arm and generally stabilises the shoulder joint.

Trapezius

General: Large, flat, kite-shaped muscle, extending over the back of the neck and the upper thorax.
Attachment: Occipital bone, seventh cervical vertebra and all thoracic vertebrae to the clavicle and scapula.
Action: Elevates the clavicle and scapula, adducts and depresses the scapula and extends the head.

Levator scapulae

General: Slender muscle that runs from the top of the spinal column to the scapula, located deeper than the muscles shown here.
Attachment: Upper four cervical vertebrae to the upper medial corner of the scapula.
Action: Elevates the scapula.

Shoulder – Anterior

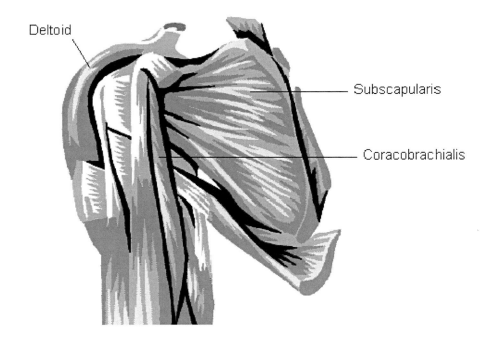

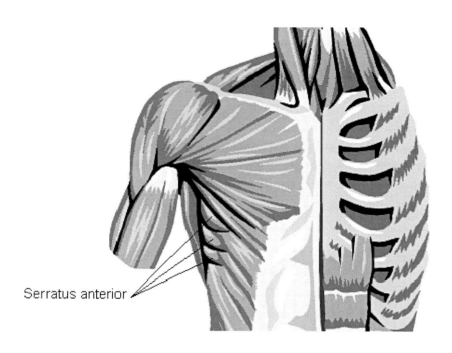

Serratus anterior

Subscapularis

General: A bulky, triangular muscle situated anterior to the scapula.
Attachment: Anterior surface of the scapula to the head of the humerus and to the articular capsule of the shoulder joint.
Action: Rotates the arm medially and stabilises the shoulder.

Coracobrachialis

General: Located between the scapula and the humerus.
Attachment: Scapula to middle of the shaft of the humerus.
Action: Flexes and adducts the arm.

Deltoid

General: Triangular muscle covering the shoulder.
Attachment: Clavicle and scapula to the humerus.
Action: Abducts the humerus, is involved in the rotation of the arm and generally stabilises the shoulder joint.

Serratus anterior

General: Sheet of muscle that runs around the sides of the thorax.
Attachment: Upper eight ribs as separate strips of muscle and to the medial border of the scapula and its anterior surface.
Action: Lateral rotation of the scapula when extending the arms or pushing.

As you have seen, the shoulder is a complex joint. The strength and stability of the shoulder is largely provided by the following **four** deep muscles:

1. **Subscapularis**
2. **Supraspinatus**
3. **Infraspinatus**
4. **Teres minor**

These four muscles and their tendons are arranged to form a nearly complete circle around the shoulder joint. This arrangement is referred to as the **rotator cuff**.

Arm – Anterior

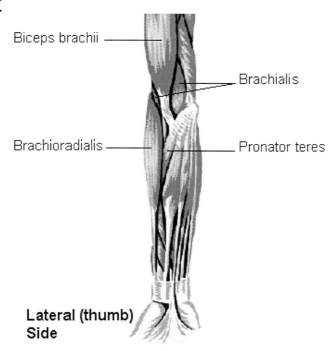

Biceps brachii — Brachialis — Brachioradialis — Pronator teres — Lateral (thumb) Side

Brachialis

General: Lies under the biceps on the anterior side of the arm.
Attachment: Distal portion of the anterior shaft of the humerus, across the elbow, to the ulna.
Action: Assists the biceps to flex the arm.

Pronator teres

General: Lies diagonally across the anterior of the elbow. The title gives its action.
Attachment: Medial side of distal end of the humerus to the lateral surface of the radius about half way down the shaft.
Action: Pronates the hand (turns palm down) and flexes the forearm.

Brachioradialis

General: Lies on the lateral (radial) side of the arm, so the title helps you to remember this one.
Attachment: Lateral and medial side of the distal end of the humerus to the styloid process at the distal end of the radius.
Action: Helps to flex the arm and aids rotation.

Biceps brachii

General: Large, two (bi-) headed muscle on the anterior surface of the upper arm.
Attachment: Both heads originate at the scapula. The main insertion is the head of the radius on the medial side, but there is also an insertion with the fascia over the pronator teres flexor muscle.
Action: Flexes the arm and supinates the hand (turns the palm up).

Flexors of the Wrist

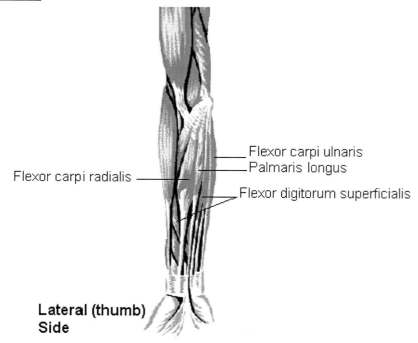

Flexor carpi ulnaris
Palmaris longus
Flexor carpi radialis
Flexor digitorum superficialis
Lateral (thumb) Side

Flexor carpi ulnaris

General: As the title suggests, this muscle flexes the wrist (carpus). It runs from the elbow, down alongside the ulna, to the hand and wrist.
Attachment: Medial distal end of the humerus and upper, posterior border of the ulna, to the fifth metacarpal, hamate and pisiform (carpals).
Action: Flexes and adducts the wrist.

Palmaris longus

General: A flexor of the wrist, that joins the wrist between the flexor carpi radialis (on the side of the radius) and the flexor carpi ulnaris (on the side of the ulna).
Attachment: Medial distal end of the humerus to the deep fascia in the centre of the palm.
Action: Flexes the wrist.

Flexor digitorum superficialis

General: The largest of the superficial flexors lying deep in the forearm. As the name suggests, it flexes the fingers (digits).
Attachment: Medial distal end of humerus, the ulna and the lateral margin of the anterior surface of the radius to the middle phalanges of each finger.
Action: Flexes the middle phalanges of each finger.

Flexor carpi radialis

General: As the title suggest, this muscle flexes the wrist (carpus). It runs from the elbow, down the forearm, across the radius to the metacarpals.
Attachment: Medial distal end of the humerus, across the radius, to the second and third metacarpals.
Action: Flexes and abducts the wrist.

Arm – Posterior

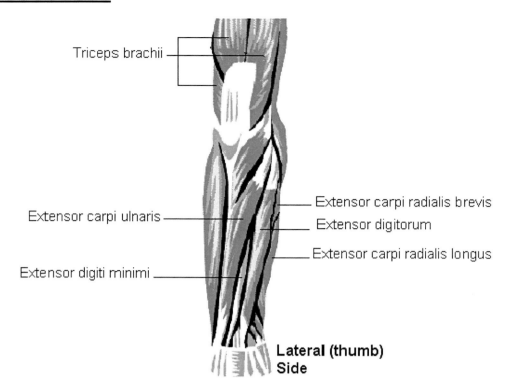

Triceps brachii

Extensor carpi ulnaris

Extensor digiti minimi

Extensor carpi radialis brevis

Extensor digitorum

Extensor carpi radialis longus

Lateral (thumb) Side

Extensor carpi radialis brevis

General: As the name suggests this muscle extends the wrist (carpus). It runs from the elbow to the middle part of the wrist.
Attachment: Lateral distal end of humerus to the third metacarpal.
Action: Extends and abducts the wrist.

Extensor digitorum

General: As the name suggests this muscle extends the fingers (digits). It runs from the elbow and splits over the top of the hand to attach to the fingers.
Attachment: Lateral distal end of humerus to the second – fifth distal and middle phalanges.
Action: Extends the phalanges.

Extensor carpi radialis longus

General: As the name suggests this muscle extends the wrist (carpus). It runs from the elbow, down the edge of the radius to the wrist.
Attachment: Lateral distal end of humerus to the second metacarpal.
Action: Extends and abducts the wrist.

Extensor digiti minimi

General: The clue is in the title again, this muscle extends the little (mini-) finger (digit).
Attachment: Tendon of the extensor digitorum to the tendon of the extensor digitorum on the fifth phalange.
Action: Extends the little finger.

Extensor carpi ulnaris

General: As the name suggests this muscle extends the wrist. It runs from the elbow and joins the wrist on the ulna side.
Attachment: Lateral distal end of humerus and the posterior border of the ulna to the fifth metacarpal.
Action: Extends and adducts the wrist.

Triceps brachii

General: A three (tri-) headed muscle, located on the posterior of the upper arm.
Attachment: One head from the scapula and two from the humerus to the top of the ulna.
Action: Extends the arm.

Hand

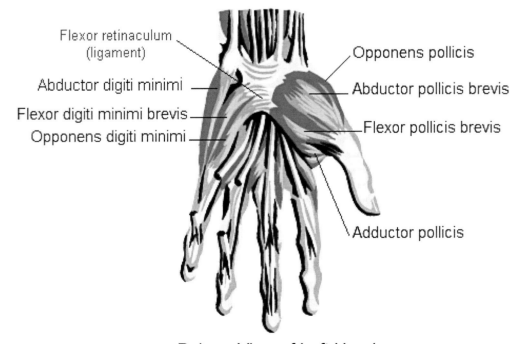

Palmar View of Left Hand

Opponens pollicis

General: One of the four muscles that make up the thenar eminence. The thenar muscles act on the thumb.
Attachment: Flexor retinaculum (a carpal ligament) and trapezium to metacarpal of thumb.
Action: Draws thumb across palm to meet little finger.

Abductor pollicis brevis

General: One of the four muscles that make up the thenar eminence. The thenar muscles act on the thumb.
Attachment: Flexor retinaculum (a carpal ligament), scaphoid and trapezium to the proximal phalange of thumb.
Action: Abducts thumb.

Flexor pollicis brevis

General: One of the four muscles that make up the thenar eminence. The thenar muscles act on the thumb.
Attachment: Flexor retinaculum (a carpal ligament), trapezium and first metacarpal, to the proximal phalange of thumb.
Action: Flexes and adducts thumb.

Adductor pollicis

General: One of the four muscles that make up the thenar eminence. The thenar muscles act on the thumb.
Attachment: Capitate and second and third metacarpals to the proximal phalange of thumb.
Action: Adducts thumb

Opponens digiti minimi

General: One of the four muscles that make up the hypothenar eminence. The hypothenar muscles act on the little finger.
Attachment: Flexor retinaculum (a carpal ligament) and hamate to the metacarpal of the little finger.
Action: Draws the little finger across the palm to meet the thumb.

Flexor digiti minimi brevis

General: One of the four muscles that make up the hypothenar eminence. The hypothenar muscles act on the little finger.
Attachment: Flexor retinaculum (a carpal ligament) and hamate to the proximal phalange of the little finger.
Action: Flexes the little finger.

Abductor digiti minimi

General: One of the four muscles that make up the hypothenar eminence. The hypothenar muscles act on the little finger.
Attachment: Pisiform and tendon of the flexor carpi ulnaris to the proximal phalange of the little finger.
Action: Abducts the little finger.

You may have noticed that we said the hypothenar eminence was made up of 4 muscles but we only showed 3!

The fourth is the **palmaris brevis** but cannot be showed on this diagram. It originates at the flexor retinaculum and the palmer aponeurosis and inserts at the skin on the ulnar border of the palm of the hand. The palmaris brevis draws the skin toward the middle of the palm, as when clenching the fist.

Other muscles in the hand are called intermediate or midpalmar. These muscles work on the digits apart from the thumb.

Thigh – Anterior

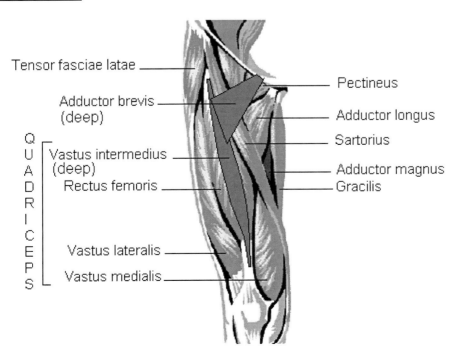

Pectineus

General: Although not called "adductor" in its name, this is an adductor of the thigh.
Attachment: From the pelvis to the femur.
Action: Adduction, medial rotation and flexion of the thigh.

Adductor longus

General: A narrower adductor muscle than the adductor magnus.
Attachment: From the pubic crest and pubic symphysis to the femur.
Action: Adduction, medial rotation and flexion of the thigh.

Sartorius

General: The longest muscle in the body. It crosses two joints, running from the outside edge of the pelvis, past the hip, down and across the leg to the tibia.
Attachment: Iliac crest to the tibia.
Action: Flexes the knee, flexes the thigh at the hip and rotates it laterally (e.g. crossing legs).

Adductor magnus

General: As the name suggests, this is the largest adductor of the thigh, with two heads. Most of this large muscle is deeper than you can see here. Its insertion runs virtually the whole length of the femur.
Attachment: From the pubis and ischium of the pelvis to the femur.
Action: Adduction and medial rotation of the thigh. The anterior part flexes the thigh, the posterior part extends it.

Gracilis

General: The most superficial muscle on the medial side of the thigh. Gracilis is Latin for "slender".
Attachment: From the pubic symphysis and pubic arch to the medial surface of the body of the tibia.
Action: Adducts the thigh and flexes the leg.

Vastus medialis

General: One of the four muscles that make up the quadriceps. The quadriceps cover the anterior thigh.
Attachment: From the femur to the patella and tibia.
Action: Extends the leg.

Vastus lateralis

General: One of the four muscles that make up the quadriceps. The quadriceps cover the anterior thigh.
Attachment: From the femur to the patella and tibia.
Action: Extends the leg.

Rectus femoris

General: One of the four muscles that make up the quadriceps. The quadriceps cover the anterior thigh.
Attachment: From the iliac spine of the pelvis to the patella.
Action: Extends the leg and flexes the thigh.

Vastus intermedius

General: One of the four muscles that make up the quadriceps. The quadriceps cover the anterior thigh. Situated deeper than the muscles shown here.
Attachment: From the femur to the patella and tibia.
Action: Extends the leg.

Adductor brevis

General: A shorter (brev-) adductor muscle than the adductor longus. Located deeper than the muscles shown here.
Attachment: From the pelvis to the proximal part of the femur.
Action: Adduction, medial rotation and flexion of the thigh.

Tensor fasciae latae

General: Positioned on the outside of the thigh at the hip.
Attachment: Iliac crest to the tibia.
Action: Abducts and flexes the thigh.

Thigh – Posterior

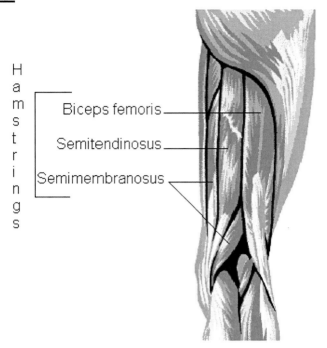

The three muscles that make up the **hamstrings** are shown above.

They all **originate** from the **ischium** but the **biceps femoris** has an **additional** origin from the **femur**.

They all **insert** at the **tibia** but the **biceps femoris** is the odd one out again – it **also** inserts at the **fibula**.

The hamstrings cause flexion of the leg at the knee and extension of the thigh at the hip.

Lower Leg – Anterior

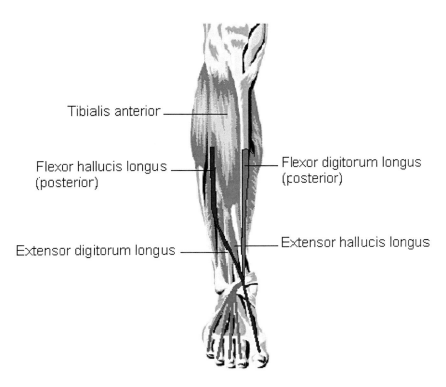

Tibialis anterior

Flexor hallucis longus
(posterior)

Flexor digitorum longus
(posterior)

Extensor digitorum longus

Extensor hallucis longus

Please Note:

The two **extensors** shown here attach to the **superior** surface of the **phalanges**.

The **flexors** shown here run down the **posterior** side of the leg and attach to the **inferior** surface of the **phalanges**.

They are shown here on this anterior view so that you can see that the **extensor** and **flexor digitorum longus** both insert at the **four outer toes** and the **extensor** and **flexor hallucis longus** insert at the **big toe**.

Flexor digitorum longus

General: Located on the **posterior** surface of the lower leg.
Attachment: Upper posterior surface of the tibia to the **inferior** surface of the distal phalanges of the four outer toes.
Action: Plantar flexes the foot (bending the foot in the direction of the sole), inverts the foot (moves the sole of the foot towards the midline of the body) and flexes the toes.

Extensor hallucis longus

General: Located on the anterior surface of the lower leg.
Attachment: Middle portion of the anterior surface of the fibula to the superior surface of the distal phalange of the big toe.
Action: Dorsiflexes the foot (moves the foot up towards the front of the lower leg), inverts the foot (moves the sole of the foot towards the midline of the body) and extends the big toe.

Extensor digitorum longus

General: Located on the anterior surface of the lower leg.
Attachment: Tibia and fibula to the superior surface of the middle and distal phalanges of the four outer toes.
Action: Dorsiflexes the foot (moves the foot up towards the front of the lower leg), everts the foot (moves the sole of the foot to face away from the midline of the body) and extends the toes.

Flexor hallucis longus

General: Located on the **posterior** surface of the lower leg.
Attachment: Lower two-thirds of the posterior surface of the fibula to the **inferior** surface of the distal phalange of the big toe.
Action: Plantar flexes the foot (bending the foot in the direction of the sole), inverts the foot (moves the sole of the foot towards the midline of the body) and flexes the big toe.

Tibialis anterior

General: On the anterior side of the lower leg.
Attachment: Tibia (just below the knee) to the first metatarsal and cuneiform (tarsal).
Action: Dorsiflexes the foot (moves the foot up towards the front of the lower leg) and inverts the foot (moves the sole of the foot to face towards the midline of the body).

Lower Leg – Posterior

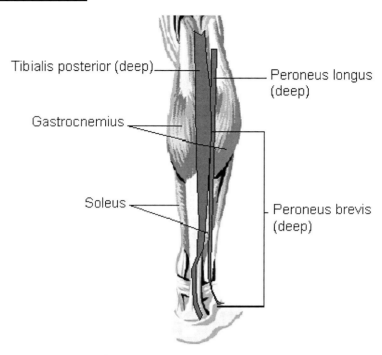

Tibialis posterior (deep)

Peroneus longus (deep)

Gastrocnemius

Soleus

Peroneus brevis (deep)

Peroneus longus

General: One of a pair of peroneal muscles on the lateral side of the lower leg, located deeper than the muscles shown here.
Attachment: Head and upper two thirds of the fibula, down over the lateral side of the ankle then across the foot to the inferior surface of the first metatarsal and first cuneiform.
Action: Plantar flexes the foot at the ankle (bending the foot in the direction of the sole) and everts the foot (turning the sole of the foot outwards).

Peroneus brevis

General: One of a pair of peroneal muscles on the lateral side of the lower leg, located deeper than the muscles shown here.
Attachment: Lower two thirds of the fibula, over the lateral side of the ankle to the inferior surface of the fifth metatarsal.
Action: Plantar flexes the foot at the ankle (bending the foot in the direction of the sole) and everts the foot (turning the sole of the foot outwards).

Soleus

General: Lies under the gastrocnemius in the calf.
Attachment: Head of the fibula and medial portion of tibia to the calcaneus (the tarsal that makes up the heel bone) via the Achilles tendon.
Action: Plantar flexes the foot (bending the foot in the direction of the sole).

Gastrocnemius

General: The main muscle of the calf, made up of medial and lateral portions.
Attachment: Femur to the calcaneus (the tarsal that makes up the heel bone) via the Achilles tendon.
Action: Plantar flexes the foot (bending the foot in the direction of the sole) and flexes the leg at the knee.

Tibialis posterior

General: Located in the calf, deeper than the muscles shown here.
Attachment: Upper shaft of the tibia and head of the fibula to the inferior surfaces of the second, third and fourth metatarsals, navicular, all three cuneiforms and the cuboid (tarsals).
Action: Plantar flexes the foot (bending the foot in the direction of the sole) and inverts the foot (moves the sole of the foot towards the midline of the body).

Trunk – Anterior

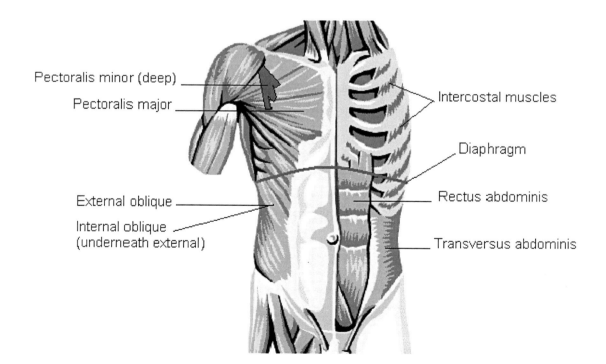

Pectoralis minor (deep)
Pectoralis major
Intercostal muscles
Diaphragm
External oblique
Internal oblique (underneath external)
Rectus abdominis
Transversus abdominis

Intercostal muscles

General: The muscles between the ribs. There are two layers, external and internal.

Attachment: External intercostals run from the inferior border of the rib above to the superior border of the rib below. Internal intercostals run from the superior border of the rib below to the inferior border of the rib above.

Action: External intercostals elevate the ribs during inspiration, increasing the size of the thorax. Internal intercostals draw adjacent ribs together during forced expiration, decreasing the size of the thorax.

Diaphragm

General: The dome-shaped muscle that separates the thorax and abdominal cavities, and plays a role in the process of respiration.

Attachment: Very bottom of sternum, costal cartilages of last six ribs, and lumbar vertebrae to a central tendon for all fibres of the diaphragm.

Action: Pulls the central tendon downwards during inspiration which flattens the dome of the diaphragm and increases the vertical length of the thorax.

Rectus abdominis

General: A broad flat muscle that runs up the length of the abdomen.

Attachment: Pubic crest and pubic symphysis to the cartilage of the fifth, sixth and seventh ribs and the very bottom of the sternum.

Action: Compresses the abdomen.

Transversus abdominis

General: A very deep sheet of muscle that runs from the lower back, around the sides and then up to the bottom of the sternum and down to the pubis. Located under the internal obliques.

Attachment: Iliac crest, lower six costal cartilages, inguinal ligament (in the groin) and lumbar fascia to the very bottom of the sternum, linea alba (a tough fibrous band that extends from the bottom of the sternum to the pubic symphysis) and pubis.

Action: Compresses the abdomen.

Internal oblique

General: The internal obliques are located under the external obliques.

Attachment: Run upwards and medially from the iliac crest, inguinal ligament in the groin and lumbar fascia to the lower four ribs, pubic bone and linea alba (a tough fibrous band that extends from the bottom of the sternum to the pubic symphysis).

Action: Contraction of both internal obliques compresses the abdomen. Contraction of one side bends the vertebral column laterally.

External oblique

General: The external obliques are the largest of the abdominal muscles. Located under the rectus abdominis the external obliques run around the sides of the abdomen.

Attachment: Eight strips from the lower eight ribs run downward and medially to the iliac crest and linea alba (a tough fibrous band that extends from the bottom of the sternum to the pubic symphysis).

Action: Contraction of both external obliques compresses the abdomen. Contraction of one side bends the vertebral column laterally.

Pectoralis major

General: A large muscle covering the anterior thorax.

Attachment: Clavicle, sternum and cartilages of the second to sixth ribs, to the upper portion of the humerus.

Action: Flexes and adducts the arm and rotates the arm medially at the shoulder.

Pectoralis minor

General: Small triangular muscle underneath the pectoralis major.

Attachment: Third, fourth and fifth ribs to the scapula.

Action: Depresses and moves the scapula anteriorly.

Trunk – Posterior

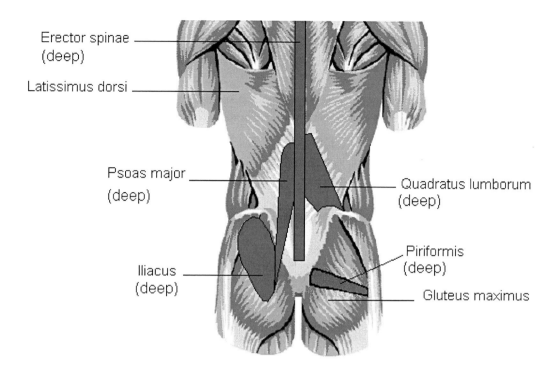

Erector spinae (deep)
Latissimus dorsi
Psoas major (deep)
Quadratus lumborum (deep)
Piriformis (deep)
Iliacus (deep)
Gluteus maximus

Quadratus lumborum

General: A rectangular muscle on either side of the lumbar region. Located deeper than the muscles shown here.
Attachment: Iliac crest to the twelfth rib and the first four lumbar vertebrae.
Action: Lateral flexion of the vertebral column.

Piriformis

General: Pear-shaped muscle in the gluteal region. Located deeper than the muscles shown here.
Attachment: Anterior sacrum to the femur.
Action: Rotates the thigh laterally and abducts it.

Gluteus maximus

General: The strongest single muscle in the body. It makes up the bulk of the buttock and, as the name suggests, is the largest of the gluteal muscles.
Attachment: Iliac crest, sacrum and coccyx to the proximal lateral side of the femur.
Action: Extends the thigh and rotates it laterally.

Gluteus medius (not showing)

General: Lies under the gluteus maximus.
Attachment: Ilium to the head of the femur.
Action: Abduction and medial rotation of the thigh.

Gluteus minimus (not showing)

General: Lies under the gluteus medius and, as the name suggests, is the smallest of the gluteal muscles.
Attachment: Ilium to the head of the femur.
Action: Abduction and medial rotation of the thigh.

Iliacus

General: A triangular muscle deep in the pelvis. Located deeper than the muscles shown here.
Attachment: Anterior surface of the ilium to the tendon of the psoas major, which attaches to the head of the femur.
Action: Flexes and rotates the thigh laterally and flexes the vertebral column.

Psoas major

General: Runs between the lower back and the thigh. Located deeper than the muscles shown here.
Attachment: Lumbar vertebrae to medial side of head of femur.
Action: Flexes and rotates the thigh laterally and flexes the vertebral column.

Latissimus dorsi

General: Wide muscle that runs down the back covering the area between the pelvis and the humerus.
Attachment: Six lower thoracic vertebrae, lumbar vertebrae, sacrum and iliac crest to the upper humerus.
Action: Extends, adducts and rotates the arm medially, draws the arm downward and backward.

Erector spinae

General: Three complex groups of overlapping muscles (iliocostalis (lateral), longissimus (intermediate) and spinalis (medial)) that create the largest muscle mass of the back. Located deeper than the muscles shown here.
Attachment: From and to various points up the length of the back.
Action: Maintain an upright position, maintain the vertebral curvatures, extend the head and vertebral column and flexion and rotation of the spine.

Summary

➢ The muscular system enables movement, supports and protects the skeleton, gives the body shape, provides strength, and helps to maintain body temperature.

➢ Muscle tissue is characterized by its ability to contract, extend without damage and return to its original shape after contraction.

➢ Skeletal muscle is mainly attached to bones (often using tendons).

➢ Skeletal muscle is striated and its movement is voluntary.

➢ Skeletal muscle is comprised of bundles of muscle fibres protected and supported by various layers of connective tissue.

➢ Muscular contraction requires both adenosine triphosphate (ATP) and calcium.

➢ The ATP is acquired either from molecules already in the cell, the breakdown of creatine phosphate, glycolysis (anaerobic respiration) or aerobic respiration.

➢ The inability of the muscle to maintain its strength of contraction due to an insufficient supply of oxygen and the accumulation of lactic acid is called muscle fatigue.

➢ During muscular contraction the thin and thick protein filaments in the myofibril slide past one another, shortening the length of the sarcomere.

➢ The involuntary, continuous, partial tension in muscles is known as muscle tone.

➢ Skeletal muscle is attached at both ends to the skeleton to facilitate movement.

➢ The muscular attachment to the bone that remains unmoved is the origin.

➢ The muscular attachment to the bone that the contraction is intended to move is the insertion.

➢ The muscle that is contracting to perform the action is called the agonist.

➢ The muscle that could oppose the movement but, in relaxing, allows the movement to take place is called the antagonist.

➢ Isotonic contractions allow the muscle to shorten or lengthen whilst maintaining a constant tension.

➢ Isometric contractions occur when the muscle does not alter in length but the tension increases.

➢ Smooth muscle is found in the walls of hollow structures.

➢ The movement of smooth muscle is involuntary.

➢ The involuntary movement of smooth muscle is governed by the autonomic nervous system, hormones and other environmental factors.

➢ The intermediate filaments, attached to the dense bodies and the sarcolemma, facilitate the contraction of smooth muscle.

➢ Cardiac muscle forms most of the heart.

➢ Cardiac muscle is striated and its movement is involuntary.

➢ Cardiac muscle contains many large mitochondria because it is largely dependent on aerobic respiration for its ATP.

➢ The main muscles of the face, head and neck are the occipitofrontalis, temporalis, corrugator supercilii, buccinator, risorius, masseter, orbicularis oculi, zygomaticus major, zygomaticus minor, mentalis, orbicularis oris, sternocleidomastoid, nasalis and platysma.

➢ The main muscles of the shoulder are the coracobrachialis, deltoid, infraspinatus, levator scapulae, rhomboids, serratus anterior, subscapularis, supraspinatus, teres major, teres minor and the trapezius. The infraspinatus, subscapularis, supraspinatus and the teres minor make up the rotator cuff.

➢ The main muscles of the arm are the biceps brachii, brachialis, pronator teres, brachioradialis, flexor carpi radialis, flexor carpi ulnaris, palmaris longus, flexor digitorum superficialis, triceps brachii, extensor carpi radialis longus, extensor carpi radialis brevis, extensor digitorum, extensor carpi ulnaris and extensor digiti minimi.

> The main muscles of the hand are the opponens pollicis, abductor pollicis brevis, flexor pollicis brevis and the adductor pollicis, which make up the thenar eminence and act on the thumb, and the abductor digiti minimi, flexor digiti minimi brevis, opponens digiti minimi and the palmaris brevis, which make up the hyothenar eminence and act on the little finger. The intermediate (midpalmar) muscles act on all the digits apart from the thumb.

> The main muscles of the leg are the rectus femoris, vastus lateralis, vastus intermedius, vastus medialis, adductor magnus, adductor longus, adductor brevis, gracilis, pectineus, tensor fasciae latae, sartorius, digitorum longus, hallucis longus, tibialis anterior, tibialis posterior, gastrocnemius, soleus, peroneus longus and the peroneus brevis.

> The main muscles in the anterior trunk are the pectoralis major, pectoralis minor, external obliques, internal obliques, intercostal muscles, diaphragm, rectus abdominis and the transversus abdominis.

> The main muscles of the posterior trunk are the quadratus lumborum, psoas major, iliacus, erector spinae, latissimus dorsi, piriformis, gluteus maximus, gluteus medius and gluteus minimus.

Questions (Answers: Page 392)

1. What type of muscle tissue is mainly attached to bones?

2. What type of muscle tissue is found in the walls of hollow structures?

3. Where in the body can cardiac muscle be found?

4. What non-elastic structures often join skeletal muscles to bone?

5. Which neurons stimulate muscular contraction?

   a. motor
   b. sensory
   c. association

6. True or False?

   Muscles have a rich blood supply to deliver the nutrients and oxygen required for the production of the energy-carrying molecule ATP, and to remove the waste products of metabolism.

7. Which connective tissue forms the fibrous outermost layer of the muscle?

   a. fascia
   b. epimysium
   c. perimysium

8. True or False?

   The epimysium is located under the fascia, encircling the whole muscle. The perimysium surrounds the bundles of muscle fibres.

9. Which connective tissue surrounds each group of muscle fibres, binding them into fascicles?

   a. epimysium
   b. perimysium
   c. endomysium

10.   What name is given to the cell membrane of a muscle fibre?

       a. sarcolemma
       b. sarcoplasm

11.   What name is given to the threads that run lengthways through the sarcoplasm of the muscle fibre?

12.   True or False?

      Myofibrils contain filaments that run the whole length of the myofibril.

13.   Which filaments are responsible for the appearance of darker striations in the myofibril?

       a. actin filaments
       b. myosin filaments

14.   True or False?

      During muscular contraction the filaments shorten.

15.   Which ion is required for muscular contraction?

16.   When is the calcium level in the sarcoplasm at its highest?

       a. when the muscle is relaxed
       b. when the muscle is contracting

17.   True or False?

      When the muscle is rapidly stimulated, the calcium may not be removed between contractions. This causes a sustained contraction called tetanus.

18.   Fill in the missing word:

      Creatine phosphate can transfer its phosphate group to adenosine _____ to form adenosine triphosphate and creatine.

19.   What chemical is broken down during glycolysis to produce two molecules of ATP and two molecules of pyruvic acid?

20.   During which phase of cellular respiration does glycolysis occur?

      a. aerobic
      b. anaerobic

21.   What is produced by the pyruvic acid if there is insufficient oxygen to allow aerobic cellular respiration?

22.   True or False?

      All lactic acid produced remains in the muscles.

23.   Where is pyruvic acid transformed into ATP in the presence of oxygen?

      a. blood
      b. nuclei of the muscle cells
      c. mitochondria

24.   What protein in the muscle carries oxygen and releases it when necessary?

25.   Put the ways in which a contracting muscle obtains its ATP in order, starting from the onset of exercise.

      a. aerobic respiration
      b. anaerobic respiration
      c. uses creatine phosphate to form ATP from ADP
      d. uses the ATP present in the muscle cells

26.   True or False?

      The inability of the muscle to maintain its strength of contraction is called muscle fatigue. It is caused by an insufficient supply of oxygen and a build up of lactic acid.

27.   True or False?

      Smooth muscle is not striated and its movement is involuntary.

28.   Which filaments in smooth muscle are attached to the dense bodies and the sarcolemma?

      a. thin
      b. thick
      c. intermediate

29. The autonomic nervous system governs the nervous stimulation of the smooth muscle. What chemicals, secreted by the glands, are also capable of triggering the muscular contraction of smooth muscle?

30. Which two muscle types are striated?

    a. skeletal and smooth
    b. skeletal and cardiac
    c. cardiac and smooth

31. Which is the only muscle type under voluntary control?

    a. skeletal
    b. smooth
    c. cardiac

32. What type of cellular respiration produces the vast majority of ATP in the cardiac muscle?

    a. aerobic
    b. anaerobic

33. True or False?

    Cardiac muscle fibres form one continuous network.

34. Skeletal attachment takes place at both ends of the muscle. Which attachment is the origin?

    a. The attachment to the bone that remains unmoved during the muscular contraction.
    b. The attachment to the bone that the muscular contraction intends to move.

35. What is the muscle that causes the movement called?

    a. agonist
    b. antagonist

36. Muscle actions are often paired as they have opposing effects. Pair these actions by writing the appropriate letter alongside the opposing action.

    a. flexors   adductors
    b. abductors   depressors
    c. levators   extensors

37. In which type of contraction does the muscle alter in length but the tension remain constant?

    a. isotonic
    b. isometric

38. Which muscle circles the eye?

39. Which muscle covers the dome of the skull?

40. Which major cheek muscle attaches at the molar area of maxilla and mandible and runs to the orbicularis oris?

41. Which cheek muscle runs from the maxilla and zygomatic arch to the mandible?

42. Which two muscles run down the neck?

    a. sternocleidomastoid and mentalis
    b. corrugator supercilii and temporalis
    c. platysma and sternocleidomastoid
    d. orbicularis oris and platysma

43. Which muscle closes and protrudes lips and shapes the lips during speech?

44. Which large, flat, kite-shaped muscle, extends over the back of the neck and the upper thorax?

45. Which triangular muscle covers the shoulder?

46. Which slender muscle runs from the top of the spinal column to the scapula?

47. True or False?

The rhomboid major and rhomboid minor originate from the 7th cervical vertebra to the 5th thoracic vertebra and insert at the medial edge of the scapula.

48.   The following muscles all insert at the humerus. Which inserts at the most distal (lowest) point?

        a. coracobrachialis
        b. deltoid
        c. infraspinatus
        d. subscapularis
        e. supraspinatus
        f. teres major
        g. teres minor

49.   Starting with the muscle that is located superiorly and working down, what is the correct order of these 4 muscles?

        a. supraspinatus, infraspinatus, teres major, teres minor
        b. teres major, teres minor, supraspinatus, infraspinatus
        c. supraspinatus, infraspinatus, teres minor, teres major
        d. supraspinatus, teres major, infraspinatus, teres minor

50.   Is the origin of the subscapularis the anterior or posterior side of the scapula?

51.   Which four muscles and their tendons make up the rotator cuff?

52.   True or False?

        Extensors of the wrist tend to attach on the posterior side of the arm, flexors on the anterior side.

53.   Which of the following muscles is the only one to be located on the posterior side of the arm?

        a. biceps brachii
        b. brachialis
        c. pronator teres
        d. triceps brachii

54.   Three of these muscles insert at the radius, but which one of them inserts at the ulna?

        a. biceps brachii
        b. brachialis
        c. pronator teres
        d. brachioradialis

55.   Three of these muscles originate at the humerus, but which one of them originates at the scapula?

        a. biceps brachii
        b. brachialis
        c. pronator teres
        d. brachioradialis

56.   Which of the following flexors flexes the middle phalanges of each finger?

        a. flexor carpi radialis
        b. flexor carpi ulnaris
        c. palmaris longus
        d. flexor digitorum superficialis

57.   Which of the following flexors inserts in the deep fascia in the centre of the palm?

        a. flexor carpi radialis
        b. flexor carpi ulnaris
        c. palmaris longus
        d. flexor digitorum superficialis

58.   Which bone provides an origin for the flexor carpi radialis, flexor carpi ulnaris, palmaris longus and the flexor digitorum superficialis?

        a. humerus
        b. scapula
        c. ulna
        d. radius

59.   Which muscle extends the little finger?

        a. extensor carpi radialis longus
        b. extensor carpi radialis brevis
        c. extensor digitorum
        d. extensor carpi ulnaris
        e. extensor digiti minimi

60.   Which muscle extends the phalanges?

        a. extensor carpi radialis longus
        b. extensor carpi radialis brevis
        c. extensor digitorum
        d. extensor carpi ulnaris
        e. extensor digiti minimi

61. Which muscle extends from the lateral distal end of the humerus to the second metacarpal?

    a. extensor carpi radialis longus
    b. extensor carpi radialis brevis
    c. extensor digitorum
    d. extensor carpi ulnaris
    e. extensor digiti minimi

62. Which emeniance is made up of four muscles that act on the little finger?

    a. thenar
    b. hypothenar

63. Which four muscles make up the thenar eminence?

    a. opponens pollicis
    b. abductor pollicis brevis
    c. abductor digiti minimi
    d. flexor digiti minimi brevis
    e. opponens digiti minimi
    f. palmaris brevis
    g. flexor pollicis brevis
    h. adductor pollicis

64. True or False?

    Both the quadriceps and the hamstrings are made up of four muscles.

65. Which large muscle of the quadriceps runs down the centre of the thigh and is used to flex the thigh as well as extend the leg?

    a. rectus femoris
    b. vastus lateralis
    c. vastus intermedius
    d. vastus medialis

66. Which muscle of the quadriceps is situated beneath the rectus femoris?

67. Which anterior thigh muscle is the longest muscle in the body?

68.   The muscles adductor magnus, adductor longus and adductor brevis are all obviously adductors. Which two of these other anterior thigh muscles are also adductors?

        a. pectineus
        b. tensor fasciae latae
        c. Sartorius
        d. gracilis

69.   Adductors of the thigh all originate at the pelvis. With the exception of the gracilis (that inserts at the tibia), which bone provides the insertion?

70.   What are the actions of the tensor fasciae latae?

        a. abduction and adduction
        b. abduction and flexion
        c. adduction and flexion
        d. flexion and rotation

71.   Which of the following insert at the distal phalange of the big toe?

        a. extensor digitorum longus and flexor digitorum longus
        b. extensor hallucis longus and extensor digitorum longus
        c. flexor hallucis longus and flexor digitorum longus
        d. extensor hallucis longus and flexor hallucis longus

72.   True or False?

        The extensor digitorum longus and the extensor hallucis longus insert on the superior surface of the phalanges. The flexor digitorum longus and the flexor hallucis longus insert on the inferior surface of the phalanges.

73.   Which muscle located on the anterior side of the lower leg runs from the tibia (just below the knee) to the first metatarsal and cuneiform (tarsal)?

        a. extensor digitorum longus
        b. extensor hallucis longus
        c. tibialis anterior

74.   Which is the main muscle of the calf?

75.   Which muscle lies under the gastrocnemius in the calf, running from the head of the fibula and medial portion of tibia to the calcaneus via the Achilles tendon?

76. Which muscle, located deep in the calf, runs from the upper shaft of the tibia and head of the fibula to the second, third and fourth metatarsals, navicular, all three cuneiforms and the cuboid?

77. Which of the peroneal muscles runs from the lower two thirds of the fibula?

78. Which of the following muscles runs up the length of the abdomen?

    a. pectoralis major
    b. pectoralis minor
    c. external obliques
    d. internal obliques
    e. intercostal muscles
    f. diaphragm
    g. rectus abdominis
    h. transversus abdominis

79. Three abdominal muscles lay over each other. Starting from the muscle that is closest to the skin, which is the correct order?

    a. transversus abdominis, internal oblique, external oblique
    b. internal oblique, transversus abdominis, external oblique
    c. external oblique, internal oblique, transversus abdominis

80. When the diaphragm contracts, what happens to the size of the thorax?

81. Which of these muscles flexes and adducts the arm and rotates the arm medially at the shoulder?

    a. pectoralis major
    b. pectoralis minor

82. Which of these muscles cannot flex the vertebral column?

    a. quadratus lumborum
    b. psoas major
    c. iliacus
    d. erector spinae
    e. latissimus dorsi

83. Which three posterior trunk muscles can cause movement in the thigh?

> a. erector spinae
> b. quadratus lumborum
> c. psoas major
> d. latissimus dorsi
> e. iliacus
> f. piriformis

84. Which of the three gluteal muscles is located deeper than the other two?

85. Which muscle is located on either side of the lumbar region and runs from the iliac crest to the twelfth rib and the first four lumbar vertebrae?

> a. quadratus lumborum
> b. psoas major
> c. iliacus
> d. erector spinae
> e. latissimus dorsi

Cardio- vascular System

This page has intentionally been left blank.

The cardiovascular system acts as a **transport mechanism**. As the blood circulates around the body it transports substances such as oxygen, nutrients, hormones and enzymes to the cells and absorbs waste products from the cells so they can be removed from the body.

It works closely with two other body systems – the **lymphatic** system and the **respiratory** system. Let's look at the links to these two systems next.

The **lymphatic system** also consists of a **network** of vessels but, unlike the cardiovascular system, there is **no pump** to encourage the fluid to circulate. The lymphatic system supports the cardiovascular system by collecting from the intercellular fluid unwanted substances that are not absorbed into the blood and **transporting** them away from the cells. The fluid contained within the lymphatic system is called **lymph**. The lymph is filtered and eventually **drained directly** into the cardiovascular system. The **kidneys** then **filter** the blood, and the waste products leave the body as urine.

The cardiovascular system can only **distribute oxygen** to the cells if it is **inhaled**. This is a role of the **respiratory system**. The oxygen is received into the **lungs** where it diffuses into the **blood** and is then transported to the cells. The oxygen is used for metabolic reactions and **carbon dioxide** is produced as a **waste** product. The carbon dioxide diffuses into the blood and is taken to the lungs. In the lungs, the carbon dioxide is extracted from the blood and removed from the body by exhalation.

As well as **transporting** substances such as oxygen, nutrients, hormones, enzymes and waste products, the blood has a number of other functions. It:

✓ **protects** against **disease** – the white blood cells (see Page 266) **devour bacteria** and **produce antibodies**. (For more on protection against disease see Immunity.)

✓ **protects** against **blood loss** – a chain of reactions cause a **blood clot** to form when the body is injured (see Blood Clotting).

✓ **transports heat** – much of the body's heat is produced by the digestion of food, muscular activity and the functioning of the liver. As the blood circulates it transports the heat to help to maintain an **even** and **constant** body temperature (see Temperature Control).

✓ **maintains** the body's **pH** (level of alkalinity/acidity).

Composition of Blood

The blood consists of a variety of **blood cells** and a watery substance called blood **plasma**. We'll look at the composition of the blood in detail. The chart below summarizes the main components that we will be discussing. Please note, it does not proportionately represent the composition of the blood.

Blood Cells 45%	Red			
	White	Granular	Neutrophils	
			Eosinophils	
			Basophils	
		Agranular	Lymphocytes	B-Cells
				T-Cells
			Monocytes	
	Platelets			
Plasma 55%	Other solutes			
	Proteins	Albumins		
		Globulins		
		Fibrinogen		
	Water			

Plasma

About **55%** of the blood is composed of plasma. Plasma is a straw-coloured fluid consisting of about **91% water**.

The high **water** content of plasma allows the blood to act as a solvent and enables the transportation of **nutrients**, **salts**, **hormones**, **enzymes**, **gases** and **excretory products**. These solutes make up about 2% of the plasma. The water content also facilitates the absorption, transportation and release of **heat**.

7% of plasma is made up of **proteins**, most of which are synthesized by the **liver**. The plasma proteins include albumins, globulins and fibrinogen. Let's look at these next…

Albumins

Albumins regulate **osmotic pressure**. This helps to maintain the water balance between the blood and the tissues, so regulating blood volume.

Globulins

This protein group includes **antibodies** (immunoglobulins) that play a vital role in **immunity** by attacking antigens. **Alpha** and **beta** globulins **transport** iron, fats and fat-soluble vitamins.

Fibrinogen

Fibrinogen plays a vital role in **blood clotting** (covered later in this section).

So, plasma (consisting of about 91% water, 7% proteins and 2% other solutes) makes up about 55% of the blood. The remaining **45%** consists of **blood cells**. There are 3 main types, red blood cells, white blood cells and platelets. We'll look at each in turn.

Red Blood Cells

Red blood cells are termed **erythrocytes**. They appear as **bi-concave discs** and are produced in the **red bone marrow**. Their primary function is to **transport** the **gases** of respiration. This is possible as red blood cells contain **haemoglobin**. Haemoglobin contains a protein (globin) and a pigment (haem) containing **iron**.

Erythrocyte production begins with a **proerythroblast**. The proerythroblast gives rise to an **early erythroblast**, which then develops into an **intermediate erythroblast**. The intermediate erythroblast is the first cell to **synthesize haemoglobin** and develops into a **late erythroblast**.

Haemoglobin synthesis is at its **maximum** in **late erythroblasts**. The late erythroblast **loses** its **nucleus**, causing the centre of the cell to indent. This leaves more room for haemoglobin and gives the cell its characteristic bi-concave shape. The late erythroblasts pass from the red bone marrow, between the cells of the capillaries, into the blood. Within a couple of days they develop into **mature erythrocytes**.

Old and worn out erythrocytes are **destroyed** in the **liver** and **spleen**. The haemoglobin is broken down and the **iron** it contains is **retained** for further haemoglobin synthesis. The rest of the pigment is excreted from the liver in bile. Erythrocytes have a life span of only about **4 months** and have to be **continuously replaced** at a rate of about 9000 million per hour. If replacement does not keep up with destruction, the ability of the blood to carry oxygen falls.

White Blood Cells

White blood cells are termed **leucocytes**. Leucocytes are generally **larger** but **less numerous** than erythrocytes. They have a nucleus and do not contain haemoglobin.

Leucocytes play an important role in **immunity**. They defend against disease by **devouring** bacteria and producing **antibodies**. In a healthy body, some leucocytes can live for months or even years, but usually they only survive for a **few hours**.

There are two major groups of leucocytes, **granular** and **agranular**.

Granular leucocytes are produced in the **red bone marrow**. A granular leucocyte has a **lobed nucleus** and, as the name suggests, contains **granules** in the cytoplasm. These granules can release **enzymes** that play a part in digesting foreign particles.

Agranular leucocytes do not have cytoplasmic granules.

There are 3 types of **granular** leucocyte, neutrophils, eosinophils and basophils.

1. Neutrophils
60 – 70% of leucocytes are neutrophils. Neutrophils **engulf** foreign particles such as bacteria (a process called phagocytosis). They then release destructive chemicals that **digest** them. Neutrophils are the first line of defense. They gather at the site of infection, where they may die and form pus.

2. Eosinophils
Eosinophils make up about 1.5% of all leucocytes. It is thought that eosinophils release enzymes that **counteract** the effects of **histamine** (a vasodilator). The number of eosinophils increases in allergic conditions.

3. Basophils
About 0.5% of leucocytes are basophils. Basophils **ingest** bacteria and are involved in inflammatory and allergic reactions. They can release **heparin** (an anticoagulant) and **histamine**, both of which intensify the inflammatory reaction.

There are 2 types of **agranular** leucocyte, lymphocytes and monocytes.

1. Lymphocytes
20 – 25% of leucocytes are lymphocytes. Lymphocytes are produced in the red bone marrow, lymph nodes, tonsils, spleen and thymus. They play key roles in immune responses. There are 2 types of lymphocyte, B-cells and T-cells. **B-cells** produce **antibodies** and **T-cells directly destroy** foreign particles (see Specific Resistance).

2. Monocytes
Monocytes make up about 4-5% of all leucocytes and are the **largest**. Monocytes develop into **macrophages** – large cells capable of devouring foreign particles such as bacteria.

We have now looked at 2 of the 3 groups of blood cells – red (erythrocytes) and white (leucocytes). The last group of blood cells to look at is the platelets.

Platelets

Platelets are also called **thrombocytes**. They are fragments of **cytoplasm** (the substance that surrounds a cell's organelles) enclosed by a cell membrane. Thrombocytes are formed in the **bone marrow**. They are disc-shaped, have **no nucleus** but contain cytoplasmic **granules**.

Thrombocytes normally have a **short life** span of just 5-9 days. Old and dead thrombocytes are removed by macrophages in the spleen and liver.

Thrombocytes help to **repair** slightly damaged **blood vessels**. When thrombocytes come into contact with damaged tissue, the cytoplasmic granules release chemicals that start a chain of reactions to form a **blood clot**.

Blood Clotting

Blood clotting (coagulation) is the conversion of blood from a liquid into a **solid**. The blood clot closes the wound, preventing further blood loss.

When a blood vessel is damaged, the smooth **muscle** in the wall of the **vessel** immediately **contracts**. This **vascular spasm** reduces the blood loss while other protection mechanisms are triggered.

As we have mentioned, the **platelets** (thrombocytes) play an important role in blood clotting. When they come into contact with a rough surface, the platelets stick to it, and to one another, to form a **platelet plug**.

Initially the platelet plug is quite loose, but it eventually becomes quite tight as it is reinforced by the blood clotting process.

The blood clotting process is a complex sequence of chemical reactions. The enzyme **thromboplastin** is a key player. Thromboplastin is produced when an injury occurs to the **platelets** or to the **tissue cells**.

The presence of thromboplastin in the blood then initiates a sequence of events…

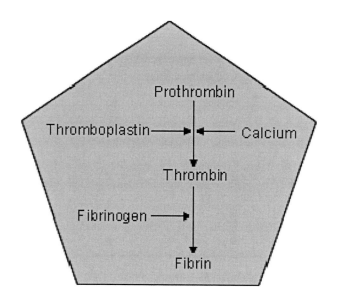

Thromboplastin changes the protein **prothrombin** (normally present in the blood) into **thrombin**. This can only take place in the presence of **calcium** which, under normal circumstances, is in the blood.

Thrombin then interacts with the soluble plasma protein **fibrinogen** to form **fibrin**. Fibrin is an insoluble protein that forms a **network** of **fibres** that strengthens into a clot.

Blood Vessels

Blood is transported around the whole body by means of an extensive network of blood **vessels**. There are three main types, arteries, veins and capillaries. We'll look at each in turn.

Arteries

Arteries take blood **away** from the heart (memory hint: **A**rteries – **A**way). They contain **oxygenated** blood. The **exception** to this is the **pulmonary arteries**. The pulmonary arteries take deoxygenated blood from the heart to the lungs.

Arteries **expand** as the blood is pumped from the heart, and then **recoil** to force the blood through the vessel. Arteries therefore have to be **elastic** and have the ability to **contract**. The anatomy of the arteries allows the elastic and contractile functions. The wall of an artery has 3 layers:

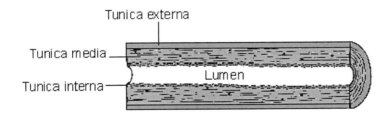

The thin outer layer is called the **tunica externa**. The tunica externa is made up of **elastic** and **collagen** fibres.

The thick middle layer consists of smooth **muscle**. This layer is called the **tunica media** and allows the artery to withstand the pressures resulting from the pumping of the heart.

The inner layer is the **tunica interna** and is composed of **endothelium** (squamous epithelial cells).

Arteries divide to form very small vessels called **arterioles**. Arterioles branch further to become capillaries.

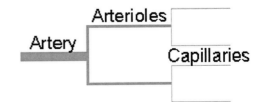

Veins

Veins take blood **back** to the heart. They contain **deoxygenated** blood. The **exception** is the **pulmonary veins**. The pulmonary veins take oxygenated blood from the lungs to the heart.

Venous blood is under **less pressure** than arterial blood. The **lumen** in a vein is larger than in an artery and the vein wall is **weaker** and **thinner**. This is particularly noticeable in the tunica media.

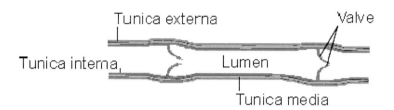

Due to the reduced pressure under which the blood flows in the veins, most veins contain **valves**. Valves **prevent** the **back-flow** of blood, so aiding its return to the heart.

Capillaries

Capillaries are **tiny, thin walled** vessels that make up dense **networks**. The capillary walls are made up of a **single layer** of **endothelium**. This structure allows the **exchange** of nutrients, gases and excretory products between the blood and the intercellular fluid, vital for internal respiration.

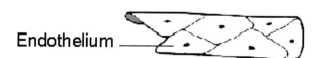

Substances in the blood pass through the thin capillary wall, into the interstitial space and then through the cell membrane into the cells. **Wastes** take the same route but in the opposite direction. This exchange of materials occurs only in capillaries, the walls of the arteries and veins are too thick.

Capillaries are formed by the multiple **division** of the **arteries**. Arteries divide to form **arterioles**, which continue to divide, getting smaller and smaller, until they become **capillaries**. The capillaries allow the **exchange** of nutrients and waste and then, as the vessels leave the capillary network, they join to form **venules**. Venules continue to merge until they become **veins**.

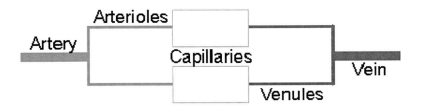

Body tissues with **high metabolic activity** have **extensive** capillary networks because their need for oxygen and nutrients is great. Tissues in low-activity areas have fewer capillaries.

Let's look at the circulation of the blood in more detail.

Heart

Blood can only flow through the blood vessels to perform its many functions if it is successfully pumped around the body.

The **heart** performs this role. The heart is a **muscular** organ that rhythmically **contracts** and **relaxes** to circulate the blood.

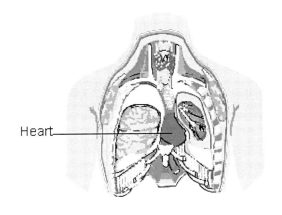

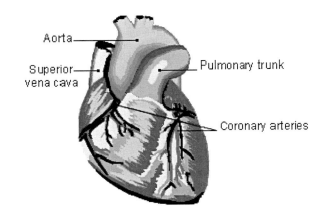

The heart is suspended by ligaments and is located between the lungs, slightly to the left of the midline in the upper thorax. It receives its own blood supply from the **coronary arteries**.

The heart is surrounded and protected by a strong, fibrous, triple-layered bag called the **pericardium**. The inner surface of the pericardium and the outer surface of the heart are both covered with a **smooth, lubricated membrane**. This enables the heart to move almost **without friction**.

The wall of the heart is composed of three layers. The **outer** layer is the **epicardium**. The **inner** layer is the **endocardium**. By far the thickest layer is the middle layer...

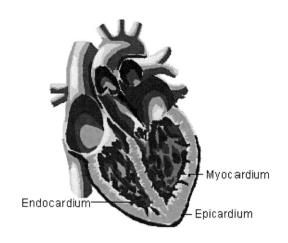

The middle layer of the heart is called the **myocardium**, or heart muscle. The specialized muscle fibres of the myocardium allow the heart to 'beat' in response to **nerve impulses**. As the nerve impulses travel through the heart, **electrical impulses** are generated which result in its **rhythmical contraction** and **relaxation**.

Circulation

The heart pumps **deoxygenated** (without oxygen) blood to the **lungs** via the **pulmonary arteries**. It receives **oxygenated** blood back from the lungs through the **pulmonary veins**.

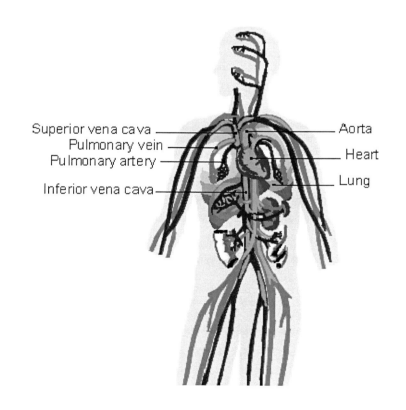

This oxygenated blood is then pumped out of the heart from the **aorta**. The aorta branches to form a complex network of arteries that circulates the blood around the body.

The deoxygenated blood is received back from the body tissues via major veins called the **superior** and **inferior vena cavae**.

Internally, the heart is comprised of **four** chambers. The **upper** chambers are called **atriums**. The **lower** chambers are called **ventricles**. The **septum** divides the left and right sides of the heart, keeping the oxygenated and deoxygenated blood separate.

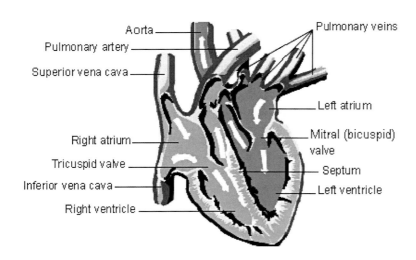

The heart receives **deoxygenated** blood from the body tissues via the superior and inferior vena cavae. This deoxygenated blood enters the **right atrium** and passes through the **tricuspid valve** to the **right ventricle**.

The deoxygenated blood leaves the right ventricle via the **pulmonary trunk** that quickly divides into the left and right **pulmonary arteries**. The pulmonary arteries transport the blood to the **lungs**.

There is a valve at the point that the pulmonary trunk leaves the right ventricle. It is called the **pulmonary semilunar valve**. The pulmonary semilunar valve has **three cusps**. The valve opens to allow blood through when pressure in the right ventricle is greater than that in the pulmonary arteries, and closes when the pressure in the ventricle falls below that of the pulmonary arteries. The valve only allows blood to flow in **one direction**. It **prevents** the **back-flow** of blood.

Oxygenated blood is brought back from the lungs in the **pulmonary veins**. The oxygenated blood from the pulmonary veins is received in the **left atrium**.

The flow of deoxygenated blood from the right ventricle to the lungs, and the return of oxygenated blood from the lungs to the left atrium, is called **pulmonary circulation**.

From the left atrium, the oxygenated blood passes through the **mitral (bicuspid) valve** to the **left ventricle**.

The left ventricle is the largest, most muscular chamber as it is responsible for pumping the oxygenated blood around the whole body. The oxygenated blood leaves the heart via the **aorta**.

There is a three-cusped valve called the **aortic semilunar valve** at the point that the aorta leaves the left ventricle. Like the pulmonary semilunar valve, this prevents the back-flow of blood.

The route through which oxygenated blood flows from the left ventricle through the aorta to all the organs of the body, and deoxygenated blood returns to the right atrium, is called **systemic circulation**.

One aspect of systemic circulation that you should be aware of is **portal circulation**. Portal circulation **detours venous blood** from the digestive organs and the spleen to the **liver** before returning the blood to the heart.

Blood, rich with nutrients, particularly after a meal, is transported to the liver via the **hepatic portal vein**. The main function of the liver is to regulate the composition of the blood (see Digestive

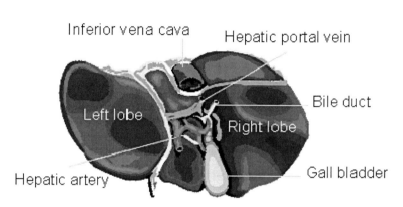

System) and so it **stores** some nutrients and **modifies** others. For example, the liver converts glucose into glycogen for storage and **detoxifies** harmful substances. The blood leaves the liver through the **hepatic veins** which drain into the **inferior vena cava** to be returned to the heart.

The network of blood vessels in the body is very complicated. When you are familiar with the **anatomical terms** for the various parts of the body you can normally get a good idea what part of the body the **vessel serves**, e.g. facial (face), occipital (posterior head), intercostal (ribs) and plantar (foot). Arteries **branch** and their off-shoots are often described using terms such as left, right, posterior, anterior, deep / internal, and superficial / external. So with a good knowledge of anatomical terms and anatomical position, the location and nomenclature of the vessels make far more sense.

The graphic on the next page shows the location of the major arteries and veins. Only the main vessels are shown. Please remember that they branch repeatedly to form the extensive network required to circulate blood to every part of the body. Other sections of the tutorial will also cover the cardiovascular connection for specific organs.

Major Arteries and Veins

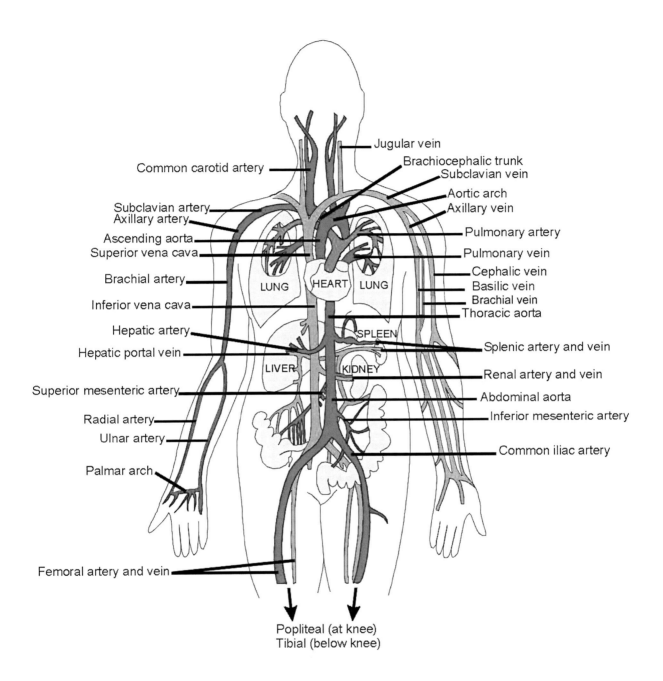

Notes:

1. The darker vessels shown here carry oxygenated blood. The lighter vessels carry deoxygenated blood.

2. To be able to give a graphical representation of the location of the major blood vessels on one diagram we have not been able to show the full body. We also show arteries in the right arm and veins in the left. This is obviously not the case in real life!

275

At rest about **60%** of the blood volume is in the **systemic veins** and **venules**. Systemic capillaries hold only about 5% and arteries and arterioles about 15%. As the systemic veins and venules contain so much of the blood they are referred to as **blood reservoirs** and from here the blood can be diverted to other areas as the need arises.

For example, if the skeletal muscles require more blood, the brain sends a signal to induce vasoconstriction in the blood reservoirs. This reduces the blood volume in the blood reservoirs and a greater blood volume can flow to the muscles.

The rapid movement of blood to areas that require it is also aided by **shunt vessels**. Shunt vessels provide short cuts from an artery to a vein, so bypassing the capillaries. **Blood shunting** enables the blood to take a shorter route to its required destination.

For example, blood shunting occurs just after a meal when the level of blood in the intestines needs to be increased to aid digestion, and during exercise when the blood is brought to the skin to help cool the body.

Blood Pressure

The strength with which the heart pumps the blood largely determines the **blood pressure**. The blood pressure is a **measurement** of the pressure exerted by the blood on the walls of the blood vessels, usually the **arteries**.

As we have seen, the blood is **pumped** from the heart by the rhythmical **contraction** and **relaxation** of the heart muscle. We mentioned earlier that the specialized muscle fibres of the myocardium allow the heart to 'beat' in response to nerve impulses. Let's look at this in a little more detail...

The cardiac nervous "excitation" begins in the **sinoatrial (SA) node**, located in the wall of the **right atrium**, just below the opening of the superior vena cava. From here, the nerve impulse, which causes muscular contraction, is conducted across to the left atrium and down through the right atrium to the **atrioventricular (AV) node**.

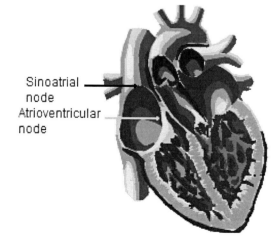

Sinoatrial node
Atrioventricular node

The AV node is located in the septum between the two atriums. From here the nerve impulse ultimately reaches the **ventricles**.

In the wake of an impulse, first the atriums contract and then, a fraction of a second later, the **stronger** ventricles contract. All four chambers then **relax** until the next impulse.

It is during the **ventricular contraction** phase of the heartbeat that the blood is being **forced** through the arteries, and so the blood pressure is at its **highest** at this time.

The phase of heartbeat involving ventricular contraction is called **ventricular systole**. The force exerted by the blood on an arterial wall during the systolic phase is called **systolic blood pressure**.

After systole (contraction), the heart muscle relaxes. The phase of heartbeat in which the cardiac **muscle** is **relaxed** is called **diastole**. The force exerted by the blood on an arterial wall during diastole is called **diastolic blood pressure**. Diastolic blood pressure is **lower** than systolic blood pressure because, during diastole, the heart is not forcing the blood through the arteries.

In a normal, young, healthy, adult male at rest, the usual **systolic** blood pressure is **120** mm Hg (millimetres of mercury) and the **diastolic** pressure is **80** mm Hg. It is written as 120/80 and expressed as "120 over 80". Abnormally high blood pressure is known as hypertension. Abnormally low blood pressure is termed hypotension.

Although the force with which the heart pumps largely determines blood pressure, it can be affected by a number of other physical factors:

Blood volume – a decrease in the volume of blood decreases the blood pressure.

Blood viscosity – the more viscous the blood, the more friction occurs between the blood and the walls of the blood vessels. The higher the resistance to blood flow, the higher the blood pressure will become to force the blood through.

Blood vessel length – the longer the blood vessel the more resistance exists to blood flow. The increased resistance will result in higher blood pressure.

Blood vessel radius – the smaller the radius of the vessel, the greater the resistance it creates to the blood flow. The blood pressure is therefore higher in narrower vessels.

Temperature – a decrease in temperature causes the blood pressure to rise. This is because the blood vessels contract in response to a decrease in temperature to reduce heat loss (see Temperature Control). Conversely, an increase in temperature causes the blood vessels to dilate, so lowering the blood pressure.

As well as those physical factors, the blood pressure will rise during **exercise** and an increase in blood pressure may also be linked to stress, diet, alcohol consumption, and smoking.

Medications can be used to regulate abnormal blood pressure but some medications, prescribed for various conditions, can also have the side effect of adversely affecting blood pressure.

The **cardiovascular centre** in the **medulla oblongata** controls blood pressure and blood flow. This centre governs heart rate, the force of ventricular contraction, and the diameter of the blood vessels.

Receptors called **baroreceptors** exist in the walls of the arteries and veins. Baroreceptors are sensitive to **pressure** and can detect **stretch**. They monitor the blood pressure and feed back the information to the cardiovascular centre. The cardiovascular centre then reacts as necessary to trigger an appropriate response.

The level of **chemicals** in the blood also triggers the cardiovascular centre. **Chemoreceptors** are sensitive to changing levels of oxygen and carbon dioxide in the blood and feed back the information to the cardiovascular centre. A detected decrease in the oxygen level or increase in the level of carbon dioxide will bring about vasoconstriction. Vasoconstriction leads to an increase in blood pressure.

Blood pressure is also influenced by the presence of certain hormones (see Endocrine System). These hormones act on the heart, alter blood vessel diameter or affect blood volume.

For example:

Adrenaline and noradrenaline are produced by the adrenal glands. They increase the heart rate and the force of the ventricular contractions.

Antidiuretic hormone (ADH), produced by the hypothalamus but released from the pituitary gland, causes vasoconstriction if there is a severe loss of blood.

The **wave of pressure** caused by the contraction of the ventricles can be felt as a **pulse** in **arteries** that lie close to the surface of the body. The most common places to feel for a pulse are on the **radial** artery in the wrist and on the **carotid** artery in the neck. The number of pulses represents the heart rate. The normal **resting pulse** for a young fit adult is **70-80 beats per minute**. Children have higher pulse rates than adults, and on average women have a higher pulse rate than men.

Like blood pressure, the pulse rate will **increase** with **exercise** and in times of **stress**.

Summary

➢ The cardiovascular system transports blood to and from the body's tissues.

➢ The blood acts as a transport mechanism for oxygen, nutrients, hormones, enzymes and waste products, protects against disease, protects against blood loss, transports heat and maintains the body's pH.

➢ The cardiovascular system is linked closely to the lymphatic system which assists with transporting waste products, and the respiratory system which inhales oxygen into the body for diffusion into the blood and eliminates the waste carbon dioxide.

➢ Blood consists of plasma, red blood cells (erythrocytes), white blood cells (leucocytes) and platelets (thrombocytes).

➢ Plasma is 91% water, 7% proteins (albumins, globulins and fibrinogen) and 2% other solutes.

➢ Erythrocytes contain haemoglobin and transport the gases of respiration.

➢ Leucocytes play vital roles in immunity. The two main groups are granular (neutrophils, eosinophils and basophils) and agranular (lymphocytes and monocytes).

➢ Thrombocytes play a role in blood clotting.

➢ In the blood clotting process, thromboplastin changes prothrombin into thrombin. Thrombin then interacts with fibrinogen to form non-soluble, fibrous fibrin.

➢ Arteries have thick, muscular walls and carry blood under pressure away from the heart.

➢ Veins carry blood back to the heart. The presence of valves helps to prevent the back-flow of blood.

➢ Capillaries have thin walls, form networks, and provide the site for the exchange of gases, nutrients and waste.

➢ The heart is the cardiovascular pump. It has four chambers - two atriums and two ventricles.

➢ Deoxygenated blood is pumped, via the pulmonary arteries, to the lungs.

➤ Oxygenated blood is received back from the lungs via the pulmonary veins.

➤ Oxygenated blood leaves the heart via the aorta to be circulated around the body.

➤ Deoxygenated blood is received back from the body's tissues via the superior and inferior vena cavae.

➤ The flow of deoxygenated blood from the right ventricle to the lungs, and the return of oxygenated blood from the lungs to the left atrium, is called pulmonary circulation.

➤ The route through which oxygenated blood flows from the left ventricle through the aorta to all the organs of the body, and deoxygenated blood returns to the right atrium, is called systemic circulation.

➤ Portal circulation detours venous blood from the digestive organs and the spleen to the liver via the hepatic portal vein, before returning the blood to the heart via the inferior vena cava.

➤ Blood pressure is a measurement of the pressure exerted by the blood on the walls of the blood vessels, usually the arteries.

➤ Systole is the phase of heartbeat involving ventricular contraction. Blood pressure during this phase is called systolic.

➤ Diastole is the phase of heartbeat in which the cardiac muscle is relaxed. Blood pressure during this phase is called diastolic.

➤ Blood pressure is controlled by the cardiovascular centre in the medulla oblongata.

➤ Blood pressure is affected by blood volume and the level of resistance to blood flow. It is also influenced by the presence of some hormones.

➤ The normal blood pressure of a young, healthy adult at rest is 120/80 mm Hg and the normal pulse rate is 70-80 beats per minute.

➤ Both blood pressure and pulse will rise during exercise.

Questions (Answers: Page 394)

1. Which system supports the cardiovascular system by removing waste products from the tissues?

2. True or False?

    The cardiovascular system and the respiratory system work together to take oxygen into the body, distribute it to the cells for use in metabolic reactions, and then excrete the carbon dioxide.

3. What straw-coloured fluid makes up more than half of the blood?

4. What is the most common component of plasma?

5. About 7% of plasma is made up of proteins. In which organ are most of these plasma proteins synthesized?

6. Which of the following plasma proteins help to regulate blood volume?

    a. albumins
    b. globulins
    c. fibrinogen

7. Which globulins include antibodies?

    a. alpha globulins
    b. beta globulins
    c. immunoglobulins

8. Which plasma protein plays a major role in blood clotting?

9. What name is given to red blood cells?

10. Where are erythrocytes produced?

11. At which state of erythrocyte development is the synthesis of haemoglobin at its maximum?

    a. proerythroblast
    b. early erythroblast
    c. intermediate erythroblast
    d. late erythroblast
    e. mature erythrocyte

12. At what stage of erythrocyte development is the nucleus lost?

    a. proerythroblast
    b. early erythroblast
    c. intermediate erythroblast
    d. late erythroblast
    e. mature erythrocyte

13. True or False?

The mature erythrocytes pass from the red bone marrow, through the capillary walls, into the blood.

14. Name one of the organs in which old or worn out erythrocytes are destroyed.

15. What name is given to white blood cells?

16. True or False?

Erythrocytes play an important role in immunity. They defend against disease by devouring bacteria and producing antibodies.

17. How are neutrophils, eosinophils and basophils categorized?

    a. granular leucocytes
    b. agranular leucocytes

18. Which is the most common type of leucocyte?

    a. neutrophils
    b. eosinophils
    c. basophils
    d. lymphocytes
    e. monocytes

19. Which type of granular leucocyte is thought to release enzymes that counteract the effects of histamine?

   a. neutrophils
   b. eosinophils
   c. basophils

20. Which type of granular leucocyte makes up only about 0.5% of all leucocytes?

21. To which group of agranular leucocytes do B-cells and T-cells belong?

   a. lymphocytes
   b. monocytes

22. Which type of lymphocyte produces antibodies?

   a. B-cells
   b. T-cells

23. Which group of agranular leucocytes become macrophages?

24. What is another term for a platelet?

25. True or False?

   Thrombocytes play a major role in the blood clotting process.

26. Which type of blood cell creates a plug to begin to prevent blood loss from an injury?

   a. red (erythrocytes)
   b. white (leucocytes)
   c. platelets (thrombocytes)

27. What must be present for the enzyme thromboplastin to change the protein prothrombin into thrombin?

28. Fill in the missing word:

   Thrombin interacts with the soluble plasma protein fibrinogen to form _____.

29.   Which vessels take blood away from the heart?

      a. arteries
      b. veins
      c. capillaries

30.   Which vessels take blood back to the heart?

      a. arteries
      b. veins
      c. capillaries

31.   Which vessels have valves to help to prevent the back-flow of blood?

      a. arteries
      b. veins
      c. capillaries

32.   Which are the smallest blood vessels?

      a. arteries
      b. veins
      c. capillaries

33.   Which layer of the artery wall is thick and muscular?

      a. tunica interna
      b. tunica media
      c. tunica externa

34.   Which is the correct sequence of structures through which the blood flows?

      a. heart, arteries, arterioles, capillaries, venules, veins, heart
      b. heart, arterioles, arteries, capillaries, veins, venules, heart
      c. heart, veins, venules, capillaries, arterioles, arteries, heart
      d. heart, venules, veins, capillaries, arteries, arterioles, heart

35.   What name is given to the strong bag, which surrounds and protects the heart?

36.   What is the middle, muscular layer of the heart called?

37.   Which arteries supply blood to the heart tissue?

38.   The heart receives oxygenated blood from the lungs via the pulmonary veins. Through which major artery does the oxygenated blood leave the heart to be circulated around the body?

39.   As oxygenated blood travels around the body, oxygen is absorbed from it and used by the tissues. Deoxygenated blood is then returned to the heart. Through which vessels does the heart receive deoxygenated blood?

40.   How many chambers are there in the heart?

41.   Which are the upper chambers of the heart?

        a. atriums
        b. ventricles

42.   True or False?

        Deoxygenated blood is on the right side of the heart. Oxygenated blood is in the left side of the heart. It is kept separate by the septum.

43.   Which chamber receives deoxygenated blood?

        a. right atrium
        b. right ventricle
        c. left atrium
        d. left ventricle

44.   Deoxygenated blood leaves the right atrium and passes through the tricuspid valve. Into which chamber is it received?

45.   Deoxygenated blood leaves the right ventricle and is taken to the lungs. Which vessels take deoxygenated blood to the lungs?

        a. superior and inferior vena cavae
        b. pulmonary arteries
        c. pulmonary veins

46.   Blood is oxygenated in the lungs. Which vessels bring the oxygenated blood back to the heart?

47. Which chamber receives oxygenated blood from the pulmonary veins?

    a. right atrium
    b. right ventricle
    c. left atrium
    d. left ventricle

48. Oxygenated blood leaves the left atrium and passes through the mitral valve. Into which chamber is it received?

49. Oxygenated blood leaves the left ventricle to be circulated around the body. Which major artery takes the oxygenated blood from the left ventricle?

50. What type of circulation is described here? "The flow of deoxygenated blood from the right ventricle to the lungs and the return of oxygenated blood from the lungs to the left atrium".

    a. pulmonary circulation
    b. systemic circulation

51. Fill in the missing word:

    _____ circulation detours venous blood from the digestive organs and the spleen through the liver before returning the blood to the heart.

52. Where does cardiac excitation normally begin?

    a. atrioventricular node
    b. sinoatrial node

53. In which phase of heartbeat does ventricular contraction take place?

    a. systole
    b. diastole

54. In which phase of heartbeat is the blood pressure at its highest?

    a. systole
    b. diastole

55. True or False?

    Resistance to blood flow will increase the blood pressure.

56. How does vasodilation affect blood pressure?

        a. decreases it
        b. increases it

57. In which part of the brain is the cardiovascular centre?

        a. cerebellum
        b. cerebrum
        c. medulla oblongata

58. Which receptors in the walls of arteries and veins are sensitive to changes in blood pressure?

59. What response is triggered when the chemoreceptors detect a decrease in the oxygen level or an increase in the level of carbon dioxide?

        a. vasodilation
        b. vasoconstriction

60. Which of these represents the usual blood pressure and pulse rate in a healthy, young adult at rest?

        a. 100/80 mm Hg   50-60 beats per minute
        b. 120/80 mm Hg   70-80 beats per minute
        c. 180/120 mm Hg   90-100 beats per minute

Digestive System

This page has intentionally been left blank.

The body is reliant on the intake of **food** for energy and nutrients. However, the carbohydrates, fats and proteins that we eat obviously cannot be absorbed into the blood and used by the body in the same form as they are ingested! The food must be **broken down** both **mechanically** and **chemically** into its smallest chemical components before the body can use it. The process in which food is broken down by the body is called **digestion**.

Before we look at the anatomy of the digestive system, let's quickly look at the chemical make up of carbohydrates, fats and proteins to help us to understand the digestion of these compounds. **Note:** Should you wish to enhance your knowledge about atoms, molecules and chemical bonding, please take the time to go through the Chemistry section.

Carbohydrates

Carbohydrates, e.g. sugars, starches, glycogen and cellulose, are energy producing compounds of carbon, oxygen and hydrogen. They make up about 2-3% of total body weight. They are all fundamentally built from units of sugar but vary enormously in size.

Monosaccharides
Monosaccharides are the **smallest** carbohydrate. **Glucose** is a monosaccharide and provides a main source of energy in the body.

Disaccharides
Disaccharides are formed by the chemical linking of **two** monosaccharides. Disaccharides include **sucrose** (table sugar) and **lactose** (milk sugar).

Polysaccharides
Polysaccharides are the largest and most **complex** carbohydrates. The principal polysaccharide is **glycogen**. Glycogen is comprised of many linked glucose units and is **stored** in the liver and skeletal muscles.

During the digestive process, the more complex carbohydrates are **broken down** into monosaccharides. These can then be can be absorbed from the intestines into the blood and used by the body.

Fats

Fats, termed **lipids**, comprise about 18-25% of body weight. Like carbohydrates they contain carbon, hydrogen and oxygen, but their chemical composition is different, making them **insoluble** in water.

Lipids include **triglycerides**. The fats and oils that we eat will usually be triglycerides. Triglycerides can be broken down into **glycerol** and **fatty acids** to provide the body's largest source of **energy**. Even in this form they are generally still too large to permeate the blood capillary walls and so they are absorbed into the lymphatic system. Excess triglycerides are stored in the **adipose tissue** to be drawn upon when required. Unrequired carbohydrates and proteins are converted into triglycerides and stored too.

Lipids are very diverse. As well as triglycerides they include steroids, carotenes, vitamins A, E and K and lipoproteins (a lipid-protein combination that is water-soluble).

Proteins

Proteins make up about 12-18% of total body weight. They contain carbon, hydrogen, oxygen and nitrogen. Proteins are much **more complex** than either carbohydrates or lipids, and as such have a larger range of functions. Some proteins have a **structural** role, e.g. building blocks for cells. Proteins form **enzymes** that act as catalysts to speed up chemical reactions, **antibodies** that play a part in immunity, and **hormones** that regulate body processes.

In the same way that monosaccharides are the building blocks for carbohydrates, **amino acids** are the **building blocks** for proteins. Amino acids **bond** to form **peptides**. When two amino acids bond the structure is called a **dipeptide**. If a third attaches it is known as a **tripeptide**. When more than three amino acids bond – and there can be up to 2,000 – the chain-like structure is called a **polypeptide**.

During the digestive process, the complex proteins that we eat are **broken down** into peptides and then into amino acids to be absorbed into the blood and made available for the body to use structurally or physiologically. Any protein derivatives produced during the digestive process are sometimes referred to as **peptones**.

As well as the 3 main food groups that we have looked at, the body requires 4 other nutritional components to remain healthy:

Vitamins

A vitamin is an essential organic compound that acts as a catalyst in metabolic processes. We have already mentioned vitamins as some are made from lipids. Vitamins are necessary in small quantities for the normal functioning of the body. A normal balanced diet will usually provide an adequate vitamin supply. A deficiency in a vitamin will usually lead to a metabolic disorder, or deficiency disease, which can be remedied by the sufficient intake of that vitamin. The main vitamins are A, B12, C, D, E and K.

Minerals

A mineral is an inorganic compound that may perform a function vital to life. Approximately 4% of the human body is made up of minerals. Without minerals the body is unable to function. The correct balance of minerals ensures that we do not dehydrate or drown in our own fluids and that the nerves and muscles work well. Minerals include calcium, phosphorous, sodium, potassium, chlorine and iron.

Fibre

Fibre, or roughage, gives bulk to the diet. Undigested fibre is passed in the faeces. This is necessary for healthy and active bowels. Good sources of roughage include skins and pulp of fruit and vegetables, and the husks of grains.

Water

Last but most certainly not least, water is the most abundant inorganic compound in the body - it makes up a large percentage of it! It is therefore essential that the body is hydrated. Water plays a major part in all the major metabolic processes. More information about the properties of water can be found in the Chemistry section.

The digestive system contains the organs involved in taking food into the body (**ingestion**), transporting it to the appropriate location, breaking it down (**digestion**), absorbing the required components (**absorption**) and eliminating waste products (**elimination**). Anatomically, the digestive system runs from mouth to anus, a route that is commonly called the **alimentary canal**. We'll look at this route now.

Food is taken through the lips into the body via the **mouth**. The mouth is also called the **buccal cavity**. It is in the mouth that the first stage of mechanical and chemical digestion begins. Mechanically, the **teeth** and the **tongue** manipulate the food. Chemically, **saliva** begins to break it down.

Saliva is secreted by three pairs of **salivary glands**. The **parotid** glands are located inferior and anterior to the ears. The **submandibular** glands are situated inferior to the base of the tongue and the **sublingual** glands are superior to the submandibular glands.

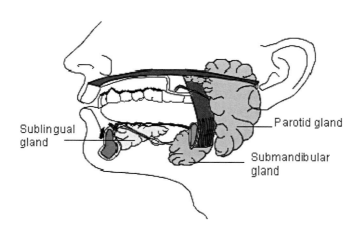

As you can see, the salivary glands lie outside of the mouth. The saliva is secreted into **ducts** that empty into it.

Saliva is alkaline and consists mainly of **water** to moisten the food, but it also contains an enzyme called **salivary amylase**. Salivary amylase begins the breakdown of **starches** (polysaccharides). The digestive processes in the mouth create a round mass of food called a **bolus**. The bolus is then **swallowed**.

On swallowing, the bolus leaves the mouth and passes into the **pharynx** (throat). It passes the entrance to the trachea, which is covered during swallowing by the epiglottis, and moves into the **oesophagus**. Food is helped down the oesophagus by waves of muscular contraction called **peristalsis**. The oesophagus takes the bolus to the **stomach**.

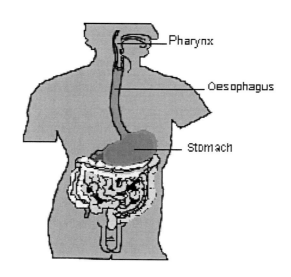

294

The stomach is a 'J' shaped **muscular sac**, located under the diaphragm to the left of the abdomen. It has 3 layers of smooth muscle:

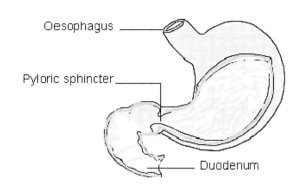

1. outer longitudinal layer
2. middle circular layer
3. inner oblique layer

The complex arrangement of muscle layers allows the stomach to contract in a variety of ways to **churn** and **break down** food.

The stomach has 4 main areas. The **cardia** surrounds the superior opening of the stomach. The **fundus** is the rounded portion above and to the right (as we look now) of the cardia. Below the fundus is the **body**. The inferior region that connects the stomach to the duodenum is called the **pylorus**.

The stomach receives food from the oesophagus. There is a sphincter muscle where the oesophagus meets the stomach. This is called the **lower oesphageal sphincter** or the **cardiac sphincter** (due to its location in the cardia, nothing to do with hearts!).

The stomach holds food received from the oesophagus for 2-6 hours before expelling it via the **pyloric sphincter** into the **duodenum**.

The stomach can hold about 1.5 litres and is the site of digestion, both mechanical and chemical. Mechanically, the peristaltic 'churning' of the stomach mixes the food. Chemically, the stomach is an **acidic** environment in which a number of **gastric juices** are secreted to break down the food.

The secretion of gastric juices is a **reflex action** that begins when food is in the mouth and continues when it enters the stomach. The gastric juices include:

Secretion	Action
Mucus	Protects the delicate inner lining of the stomach.
Hydrochloric acid	Kills bacteria. Neutralizes saliva. Inhibits the secretion of gastrin. Acts on pepsinogen.
Pepsinogen (enzyme)	On contact with hydrochloric acid, pepsinogen is converted to pepsin, a protein-digesting enzyme which begins to break down proteins into peptides.
Rennin (enzyme)	Coagulates the milk protein casein.
Intrinsic factor	Allows the absorption of vitamin B12.
Gastrin (hormone)	Stimulates the secretion of hydrochloric acid and pepsinogen. Increases the muscular activity of the stomach. Relaxes the pyloric sphincter.

The digestive processes that take place in the stomach create a **semi-fluid** mixture of food and gastric juices called **chyme**. With the exception of some water and certain drugs (including alcohol), very few components of the chyme are absorbed from the stomach into the blood. The chyme leaves the stomach via the **pyloric sphincter** and enters the **duodenum**.

The duodenum is the first part of the **small intestine**.

The small intestine consists of a convoluted muscular passageway about 6 metres long.

This passageway runs from the pyloric sphincter to the **ileocaecal sphincter** at the entrance to the large intestine.

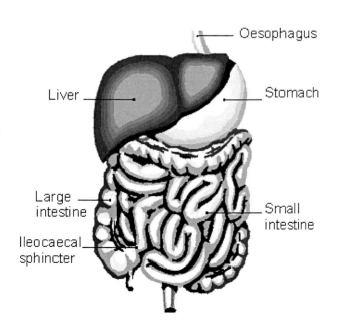

The **duodenum** is the **shortest** part of the small intestine. After about 25cm it runs into the **middle** part of the small intestine called the **jejunum**. The jejunum, about 2.5 metres long, then becomes the **ileum**.

The ileum is the **longest** section, running for about 3.5 metres before joining the large intestine.

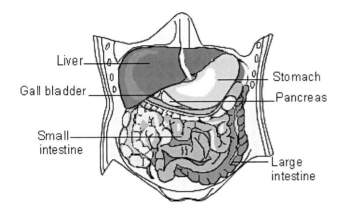

Digestion continues in the **small intestine**.

The small intestine produces alkaline intestinal juice. Also, the epithelial cells produce enzymes that continue the digestive process. We'll look at these later.

Successful digestion, however, also depends on secretions from the pancreas, liver and gall bladder. We'll look at these organs next.

Pancreas

The pancreas is located inferior and slightly posterior to the stomach. It is 12-15cm long. **Pancreatic juice** is introduced into the **duodenum** via two pancreatic ducts.

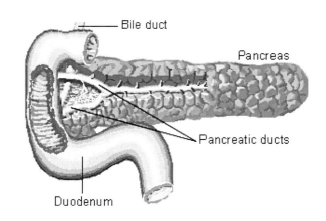

Pancreatic juice is a clear liquid consisting mostly of water, some salts and several enzymes. The enzymes include:

- ✓ **pancreatic amylase** – digests **carbohydrates** by breaking down polysaccharides into disaccharides

- ✓ **trypsin and chymotrypsin** – continue to break down **proteins** into peptides

- ✓ **lipase** – breaks **lipids** down into glycerol and fatty acids

The pancreas is made up of small clusters of glandular epithelial cells. About **99%** of these cells are arranged in clusters called **acini**. The acini are responsible for producing the **pancreatic juice**. Because the pancreatic juice is secreted via a **duct** to the **epithelial** surface of the duodenum, the pancreas is classified as an **exocrine** gland.

In the remaining **1%** of the pancreas, the cells are arranged in clusters called **islets of Langerhans**. These clusters secrete the **hormones insulin** and **glucagon** directly (not via a duct) into the **blood**. This also classifies the pancreas as an **endocrine** gland (see Endocrine System).

The secretion and content of pancreatic juice is regulated by **nervous** and **hormonal** stimulation. When the food is in the **stomach**, **nerve** impulses are transmitted to the pancreas to stimulate the secretion of pancreatic juice.

The content of the pancreatic juice is regulated by hormones secreted by the small intestine. When **acidic** chyme leaves the stomach and enters the small intestine, the small intestine secretes the hormone **secretin**. Secretin stimulates the production of **alkaline pancreatic** secretions.

In response to **partially digested fats** and **proteins** in the small intestine, the small intestine secretes the hormone **cholecystokinin** (CCK). CCK stimulates a pancreatic secretion that is rich in **digestive enzymes**.

Liver

The liver is the **heaviest** gland in the body. The graphic here shows the posterior view. It is located to the right of the upper abdominal cavity, just inferior to the diaphragm. The liver consists of two main lobes and two smaller lobes, each made up of millions of smaller lobules.

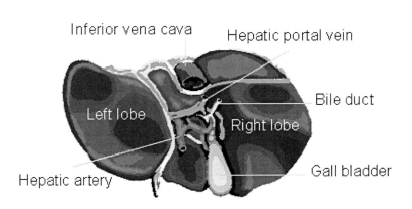

The liver is highly vascular because its main function is to regulate the composition of the blood. Its blood supply is therefore different to any other part of the body. As you would expect, the liver receives oxygenated blood. The **oxygenated** blood is supplied by the **hepatic artery**.

The liver also receives **deoxygenated** blood from the **digestive organs** and the **spleen**. This **deoxygenated** blood is received from the **hepatic portal vein**. Harmful substances, absorbed from the stomach and intestines into the blood, are extracted from the blood by the liver and destroyed. The **inferior vena cava** then transports the blood from the liver back to the heart.

The liver **produces** and **secretes bile**. Bile is partially an excretory product and partially a digestive secretion. It consists of salts, pigments, cholesterol and traces of other substances. The bile is drained from the liver and stored in the **gall bladder**.

The liver has many other functions. The liver:

✓ helps to **maintain** the **blood-sugar** level by converting glucose to glycogen when the blood-sugar level is high, and vice-versa when it is low
✓ **stores** and breaks down **fats**
✓ **metabolizes proteins**
✓ **manufactures** some of the **proteins** of blood plasma
✓ **manufactures** some of the blood **clotting factors**
✓ **manufactures vitamin A** from carotene
✓ **stores vitamins A, B12, D, E and K** and **iron**
✓ **detoxifies** or excretes drugs and poisons
✓ **inactivates** certain **hormones**
✓ **destroys** worn out **blood cells**
✓ produces **heat**

Gall Bladder

As we have mentioned, **bile**, produced by the liver, is stored in the **gall bladder**. The gall bladder is a small **sac** located posterior to the liver. The gall bladder adds **mucus** to the bile and increases its **concentration** by absorbing some water from it.

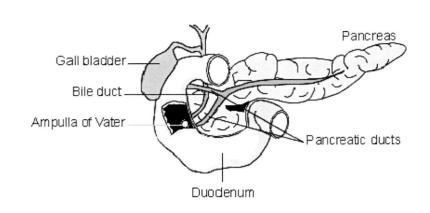

When the bile is required, the gall bladder contracts and bile is released into the bile duct. The bile duct joins a pancreatic duct and they enter the duodenum together at the **ampulla of Vater**. Bile plays a role in the **emulsification** of **fats**, breaking down the large fat globules into smaller ones. It also helps to **lubricate** the intestines.

The secretion of bile is regulated by a number of factors, including nervous and hormonal stimulation. You will notice some similarities between the regulation of bile and the regulation of pancreatic juice, which we covered earlier in this section.

When the food is in the **stomach**, **nerve** impulses are transmitted to the **liver** to stimulate the **production** of bile. When **acidic chyme** leaves the stomach, the small intestine secretes the hormone **secretin**. Secretin stimulates the liver to produce **alkaline bile**.

The hormone **cholecystokinin** (CCK) also has a part to play. CCK is secreted in the small intestine in response to partially digested fats and proteins. CCK stimulates the **contraction** of the walls of the **gall bladder**. This squeezes the stored bile into the bile duct. CCK also relaxes the sphincter at the **ampulla of Vater** to allow the bile to flow into the duodenum.

The **flow** of **blood** through the liver has an impact on bile secretion too. As blood flow increases, so does bile production to some extent. The presence of large amounts of **bile salts** in the blood also increases the rate of bile production.

Let's recap on the digestive process covered so far:

In the mouth, the food is mechanically digested by the teeth and tongue, and chemically digested by the saliva. After swallowing, the peristaltic action of the oesophagus takes the food to the stomach where it is churned and chemically digested by the gastric juices. Chyme leaves the stomach via the pyloric sphincter and enters the duodenum. The duodenum is the first part of the small intestine. Here, pancreatic juice and bile are added to the intestinal secretions.

As the **chyme** moves through the **small intestine**, the alkaline intestinal juice, pancreatic juice and bile continue the digestive process. The **epithelium** of the small intestines that lines the **villi** also produces several enzymes called **brush border enzymes**. The brush border enzymes **complete** many of the digestive processes. The brush border enzymes include:

✓ **Maltase**, **sucrase** and **lactase**, which **complete** the digestion of carbohydrates by breaking down the disaccharides and some remaining polysaccharides into monosaccharides.

✓ **Peptidases**, which **complete** the digestion of proteins by breaking the **peptides** down into **amino acids**.

Once the carbohydrates, proteins and fats have been successfully broken down into their smallest components (namely **monosaccharides, amino acids, glycerol** and **fatty acids**) digestion is **complete**.

These nutrients are now **small** enough to be **absorbed** through the epithelial lining of the small intestine. The **monosaccharides** and **amino acids** can be absorbed directly into the **blood**, but the larger **fat** components cannot and so enter the **lymphatic** system.

For successful absorption, there must be a good **blood supply** and **lymphatic** connection to absorb the nutrients, and a large **surface area** to give sufficient opportunity for the process to take place.

The small intestine is ideally suited and is the site where most absorption occurs...

The small intestine receives a good blood supply from the **superior mesenteric artery** and structurally it offers a large surface area. Not only is the small intestine **long**, but its inner layer extends into numerous finger-like projections called **villi**.

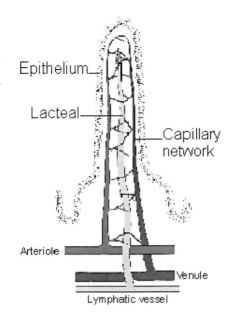

Each villus contains a network of **capillaries** and a **lacteal** (a lymphatic vessel) to facilitate absorption. **Nutrients** are **absorbed** through the epithelial lining of the small intestine. The digested **fats** enter the **lymphatic** system and the digested **proteins** and **carbohydrates** permeate the blood capillaries to enter the **blood**.

The **small intestine** also absorbs about **90%** of the **water** that makes its way into it. Only about 10% passes into the large intestine.

The water is absorbed directly into the **blood**, or is transferred to the blood by the **lymphatic** system. Water that is **not** required by the body is filtered from the blood by the kidneys and excreted in the **urine**.

The small intestine leads, via the ileocaecal sphincter, to the **large intestine**.

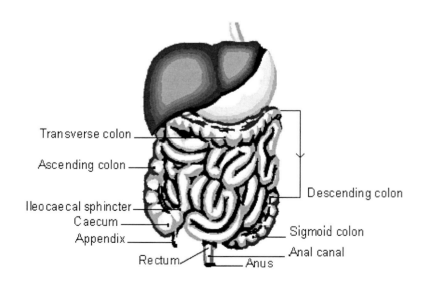

The large intestine is about **1.5 metres** long. It is much **wider** than the small intestine and does **not** have villi. The large intestine incorporates the caecum, ascending colon, transverse colon, descending colon, sigmoid colon, rectum and anal canal. It terminates at the anus. The appendix is also a part of the large intestine but it does not perform a digestive function.

The large intestine receives the remaining chyme from the small intestine. It continues the **absorption** of **water** (leaving only a tiny percentage, about 0.01%) and **nutrients** from the digested food. It then prepares undigested food and waste for expulsion as **faeces**.

The large intestine secretes **mucus** but not enzymes. It does, however, contain **bacteria** that ferment any remaining carbohydrates and release **gases**. The bacteria also break down any remaining proteins. The bacterial processes produce vitamin K and some B vitamins that are required for normal metabolism. Some of the substances produced in the large intestine are **absorbed** and the rest are incorporated in the faeces.

The solid or semi-solid faeces are passed through the sphincters at the top and bottom of the **anal canal** and are expelled through the **anus**. The expulsion of the faeces completes the mouth to anus digestive process.

Summary

➢ The digestive system is responsible for the ingestion, digestion, absorption and elimination of food.

➢ The process begins in the mouth, where food is ingested and then broken down mechanically by the teeth and tongue, and chemically by saliva.

➢ Salivary amylase begins to break down starches (polysaccharides).

➢ The bolus leaves the mouth and passes through the pharynx and oesophagus into the stomach.

➢ In the stomach, acidic gastric juices are secreted to break down the food.

➢ The gastric enzyme pepsin begins to break down proteins into peptides.

➢ The food, now called chyme, passes through the pyloric sphincter into the small intestine. The small intestine produces alkaline intestinal juice to continue digestion.

➢ The first part of the small intestine is the duodenum. Here, bile (produced in the liver and stored in the gall bladder) and pancreatic secretions further aid the digestive process.

➢ Bile emulsifies lipids.

➢ Pancreatic amylase digests carbohydrates by breaking down polysaccharides into disaccharides.

➢ Trypsin and chymotrypsin continue to break down proteins into peptides.

➢ Lipase breaks lipids down into glycerol and fatty acids.

➢ The brush border enzymes maltase, sucrase and lactase complete the digestion of carbohydrates by breaking them down into monosaccharides.

➢ The brush border peptidases complete the digestion of proteins by breaking the peptides down into amino acids.

➢ As the food passes through the duodenum, jejunum and ileum, nutrients and about 90% of the water are absorbed.

➢ The chyme passes through the ileocaecal sphincter into the large intestine.

➤ The large intestine continues the absorption of water and nutrients, and prepares undigested food for expulsion as faeces.

➤ The faeces are expelled through the anus to complete the digestive process.

Questions (Answers: Page 395)

1.   Which are the most complex carbohydrates?

      a. polysaccharides
      b. disaccharides
      c. monosaccharides

2.   Which type of carbohydrates are sucrose and lactose?

3.   Which two compounds make up triglycerides?

      a. glycerol and fatty acids
      b. glucose and fatty acids
      c. glycogen and fatty acids

4.   What are the building blocks of proteins?

5.   What term is given to the digestive tract that runs from 'mouth to anus'?

      a. elementary canal
      b. digestive channel
      c. alimentary canal

6.   How many pairs of salivary glands are there?

      a. 2
      b. 3
      c. 4
      d. 6

7.   Saliva contains the enzyme salivary amylase. Which food type does salivary amylase begin to break down?

      a. proteins
      b. starches
      c. roughage
      d. fats

8. On swallowing, the food leaves the mouth as a round mass called a bolus. Into which structure does it pass?

    a. pharynx
    b. oesophagus
    c. stomach
    d. trachea

9. Fill in the missing word:

    The food passes the entrance to the trachea, which is covered during swallowing by the epiglottis, and moves into the _____ .

10. What type of environment does the stomach provide for digestion?

    a. acidic
    b. alkaline
    c. neutral

11. Which of the following is NOT secreted in the gastric juices?

    a. rennin
    b. gastrin
    c. trypsin
    d. pepsinogen

12. Through which opening does the food leave the stomach?

13. Fill in the missing word:

    Chyme passes from the stomach, through the pyloric sphincter, into the _____.

14. The small intestine runs from the stomach to the large intestine. It has three parts. Starting at the stomach, in which order do they occur?

    a. ileum, duodenum, jejunum
    b. jejunum, duodenum, ileum
    c. duodenum, ileum, jejunum
    d. duodenum, jejunum, ileum

15. All of the following are enzymes secreted in the pancreatic juice. Which pancreatic enzyme digests fats?

    a. lipase
    b. pancreatic amylase
    c. trypsin and chymotrypsin

16. Which pancreatic enzyme breaks down carbohydrates?

17. What substances do trypsin and chymotrypsin digest?

18. Which pancreatic cells produce the pancreatic juice?

    a. acini
    b. islets of Langerhans

19. What is secreted by the islets of Langerhans?

    a. enzymes
    b. hormones
    c. gastric juice
    d. pancreatic amylase

20. When the food is in the stomach, the pancreas is stimulated to produce pancreatic juice. Is this a nervous or hormonal stimulation?

    a. nervous
    b. hormonal

21. Which hormone, produced by the small intestine, stimulates the pancreas to secrete juice rich in digestive enzymes?

    a. pancreatic amylase
    b. cholecystokinin
    c. secretin
    d. trypsin

22. Which hormone, secreted by the small intestine in response to receiving acidic chyme, stimulates the production of alkaline pancreatic secretions?

23. Which vessel supplies oxygenated blood to the liver?

    a. hepatic artery
    b. hepatic portal vein
    c. inferior vena cava

24. Which vessel takes deoxygenated blood away from the liver to the heart?

    a. hepatic artery
    b. hepatic portal vein
    c. inferior vena cava

25. The hepatic portal vein delivers deoxygenated blood to the liver. Where does this deoxygenated blood come from?

26. What is produced and secreted by the liver and then stored in the gall bladder?

27. Bile is released from the gall bladder via the bile duct. Where does the bile duct join the small intestine?

    a. duodenum
    b. jejunum
    c. ileum

28. Which food component does bile break down?

    a. carbohydrates
    b. proteins
    c. fats

29. Which hormone, secreted by the small intestine in response to acidic chyme, stimulates the liver to produce alkaline bile?

30. Fill in the missing word:

Cholecystokinin (CCK) stimulates the contraction of the walls of the gall bladder and relaxes the sphincter at the ampulla of _____ .

31. True or False?

The brush border enzymes maltase, sucrase and lactase complete the digestion of carbohydrates.

32. What are produced when the brush border enzyme peptidase completes the digestion of proteins?

33. What finger-like projections give the small intestine a large surface area for absorption?

34. Approximately what percentage of water is absorbed from the small intestines?

    a. 10%
    b. 50%
    c. 90%
    d. 100%

35. Fill in the missing word:

    The small intestine leads, via the _____ sphincter, to the large intestine.

36. True or False?

    Like the small intestine, the large intestine has villi to aid absorption.

Endocrine System

This page has intentionally been left blank.

312

The endocrine system consists of **ductless glands** that secrete **hormones** directly into the blood.

A comparison must be drawn here between endocrine glands and exocrine glands. Exocrine glands make their secretions via a duct onto epithelial surfaces such as those in body cavities. Endocrine glands secrete hormones into the spaces between the cells. This enables the hormones to diffuse directly into the capillaries to be carried away in the blood.

A hormone is a **chemical messenger**. Although they are only released in **small** quantities, they have profound effects on the body. They influence not only how the body **functions** but also how it **appears** from stature to hair distribution, fat distribution and fluid retention.

There are over **50** hormones that control many body functions. Let's take a look at some of their functions. Hormones:

- ✓ regulate the chemical composition and volume of the **extracellular fluid**
- ✓ help to regulate **metabolism** and energy balance
- ✓ help to regulate contraction of smooth and cardiac **muscles** and secretions by **glands**
- ✓ help maintain **homeostasis**
- ✓ regulate some **immune** responses
- ✓ play a role in **growth** and **development**
- ✓ contribute to the basic processes of **reproduction**

Most hormones are released in short bursts. The release of hormones is stimulated or inhibited by signals from the nervous system, chemical changes in the blood or levels of other hormones.

The 'master' of the endocrine system is the **hypothalamus**.

The hypothalamus is located in the **diencephalon** in the heart of the **brain**. The hypothalamus receives information about many of the body processes and so provides the link between the nervous system and the endocrine system.

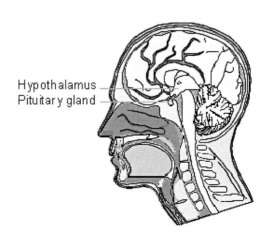

Hypothalamus
Pituitary gland

The hypothalamus performs many functions. It:

- ✓ controls the autonomic nervous system
- ✓ governs many of the body's activities
- ✓ governs many of the body's 'drives' (e.g. hunger, thirst and sexual behaviour)
- ✓ influences emotions
- ✓ receives sensory information from the external and internal environments

The ability of the hypothalamus to **secrete hormones** is crucial to its regulatory roles. The hormones produced by the hypothalamus travel in the blood to the **pituitary gland**. Here they are either stored and secreted as needed, or they act to release or inhibit hormones produced by the pituitary gland itself.

The pituitary gland is located just **beneath** the hypothalamus. It is the size of a large pea. It has two main portions – the **anterior** lobe and the **posterior** lobe.

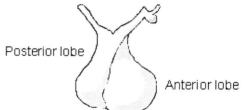

Posterior lobe

Anterior lobe

Some of the hormones secreted by the pituitary gland stimulate or inhibit the release of hormones from **other** endocrine glands. This capability of the pituitary to **control other** endocrine glands makes it a key player in the endocrine system.

The **posterior** lobe of the pituitary gland does not produce hormones. It does, however, **store** and **release** two hormones **produced** by the **hypothalamus**. They are:

1. **Oxytocin** – stimulates the contraction of the uterine muscles during birth and milk ejection after birth. During childbirth and suckling, the uterus and breasts send sensory messages to the hypothalamus. The hypothalamus then sends nerve impulses to the pituitary to release the hormone.

2. **Antidiuretic hormone** (ADH) (vasopressin) – decreases urine production and causes the contraction of the arteries. Its release is triggered by dehydration. A reduced concentration in the blood is detected in the hypothalamus, which stimulates the pituitary to release this hormone.

The **anterior** lobe of the pituitary gland **produces** and releases **six** major hormones:

1. **Growth hormone** (somatotrophin) – controls body growth
2. **Prolactin** – stimulates the mammary glands to produce milk
3. **Adrenocorticotrophic hormone** (ACTH) – stimulates secretions from the adrenals
4. **Thyroid stimulating hormone** (TSH) – controls secretions from the thyroid
5. **Gonadotrophic hormones** (e.g. follicle stimulating hormone (FSH) and luteinizing hormone (LH)) – stimulate the activities of the ovaries and testes
6. **Melanocyte stimulating hormone** – stimulates the production of melanin (a pigment found in the skin and hair)

The release of these **anterior** lobe hormones is controlled by the **hypothalamus**.

The hypothalamus continually **monitors** the **blood** for **levels** of **anterior** lobe hormones. When a level **falls**, the **hypothalamus** secretes an appropriate **releasing** hormone. This hormone is **transported** to the **anterior** lobe of the pituitary, where it **stimulates** the **release** of the hormone.

The **increased** level in the blood is then **detected**. As a result, the hypothalamus secretes an appropriate **inhibiting** hormone. When it is received in the pituitary the release of the anterior lobe hormone is **inhibited** and the level in the blood **decreases**. This **negative feedback system** (see Homeostasis) is continually in action.

We'll now take a look at the other main endocrine glands: the thyroid gland, parathyroid glands, adrenals, pancreas, ovaries, testes, pineal gland and thymus.

Thyroid Gland

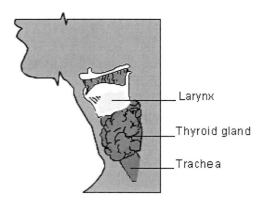

Larynx

Thyroid gland

Trachea

The thyroid gland is located just **inferior** to the **larynx**. There are **two** main lobes, one either side of the trachea.

Under the influence of **thyroid stimulating hormone** (secreted from the anterior lobe of the pituitary gland), the thyroid removes iodine from the blood and produces, stores and secretes hormones.

The thyroid hormones regulate **growth** and **development**. They also control **metabolic rate** and the activity of the **nervous system**. The main thyroid hormone is **thyroxine**.

Calcitonin is also secreted by the thyroid. Calcitonin **lowers** the blood levels of **calcium** and **phosphates** by accelerating their absorption into bone and inhibiting bone breakdown.

Parathyroid Glands

There are **four** small, oval parathyroid glands attached to the **posterior** surface of the **thyroid**.

These glands produce **parathyroid hormone**. Parathyroid hormone **decreases** the blood **phosphate** level and **increases** the blood **calcium** level.

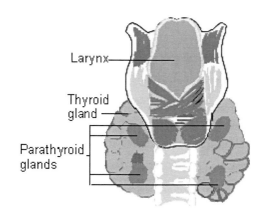

Larynx

Thyroid gland

Parathyroid glands

Parathyroid hormone increases the number and the activity of **osteoclasts** (bone-destroying cells). The subsequent breakdown of bone releases **calcium** and **phosphates** into the blood. Parathyroid hormone also impacts on the kidneys, altering the rate at which they reabsorb and excrete calcium and phosphates. In the case of phosphates, more are removed by the kidneys than are released from the bone, hence the blood-phosphate level falls.

Adrenal Glands

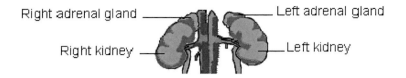

Right adrenal gland ____ ____ Left adrenal gland

Right kidney ____ ____ Left kidney

There are **two** adrenal glands, one on **top** of each **kidney**. They are sometimes called suprarenal glands (supra- = over, renal = kidney).

The **outer** layer is called the **adrenal cortex**. The **inner** layer is called the **adrenal medulla**.

The **adrenal medulla** produces the two 'fight or flight' hormones, released when the body is under **stress**, to help it cope and prepare for an emergency. Chemically, these 2 hormones are very similar.

1. **adrenaline** (also known as epinephrine) causes an increase in metabolic rate, heart rate, respiratory rate and blood pressure, and the constriction of the blood vessels. Adrenaline accounts for 80% of secretions from the adrenals.

2. **noradrenaline** (also known as norepinephrine) has the same effect as adrenaline and is also a neurotransmitter, secreted from the nerve endings of the sympathetic nervous system.

The **adrenal cortex** is rich in **vitamin C** and **cholesterol**. It secretes:

1. **cortisol** and **corticosterone** - stimulate the conversion of fats and proteins to glucose

2. **aldosterone** - controls sodium and potassium concentrations

3. **androgens** and **oestrogens** - male and female sex hormones

Occasionally tumours of the adrenal gland can cause sufficient secretions of oestrogens to cause a male to develop breasts. This excessive benign growth of the male mammary glands is called **gynecomastia**.

Pancreas

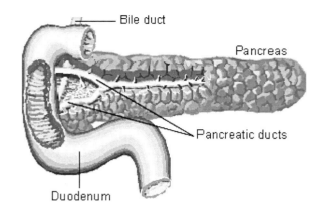

Bile duct

Pancreas

Pancreatic ducts

Duodenum

The pancreas is located inferior and slightly posterior to the stomach. It is 12-15cm long.

About **99%** of the pancreatic tissue is involved in producing **digestive enzymes** (see Digestive System) that are released into the digestive tract via a duct. This function classifies the pancreas as an **exocrine** gland. It is, however, also an endocrine gland...

The cells in the remaining **1%** of the pancreas are arranged in clusters called **islets of Langerhans**. These clusters secrete **hormones** into the **blood**, classifying the pancreas as an **endocrine** gland.

The pancreas secretes two hormones that are responsible for regulating the blood-glucose level:

1. **insulin** – decreases the blood-glucose level. It does this in a number of ways including accelerating the transport of **glucose** from the blood into the cells, converting glucose into glycogen or into fatty acids, and decreasing the amount of glycogen that is converted into glucose. Insulin is secreted in response to an **increased** blood-glucose level.

2. **glucagon** – increases the blood-glucose level. Glucagon causes the release of glucose into the blood, accelerates the breakdown of glycogen into glucose in the liver and converts other nutrients into glycogen, again in the liver. Glucagon is secreted in response to a **decrease** in the blood-glucose level.

Ovaries

The **ovaries** are the principal structures of the female reproductive system (see Reproductive System). They are classified as endocrine glands because they secrete hormones.

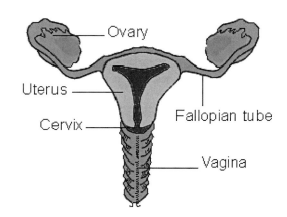

The ovaries secrete:

1. **oestrogen** - the female sex hormone concerned with the **development** and **maintenance** of the **reproductive system** and the development of **secondary sex characteristics**. Oestrogen promotes **fat distribution** to the breasts, abdomen and hips, influences **voice** pitch and the width of the **pelvis** and controls the distribution of **hair**. Oestrogens also help to control the **fluid** balance.

2. **progesterone** - female sex hormone produced in the ovaries after ovulation. It helps to prepare the uterus for the implantation of the fertilized ovum, develops the placenta and prepares the mammary glands for milk secretion.

3. **inhibin** - inhibits the secretion of follicle stimulating hormone (FSH - produced by the anterior lobe of the pituitary gland) towards the end of the menstrual cycle.

4. **relaxin** - dilates the cervix and helps the pelvic girdle to widen during childbirth.

Two of the hormones produced by the ovaries, oestrogen and progesterone, play a part in the **menstrual cycle**. Menstruation and menopause are covered in the Reproductive System.

The hormonal balance alters throughout the life of a female. We'll take a look at the hormonal influences during two significant life stages – puberty and pregnancy.

Please note that not all of the hormones that will be mentioned here are secreted from the ovaries. As a recap, the ovaries secrete oestrogen, progesterone, inhibin and relaxin. We'll state the secreting gland for you for the other female hormones as we go.

Puberty

Prior to puberty, levels of **luteinizing hormone** (anterior lobe of pituitary gland) and **follicle stimulating hormone** (anterior lobe of pituitary gland) are **low**.

At about **6-7 years**, there is an increase in **androgens** (adrenal cortex). These substances stimulate **male** characteristics and are responsible for the growth of pubic and axillary **hair**.

The onset of **puberty** is characterized by **sleep-associated** surges in **luteinizing hormone** and **follicle stimulating hormone**.

As puberty progresses, the levels of these two hormones increase throughout the day. These increases stimulate the ovaries to secrete **oestrogens**, responsible for the **secondary sexual characteristics**. The breasts begin to develop, and the uterine tubes, uterus and vagina grow. The oestrogens are also involved in the onset of **menstruation**, which occurs at about 12 years.

Pregnancy

During the first **3-4 months** of pregnancy, the ovaries continue to secrete **oestrogens** and **progesterone**. These hormones maintain the lining of the **uterus** and prepare the mammary glands for **lactation** (the secretion and ejection of milk from the mammary glands). Progesterone also **inhibits uterine contractions**.

Early in the gestation period, **human chorionic gonadotrophic** hormone stimulates an increased secretion of oestrogens and progesterone from the ovaries. Human chorionic gonadotrophic hormone is a substance produced by the **placenta**. It **mimics luteinizing hormone** (anterior lobe of pituitary gland) – hence its effects.

From the third month onwards, the **placenta** itself provides sufficiently high levels of oestrogens and progesterone to maintain the uterus and prepare for lactation. The secretion of human chorionic gonadotrophic hormone is therefore greatly reduced because its effects are no longer required.

The **ovaries** and the **placenta** produce **inhibin**. Inhibin **inhibits** the secretion of **follicle stimulating hormone** (anterior lobe of pituitary gland), thus preventing the development of ova.

At the end of gestation, the level of **progesterone falls**. Labour cannot begin until this occurs as progesterone inhibits uterine contraction.

Oxytocin (posterior lobe of pituitary gland) stimulates uterine contraction. The **ovaries** and the **placenta** secrete **relaxin**. Relaxin helps to **dilate** the cervix and **relaxes** appropriate ligaments and joints to assist the **labour**.

During pregnancy the level of **prolactin** (anterior lobe of the pituitary gland) rises. Prolactin promotes **lactation** but the presence of high levels of oestrogens and progesterone inhibit its action.

Post-labour, the level of oestrogens and progesterone decrease, and so prolactin is allowed to function.

The sucking action of the infant on the nipples **stimulates** the secretion of **prolactin**. It also stimulates the release of **oxytocin** (posterior lobe of pituitary gland). Oxytocin causes muscular contraction of the muscular epithelial cells of the mammary glands to **eject** milk.

Testes

The **testes** are the principal structures of the male reproductive system.

They are classified as endocrine glands as they secrete:

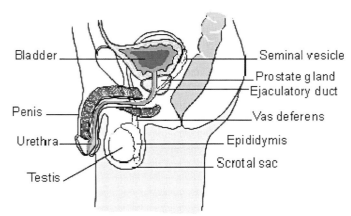

1. **testosterone** - the primary male sex hormone. It controls the **development**, **growth** and **maintenance** of the reproductive system and the development of **secondary sex characteristics** (i.e. muscular and skeletal growth, pubic, axillary, facial and chest hair, thickening of the skin, increased sebaceous gland secretions and enlargement of the larynx to deepen the voice). Testosterone also stimulates the production of **sperm**.

2. **inhibin** - inhibits the secretion of follicle stimulating hormone (produced by the anterior lobe of the pituitary gland) to control sperm production.

The levels of testosterone and other male sex hormones alter as life progresses. **Puberty** is a key time for these changes. Puberty in males takes place between the ages of 10 – 17.

We'll look at male hormonal changes next. As we did for the female, we'll state the secreting gland for the male hormones not secreted by the testes.

Prior to puberty, levels of **luteinizing hormone** (anterior lobe of pituitary gland), **follicle stimulating hormone** (anterior lobe of pituitary gland) and **testosterone** are **low**.

The secretion of **androgens** (predominantly testosterone, but also other androgens from the adrenal cortex) and **growth hormone** (anterior lobe of the pituitary gland) causes a growth spurt at around the age of 7.

Sleep-associated surges in luteinizing hormone and (to a lesser extent) follicle stimulating hormone are indicative of the onset of puberty. As puberty progresses, increased levels of these hormones are permanent, along with an associated increase in the level of testosterone.

The increase in **testosterone** during puberty causes the testes, penis, prostate gland, seminal vessels and epididymis to increase in size. It also initiates spermatogenesis.

The high level of testosterone during puberty also causes a growth spurt and the secondary sex characteristics (e.g. growth of pubic and body hair, change in voice pitch, body shape and muscle development).

At about the age of 55, there is a **decline** in the **testosterone** level. This can be called the male menopause. A fall in the testosterone level leads to less muscle strength, fewer viable sperm, and a decrease in sexual desire. The male may feel weak, show signs of depression and suffer sexual dysfunction. However, unlike women who lose the ability to conceive after the menopause, a healthy man can often retain the ability to successfully reproduce well into his 80's or even 90's.

Pineal Gland

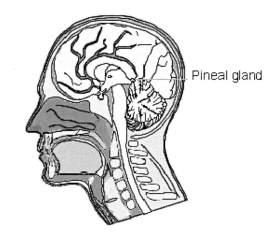

Pineal gland

The pineal gland is attached to the roof of the third cerebral ventricle in the brain. It consists of masses of neuroglia and secretory cells.

During darkness, the pineal gland secretes **melatonin**. This hormone is thought to induce sleep, help to maintain body rhythms and inhibit sexual activity.

Thymus Gland

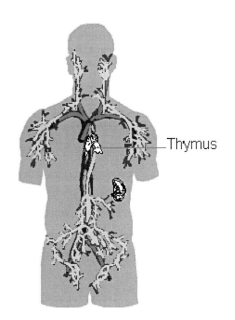

Thymus

The **thymus** consists of two lobes located in the upper chest, between the sternum (breast bone) and the lungs. It has a role to play in **immunity** as well as being an endocrine gland.

The thymus secretes a number of **thymus stimulating hormones**. As this collective name suggests, these hormones stimulate their originating gland. In stimulating itself, the thymus promotes its main role of producing and maturing T-cell lymphocytes.

Summary

➢ The endocrine system consists of a number of ductless glands that secrete hormones.

➢ Hormones are chemical messengers that control many body functions such as growth, metabolism and sexual development.

➢ The hypothalamus, located at the base of the brain, is the master of the endocrine system.

➢ Hormones secreted by the hypothalamus travel in the blood to the pituitary gland.

➢ The posterior lobe of the pituitary gland stores and releases hormones produced by the hypothalamus. They are oxytocin and antidiuretic hormone.

➢ The anterior lobe of the pituitary gland produces its own hormones - growth, prolactin, adreno-corticotrophic, thyroid stimulating, gonadotrophic and melanocyte stimulating. Their release is controlled by the hypothalamus.

➢ The other endocrine glands are the thyroid, parathyroids, adrenals, pancreas, ovaries, testes, pineal gland and thymus.

➢ The thyroid mainly secretes thyroxine.

➢ The parathyroid glands produce parathyroid hormone.

➢ The adrenal medulla secretes adrenaline and noradrenaline.

➢ The adrenal cortex secretes cortisol, corticosterone, aldosterone, androgens and oestrogens.

➢ The islets of Langerhans of the pancreas secrete insulin and glucagon.

➢ The ovaries secrete oestrogen, progesterone, inhibin and relaxin.

➢ The testes secrete testosterone and inhibin.

➢ The pineal gland secretes melatonin.

➢ The thymus secretes a number of thymus stimulating hormones.

Questions (Answers: Page 396)

1.   True or False?

Endocrine glands are ductless and secrete hormones that pass directly into the blood.

2.   Fill in the missing word:

The hypothalamus is the 'master' of the endocrine system. Hormones secreted by the hypothalamus are released into the blood and taken to the _____ gland where they are either stored or secreted as needed.

3.   Which lobe of the pituitary gland does not produce its own hormones, but stores and releases hormones produced by the hypothalamus?

      a. anterior
      b. posterior

4.   Which posterior lobe pituitary hormone decreases urine production and causes the contraction of the arteries?

      a. oxytocin
      b. antidiuretic hormone

5.   The anterior lobe of the pituitary gland produces its own hormones. Which of these anterior lobe hormones stimulates secretions from the adrenals?

      a. growth hormone (somatotrophin)
      b. prolactin
      c. adrenocorticotrophic hormone
      d. thyroid stimulating hormone
      e. gonadotrophic hormones
      f. melanocyte stimulating hormone

6.   Which of these anterior lobe pituitary gland hormones stimulate the activities of the ovaries and testes?

      a. growth hormone (somatotrophin)
      b. prolactin
      c. adrenocorticotrophic hormone
      d. thyroid stimulating hormone
      e. gonadotrophic hormones
      f. melanocyte stimulating hormone

7.   Which hormone stimulates the mammary glands to produce milk?

        a. growth hormone (somatotrophin)
        b. prolactin
        c. adrenocorticotrophic hormone
        d. thyroid stimulating hormone
        e. gonadotrophic hormones
        f. melanocyte stimulating hormone

8.   The anterior lobe pituitary hormones are produced and released by the pituitary gland, but what structure controls their release?

9.   What hormone, produced by the anterior lobe of the pituitary gland, stimulates the thyroid gland?

10.   What is the main hormone produced by the thyroid gland?

11.   What hormone secreted by the thyroid gland lowers levels of calcium and phosphates in the blood by accelerating their absorption into the bone?

12.   How many parathyroid glands are there attached to the rear surface of the thyroid?

13.   Which part of the adrenal gland produces the 'fight or flight' hormones?

        a. adrenal cortex
        b. adrenal medulla

14.   Name one of the two 'fight or flight' hormones.

15.   True or False?

        The adrenal cortex is rich in vitamin C and cholesterol but it does not secrete hormones.

16.   True or False?

        Most of the pancreas is involved in secreting hormones.

17.   Which pancreatic hormone decreases the blood-glucose level?

18. In which organ is glycogen broken down into glucose under the influence of glucagon?

19. Which ovarian hormone is concerned with the development and maintenance of the reproductive system and the development of secondary sex characteristics?

20. Which ovarian hormone is produced after ovulation and helps to prepare the uterus for the implantation of the fertilized ovum?

   a. progesterone
   b. inhibin
   c. relaxin

21. Which ovarian hormone dilates the cervix during childbirth?

   a. progesterone
   b. inhibin
   c. relaxin

22. Which two hormones have sleep-associated surges at the onset of puberty in a female?

   a. luteinizing hormone and oestrogen
   b. follicle stimulating hormone and oestrogen
   c. progesterone and oestrogen
   d. luteinizing hormone and follicle stimulating hormone

23. Fill in the missing word:

   Increases in the levels of luteinizing hormone and follicle stimulating hormone stimulate the ovaries to secrete _____, responsible for the secondary sexual characteristics.

24. Which hormone inhibits uterine contractions?

25. True or False?

   Early in the gestation period, human chorionic gonadotrophic hormone, produced by the placenta, mimics luteinizing hormone and therefore stimulates an increased secretion of oestrogens and progesterone from the ovaries.

26. Which hormone, secreted by the posterior lobe of the pituitary gland, stimulates uterine contractions?

27.   True or False?

Prolactin promotes lactation. The level of prolactin rises during pregnancy but it cannot function in the presence of high levels of oestrogens and progesterone.

28.   Which hormone causes muscular contraction to eject milk from the mammary glands?

29.   What is the primary male sex hormone produced by the testes?

30.   What hormone, secreted by the ovaries in females and the testes in males, inhibits the secretion of follicle stimulating hormone?

31.   Fill in the missing word:

Sleep-associated surges of mainly_____ hormone signal the onset of puberty in the male.

Nervous System

329

This page has intentionally been left blank.

The nervous system is the name given to the collection of nerve cells that **receive**, **transmit** and **respond** to stimuli from the external and internal environments.

The nervous system has three main functions:

1. **Senses changes** in the body and outside of the body.

2. **Analyzes** these changes, **stores** information if necessary, and **decides** how to respond. This is called **integration**.

3. **Responds** by either creating muscle movement or by inducing glandular secretions.

There are 2 main types of nerve cell, **neurons** and **neuroglia**.

Neurons are specialized to be able to **transmit nerve impulses**. We'll look at neurons in detail in a moment.

Neuroglia perform the function of connective tissue. They **support** and **protect** the neurons, and maintain **homeostasis** of the fluid that surrounds them. Neuroglia are smaller and more numerous than neurons.

Neurons

There are **3** types of neuron - sensory, motor and association.

1. Sensory Neurons
As the name suggests, **sensory** neurons transmit information **received** from the **sensory** receptors. They carry information about the **internal** or **external** **stimuli**. They are also called **afferent** neurons.

2. Motor Neurons
Motor neurons transmit information to the part of the body that has to **respond** to the sensory stimulus. These responsive body parts are called **effectors** and are **muscles** or **glands**. Motor neurons stimulate the muscle to contract or the gland to produce its secretion. Motor neurons are also called **efferent** neurons.

3. Association Neurons
Association neurons (also called connecting neurons) carry nerve impulses **from one** neuron **to another**. They do not contact sensory receptors or effectors. Approximately **90%** of all neurons are association.

Synapses

Sensory, motor and association neurons **link** to form a **network** capable of transmitting nerve impulses (tiny electrical currents) throughout the body.

One neuron **meets** another neuron at a junction called a **synapse**. A synapse also exists at the junction between a **motor neuron** and a **muscle** or **gland**.

The neuron carrying the nerve impulse **to** the synapse is called the **presynaptic** neuron. The neuron that **receives** the message and **conducts** the impulse **away** from the synapse is the **postsynaptic** neuron.

As well as facilitating the transmission of nerve impulses between neurons, synapses allow the information to be **analyzed** and **filtered**. As a result, some signals are transmitted while others are blocked.

There are 2 types of synapse – electrical and chemical.

1.   Electrical
At an electrical synapse, there is **contact** between the two neurons. This contact is made at a **gap junction** (don't be put off by the word gap – we know it doesn't exactly conjure up an image of contact!). A gap junction contains approximately 100 **tubular** protein **structures** that literally form **tunnels** between the neurons. These protein structures are called **connexons**. The nerve impulse is therefore able to **conduct** directly from one neuron to another.

2.   Chemical
At a chemical synapse, there is **no contact** between the neurons. They are very close to each other but they are separated by a space filled with **extracellular fluid**. This space is called the **synaptic cleft**.

Nerve impulses cannot cross the synaptic cleft without the help of a **chemical** called a **neurotransmitter**. The neurotransmitter is released by the presynaptic neuron. The neurotransmitter **diffuses** across the synaptic cleft, and then acts on the receptors of the postsynaptic neuron to create a nerve impulse.

The original electrical signal is therefore changed at the synapse to a chemical signal. The chemical stimulation of the postsynaptic neuron creates an electrical signal again.

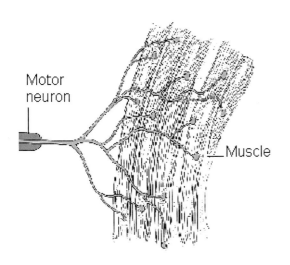

Motor neuron

Muscle

Motor neurons communicate with **muscles** at a **chemical** synapse called a **neuromuscular junction**. The region of the muscle adjacent to the motor neuron is called the **motor end plate**. The motor neuron releases a neurotransmitter called **acetylcholine**. The motor end plate contains **acetylcholine receptors** that, on detection of acetylcholine, trigger muscular contraction.

Electrical synapses are **faster** at transmitting signals than chemical synapses. As you will remember, at an electrical synapse the nerve impulse is conducted. At the chemical synapse, the nerve impulse is changed from an electrical signal to a chemical signal and then reverted back again. This all takes time!

As well as being slower, **chemical** synapses can only transfer information **one way**. This is because only the presynaptic neurons can release the vital neurotransmitter.

Now we have looked at how sensory, motor and association neurons work together to transmit nerve impulses from the sensory receptors to the effectors, let's look at their structure…

Neurons **vary** in **size**. They range from tiny cells that only transmit signals over a distance of less than 1mm, to the longest cells in the body. Some neurons stretch from the waist to the foot! Sensory, motor and association neurons all have some common features.

This is a **sensory (afferent) neuron** but, as we have said, the general features are typical for all.

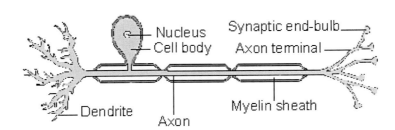

Nucleus
Cell body
Synaptic end-bulb
Axon terminal
Dendrite
Axon
Myelin sheath

The **dendrites receive** the **nerve impulses**. They create a 'tree-shaped' end to the neuron. The impulses are carried away from the dendrites by the long **axon**. The axon may be surrounded by a **myelin sheath**. The myelin sheath is a lipid and protein covering that **insulates** the axon and **increases** the **speed** of conduction.

In the **peripheral nervous system**, flattened cells arrange themselves around the axon of the neuron. These cells are called **Schwann cells** or **neurolemmocytes**. They produce the myelin sheath around the axon of peripheral nervous system neurons. At intervals along an axon, the myelin sheath has gaps called **nodes of Ranvier** or **neurofibral nodes**.

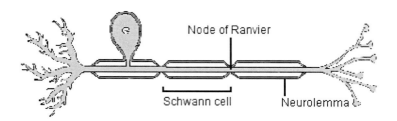

In the peripheral nervous system the myelin sheath of the Schwann cell has an outer layer called the **neurolemma**. This is a nucleated cytoplasmic layer. When an axon is injured, the neurolemma **aids regeneration** by forming a tube that guides and stimulates re-growth of the axon.

The axon branches into **axon terminals**. The end of each axon terminal is swollen into a **synaptic end-bulb**. The synaptic end-bulbs contain **synaptic vesicles** that contain a **neurotransmitter**.

To transmit the nerve impulse from one neuron to another, the **axon terminal** of the presynaptic neuron **meets** the **dendrites** of the postsynaptic neuron at the synapse.

The **cell body** contains the **nucleus**. The nucleus is surrounded by cytoplasm and contains typical organelles (see Cells).

The main structural difference between neurons is the position of the cell body. As you have seen, in the sensory neuron the cell body is positioned to one side of the axon. (Memory Hint: In the sensory neuron, the cell body resembles the eye – the sensory organ of sight.) Let's look at motor and association neurons.

The cell body of the **motor** neuron is located in the **centre** of the dendrites (see bleow). In the **association** neuron, the cell body is centrally positioned just **behind** the **dendrites**, in front of the axon.

Motor (efferent) neuron

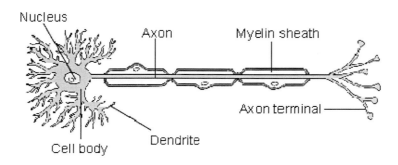

Association neuron

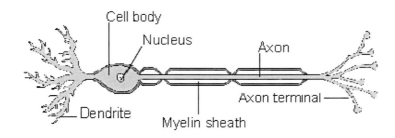

Neurons have **very limited** powers to replicate or repair themselves. At about 6 months of age, virtually all developing neurons lose their ability to undergo mitosis. Therefore when a neuron is destroyed it is **permanently lost** and only some types of damage can be repaired.

As we have discussed, damage to **myelinated** axons may be repaired in the **peripheral nervous system**. However this can only happen if the cell body remains intact and if the Schwann cells remain active. In the **central nervous system**, there is **little or no repair** of damage to neurons. Axons in the CNS do not have neurolemmas, axon re-growth is inhibited and scar tissue rapidly forms in the injured area, providing a physical barrier to regeneration.

As a part of the **natural ageing process**, the body **loses neurons**. As these are not replaced there is a decreased capacity for sending nerve impulses to and from the brain so that less information is processed. This causes conduction speed of the impulses, voluntary motor movements and reflexes to slow. Degenerative neurological changes in the sense organs can alter vision, hearing, taste, smell and touch. Not very cheery really!

All components of the nervous system are made up from neurons.

The **axon** of a neuron is also referred to as a **nerve fibre**. When nerve fibres occur in **bundles**, surrounded by a protective covering, they are referred to as a **nerve**.

A group of nerve **cell bodies**, usually bound by a sheath, is referred to as a **ganglion**.

The nervous system as a whole consists of the **central nervous system** and the **peripheral nervous system**.

We'll look at the central nervous system first.

Central Nervous System

The central nervous system consists of the **brain** and the **spinal cord**.

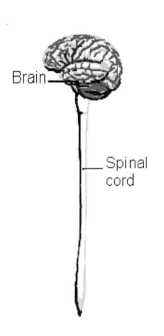

Brain

Spinal cord

The central nervous system **receives sensory** information from **all** parts of the body.

On receipt of this information, the central nervous system **analyzes** the information. Thoughts, emotions and memories are generated and stored.

The central nervous system usually **responds** to nerve impulses by **stimulating** muscles or glands, so creating an appropriate **response** to the original stimulus.

Brain

The **brain** is the most highly developed part of the nervous system. The brain weighs only about 2% of total body weight but uses **20%** of the **oxygen** at rest. It is therefore, by necessity, highly **vascular**. A vast network of arteries supplies the brain with blood. The main artery is the **carotid**, and the external and internal **jugulars** are the principal veins.

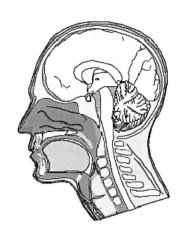

Although there is an extensive blood supply to the brain, not all substances can pass freely from the blood to the brain cells. The passage of some substances is slowed or prevented by a **semi-permeable** barrier of **specialised capillaries** that are less leaky than others, **astrocytes** (neurological cells that support neurons in the brain and spinal cord and attach the neurons to blood vessels) and a continuous basement **membrane**.

This "**blood-brain barrier**" allows the **free** passage of nutrients such as glucose, oxygen and water, **slows** the passage of substances such as creatine, urea and most ions, and **prevents** the passage of proteins and most antibiotics. The blood-brain barrier helps to **protect** the brain from harmful substances and pathogens, but lipid-soluble substances such as alcohol, caffeine, nicotine, heroin and most anaesthetics pass rapidly from the blood into the brain cells.

An **injury** to the brain may cause a **breakdown** in the blood-brain barrier and leave the nervous system **open** to the invasion of harmful substances that are usually kept out. However, on the other hand, the blood-brain barrier may also prevent the entry of drugs that could be used as therapy for CNS disorders.

The brain can be divided into 4 principal areas:

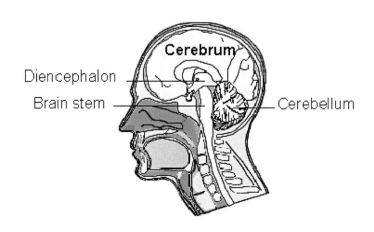

1.   The largest area is the **cerebrum**.

2.   The area at the top of the spinal cord is called the **brain stem**.

3.   Superior to the brain stem is the **diencephalon**.

4.   Inferior to the cerebrum and posterior to the brain stem is the **cerebellum**.

We'll look at each of these areas in detail later.

The **outer** portion of the brain is made up of **grey matter**. Grey matter consists either of neuron cell bodies, dendrites and axon terminals, or bundles of **unmyelinated** axons and neuroglia. The grey matter provides the site for **integration**.

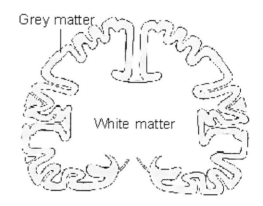

Vertical Cross-Section

The **inner** tissue of the brain is mainly **white matter**. White matter is composed of bundles of **myelinated** axons. The whitish colour of the myelin (lipid and protein) gives the white matter its colour. Some areas of grey matter are located within the white matter. The white matter conducts nerve impulses.

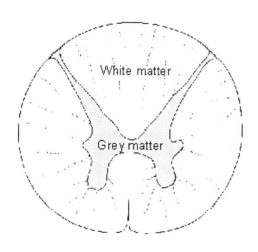

Both white matter and grey matter continue into the **spinal cord**. The grey matter appears in a **butterfly** shape. The white matter surrounds it.

The brain tissue is protected by the **cranium** (skull). It is also surrounded by **three** membranes, known as the **meninges**.

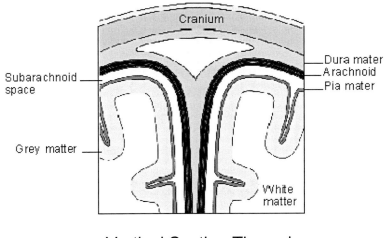

Vertical Section Through
the Top Portion of the Skull

The outer meninge is called the **dura mater** (Memory Hint: outer **D**oor = **D**ura). The middle meninge is the **arachnoid**, and the inner is the **pia mater**. These membranes also surround the **spinal cord**.

Cerebrospinal fluid (CSF) exists in the **subarachnoid** space between the arachnoid and the pia mater. Cerebrospinal fluid continually **circulates** around the brain and the spinal cord. CSF also fills **four** cavities, called **ventricles**, within the brain. The positions of the fluid-filled ventricles are shown here.

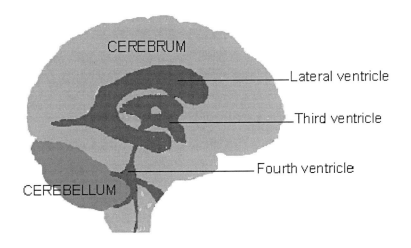

Midsagittal (front to back)
Section Through the Brain

A lateral ventricle is located in each of the cerebral hemispheres.

The third ventricle is positioned in the area of the diencephalon.

The **fourth ventricle** is located between the brain stem and the cerebellum.

Cerebrospinal fluid both **protects** and **nourishes**. It allows the brain to 'float' in the cranial cavity. In doing so it acts as a **shock absorber** to prevent the brain from crashing against the cranium.

The fluid itself provides an optimal **chemical environment** for neurons to transmit their messages. It is also the medium through which **nutrients** and **waste products** are **exchanged** between the blood and the nervous tissue.

Let's look at the 4 principal areas of the brain in turn. We'll look at them in this order:

1. Cerebrum
2. Diencephalon
3. Cerebellum
4. Brain stem

1. Cerebrum

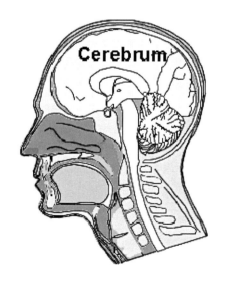

The **cerebrum** is the most prominent part of the brain.

It consists of two cerebral **hemispheres**, joined by a band of nerve fibres.

The **surface** of each cerebral hemisphere is made of grey matter and is called the **cerebral cortex**. Beneath the cerebral cortex is the white matter.

The cerebrum is the site of many functions such as vision, hearing, touch, smell, voluntary muscle activity, speech, intelligence, memory and emotional processes. These functions take place in various areas, or **lobes**, of the cerebrum.

Each cerebral hemisphere has **four** main lobes.

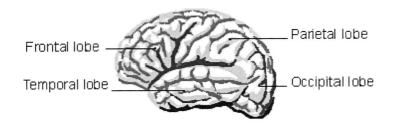

Frontal lobe: Used in the planning and execution of activities. Sends messages through the efferent nerves to the muscles. Controls facial and neck muscles, voluntary eye movement and speech.

Parietal lobe: Used for sensory reception and perception. Receives information about taste, touch, pressure, joint and muscle position, temperature and pain. Also involved with intelligence, thought and memory.

Occipital lobe: Receives visual information from the eyes.

Temporal lobe: Associated with sensory perception. Receives information from the ears and the olfactory system. Also involved in the interpretation of olfactory information.

2. Diencephalon

The **diencephalon** is situated in the heart of the brain. It consists of the **thalamus** and the **hypothalamus**.

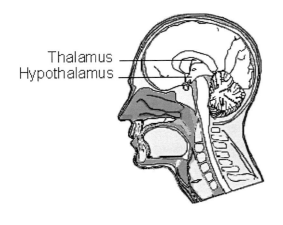

The **thalamus** is an oval mass of mainly grey matter. It **relays** sensory and motor impulses to and from the appropriate centres in the cerebral hemispheres.

It also allows crude appreciation of some sensations of pain, temperature and pressure, and has some functions in emotion and memory.

The **hypothalamus** (hypo- = low) is located **below** the thalamus. It controls many of the body's activities and is one of the major **regulators** of homeostasis. It receives information from sound, taste and smell receptors and constantly monitors many aspects of the internal environment, such as blood pressure, temperature and hormonal concentrations. It functions in anger, aggression, hunger and thirst.

The hypothalamus is the 'master' of the Endocrine System and so is also covered in that section.

3. Cerebellum

The posterior part of the brain is called the **cerebellum**. The cerebellum is the second largest area of the brain and occupies the inferior and posterior part of the cranial cavity. It is partially hidden by the cerebral hemispheres.

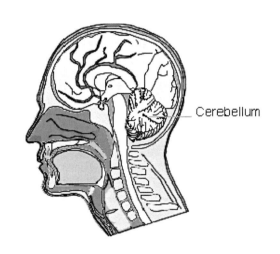

Cerebellum

The cerebellum monitors the **position** of the **limbs** and the **tension** in their **muscles**. It controls **fine movements**, **posture**, **balance** and **locomotion** by making any necessary adjustments to the messages sent out to the voluntary muscles by the cerebrum.

Let's look at the last area of the brain, the brain stem…

4. Brain Stem

The **brain stem** is the area at the top of the spinal cord. It includes the **midbrain**, **pons** and **medulla oblongata**.

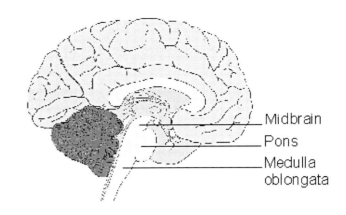

Midbrain
Pons
Medulla oblongata

The **midbrain** extends from the pons to the lower portion of the diencephalon. The midbrain **relays motor impulses** from the cerebral cortex to the pons, medulla oblongata and the spinal cord. It also **relays sensory impulses** from the spinal cord to the thalamus.

The midbrain also co-ordinates **movements** of the:

✓ **eyeballs**, in response to visual stimuli
✓ **head** and **trunk** in response to auditory stimuli (sound)

The **pons** (literally meaning bridge) consists of a thick band of nerve fibres. As the name suggests, the pons forms a **bridge** between the brain and the spinal cord. It connects the medulla oblongata with the upper parts of the brain stem. The pons also links parts of the brain with each other. It links the two hemispheres of the cerebrum.

The **medulla oblongata** (often referred to simply as the medulla) is a continuation of the spinal cord. It contains all the nerve tracts that connect the spinal cord to the various parts of the brain.

Most of the nerve tracts **cross over** from one side to the other as they pass through the medulla. Sensory impulses from one side of the body are therefore received in the cerebral cortex on the **opposite** side of the body.

Areas in the medulla oblongata regulate some vital processes including:

✓ heartbeat
✓ blood vessel diameter
✓ the basic rhythm of breathing

It also co-ordinates swallowing, vomiting, coughing, sneezing and hiccuping, and has a part to play in maintaining equilibrium and posture.

Before we go any further, here's a chance to recap on the 4 principal areas of the brain.

Area	Features	Components	Functions
Cerebrum	Largest area of brain. Consists of two cerebral hemispheres, each with 4 main lobes.	Frontal lobe	Planning and executing of activities. Controls facial and neck muscles, voluntary eye movement and speech.
		Parietal lobe	Sensory reception and perception. Receives information about taste, touch, pressure, joint and muscle tension. Also involved with intelligence, thought and memory.
		Occipital lobe	Receives visual information.
		Temporal lobe	Sensory perception. Receives auditory and olfactory information.
Diencephalon	Situated at the heart of the brain.	Thalamus	Relays sensory and motor impulses.
		Hypothalamus	Regulator of homeostasis.
Cerebellum	Inferior and posterior part of the brain.		Monitors limb position. Controls fine movement, posture, balance and locomotion.
Brain Stem	Area at the top of the spinal cord.	Midbrain	Relays motor and sensory impulses between the brain and spinal cord. Co-ordinates movements of the eyeballs (in response to visual stimuli) and the head and trunk (in response to auditory stimuli).
		Pons	Connects medulla oblongata with the upper part of brain stem. Links the cerebral hemispheres.
		Medulla oblongata	Regulates heartbeat, blood vessel diameter and basic rhythm of breathing. Co-ordinates swallowing, vomiting, coughing, sneezing, hiccuping and helps to maintain equilibrium and posture.

One other part of the brain worth a mention is the **limbic system**. The limbic system consists of a ring of structures that encircle the brain stem. They are on the inner border of the cerebrum and the floor of the diencephalon.

The limbic system functions in **emotional** aspects of behaviour and also plays a role in **memory**. This connection may be the reason why events that cause a strong emotional response are committed to memory with greater ease. The limbic system has a function in emotions such as pleasure, pain, anger, fear, sexual feelings and affection.

Twelve pairs of **cranial nerves** originate from the brain. **Most** of them supply the sensory organs and muscles in the **head**, but some do extend to other parts of the body. For example, the tenth cranial nerve is the vagus nerve. The vagus nerve serves the larynx, pharynx, liver, spleen, lungs, pancreas, heart and oesophagus.

Please note that the cranial nerves are **not** a part of the central nervous system. They are included in the **peripheral nervous system** and so are covered in more detail later.

We have completed our look at the brain. Let's move on and look at the other component of the central nervous system – the spinal cord.

Spinal Cord

The spinal cord is a long mass of nerve tissue. It runs from the **medulla oblongata** of the brain, down through the vertebral column until the upper border of the **second lumbar** vertebra (see Skeletal System).

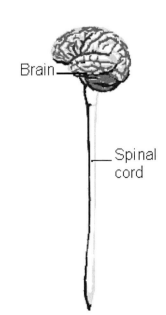

As we have already seen, the spinal cord is composed of both grey matter (in a butterfly shape) and white matter, and is surrounded by 3 meninges (dura mater, arachnoid and pia mater). Like the brain, cerebrospinal fluid circulates in the subarachnoid space.

Let's look at the structure of the spinal cord…

The spinal cord is roughly cylindrical but slightly flattened. In the centre of the spinal cord there is a **central canal**. This runs the length of the spinal cord and is continuous with the fourth ventricle of the brain.

The **white** matter contains bundles of nerve fibres called **nerve tracts**. A nerve tract contains fibres with a **common origin** or **destination** that carry similar **information**. Tracts may extend long distances up or down the spinal cord.

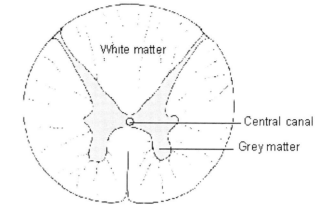

There are 2 types of nerve tract:

1. Sensory Tracts
Consist of nerve fibres that carry information **from** the **sensory** receptors to the brain. Sensory tracts run **up** the spinal cord and are referred to as **ascending** tracts.

2. Motor Tracts
Consist of nerve fibres that carry impulses **from** the **brain** to the effectors. Motor tracts run **down** the spinal cord and are referred to as **descending** tracts.

The nerve tracts in the **white** matter **conduct** the sensory and motor nerve impulses.

In the **grey** matter, each piece of sensory information received is **analyzed** in conjunction with every other piece of available information. Some information may be **stored**, and the **decision** made as to an appropriate **response**. This process is called **integration** and facilitates **memory** and **learning**.

The spinal cord has **31 pairs** of **spinal nerves**. Spinal nerves are the paths of communication between the spinal cord and **most of the body**. Although the spinal nerves originate from the spinal cord, they are not a part of the central nervous system. They are a part of the **peripheral nervous system**. We'll look at the peripheral nervous system now.

Peripheral Nervous System

The **peripheral nervous system** includes **all** components of the nervous system **except** the **brain** and **spinal cord**. It includes the **network of nerves**, originating at the cranial and spinal nerves, that connects to all organs and peripheral regions of the body. It also incorporates **ganglia** situated outside of the brain and spinal cord.

This system of nerves **conveys sensory** impulses from stimuli for processing by the central nervous system, and then **transmits** the consequent **motor** impulses to the muscles and glands. Many of the responses to the receipt of sensory information are **automatic**. These fast, predictable responses to changes in the environment are called **reflexes**. Reflexes help to maintain homeostasis.

The route taken through the nervous system from the sensory stimulus to the effector is called a **reflex arc**.

A reflex arc has 5 components:

1. Receptor
The receptor responds to the stimulus (a change in the internal or external environment) by triggering a nerve impulse.

2. Sensory Neuron
The nerve impulse is conducted to the axon terminals of the sensory neuron, located in the grey matter of the spinal cord or brain stem.

3. Integration Centre
This is a region within the grey matter of the central nervous system, which analyzes the sensory information, perhaps stores it, and determines the response required. For the simplest reflex arc, this is a single synapse between a sensory neuron and a motor neuron. Usually, however, the integration centre consists of one or more association neurons, which may relay the information to other association neurons as well as to a motor neuron.

4. Motor Neuron
Impulses generated by the integration centre are conducted along the motor neuron to the part of the body that has to respond to the original sensory stimulus.

5. Effector
The effector responds. This may be the contraction of a muscle or the secretion of a substance by a gland. This action is called the reflex.

As we have already mentioned, the network of nerves that make up the peripheral nervous system originate as either **cranial** or **spinal** nerves.

The cranial nerves originate from the brain. Most of them supply the sense organs and muscles in the head. The spinal nerves are the paths of communication between the spinal cord and most of the body.

Cranial Nerves

There are **12 pairs** of cranial nerves. Some cranial nerves contain only sensory fibres and are called **sensory** nerves. The others contain both sensory and motor fibres and are called **mixed**.

Each cranial nerve has an assigned **Roman numeral**. The numbering begins with the cranial nerve that originates at the anterior of the brain.

For your information we will list the cranial nerves on the next page, but will not be asking you any questions about them.

Here's a summary of the cranial nerves:

Cranial Nerve	Roman Numeral	Nerve Type	Function
Olfactory	I	Sensory	Smell
Optic	II	Sensory	Vision
Oculomotor	III	Mixed, but primarily motor	Motor: Movement of eyelid and eyeball, accommodation of lens for near vision, constriction of pupil Sensory: Proprioception (muscle sense)
Trochlear	IV	Mixed, but primarily motor	Motor: Movement of eyeball Sensory: Proprioception
Trigeminal	V	Mixed	Motor: Chewing Sensory: Conveys sensations of touch, pain and temperature. Proprioception
Abducens	VI	Mixed, but primarily motor	Motor: Movement of eyeball Sensory: Proprioception
Facial	VII	Mixed	Motor: Facial expression, secretion of saliva and tears Sensory: Proprioception and taste
Vestibulocochlear	VIII	Sensory	Conveys impulses associated with hearing and equilibrium
Glossopharyngeal	IX	Mixed	Motor: Secretion of saliva Sensory: Taste, regulation of blood pressure, proprioception
Vagus	X	Mixed	Motor: Smooth muscle contraction and relaxation, secretion of digestive fluids Sensory: Sensations from organs, proprioception
Accessory	XI	Mixed, but primarily motor	Motor: Swallowing, movement of head Sensory: Proprioception
Hypoglossal	XII	Mixed, but primarily motor	Motor: Movement of tongue Sensory: Proprioception

Spinal Nerves

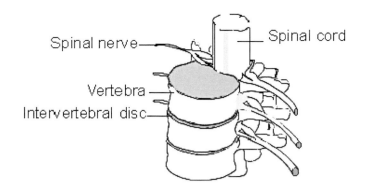

There are **31 pairs** of spinal nerves. They are numbered and named according to the area of the spinal cord from which they **emerge**.

The first pair of spinal nerves originate between the atlas (the first cervical vertebra) and the occipital bone that makes up most of the base of the cranium. All the other pairs emerge from between neighbouring vertebrae.

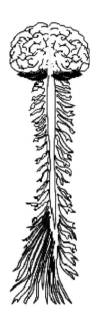

There are 8 cervical spinal nerves, 12 thoracic, 5 lumbar, 5 sacral and 1 coccygeal. (For more information on the skeletal structure of the vertebral column, see the Skeletal System.)

Remember that the spinal cord ends near the second lumbar vertebra. The lower lumbar, sacral and coccygeal nerves therefore originate higher up the spinal cord than their title suggests, and descend down the vertebral column to emerge between the appropriate vertebrae.

Each spinal nerve has 2 points of attachment.

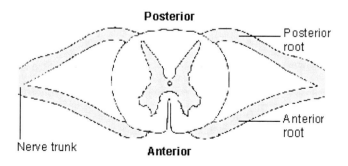

The **posterior root** contains the **sensory** fibres and the **anterior root** contains **motor** fibres. These 2 roots combine before emerging from the vertebral column to form the **nerve trunk**. All spinal nerves are therefore **mixed**.

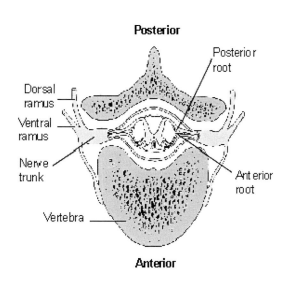

Posterior

Posterior root

Dorsal ramus

Ventral ramus

Nerve trunk

Anterior root

Vertebra

Anterior

Soon after emerging from between the vertebrae, the nerve trunks **branch**. These branches are known as **rami**.

The **dorsal ramus** of a spinal nerve runs to the deep muscles and skin of the dorsal (posterior) surface of the trunk. The **ventral ramus** serves the muscles and structures of the upper and lower extremities and the lateral (side) and ventral (anterior) trunk.

With the **exception** of the **thoracic** spinal nerves, which supply the intercostal muscles, the **ventral rami** do **not** go directly to the body structures. Instead, they join and form **networks** on both sides of the body.

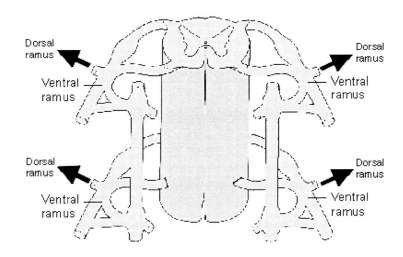

Dorsal ramus

Dorsal ramus

Ventral ramus

Ventral ramus

Dorsal ramus

Dorsal ramus

Ventral ramus

Ventral ramus

These networks are called **plexuses**. Nerves then emerge from the plexuses to serve the appropriate parts of the body. These emerging nerves may also branch.

The main plexuses are the cervical plexus, brachial plexus, lumbar plexus, sacral plexus and coccygeal plexus.

The network created by the spinal nerves is highly complicated. Here we will simply describe each plexus, and name the principal nerves included.

1. Cervical Plexus

Origin of Nerves: Ventral rami of **C1-C4, some C5**
Position: On each side of the neck, alongside the first four cervical vertebrae.
Supplies: The **skin** and **muscles** of the **head**, **neck** and **upper** part of the **shoulder**.
Major Nerves:
- Ansa cervicalis - muscles of the neck
- Lesser occipital - skin and scalp behind and above ear
- Great auricular - skin in front, below and over ear and parotid gland
- Transverse cervical - skin over anterior aspect of neck
- Supraclavicular - skin over upper portion of chest and shoulder
- Phrenic - diaphragm
- Segmental - deep muscles of the neck

2. Brachial Plexus

Origin of Nerves: Ventral rami of **C5-C8** and **T1**
Position: Extends downwards and laterally on either side of the last four cervical and first thoracic vertebrae. Passes over the first rib behind the clavicle and enters the axilla.
Supplies: Entire nerve supply to **shoulder** and **upper limb**.
Major Nerves:
- Axillary – some shoulder muscles, skin over the shoulder and upper posterior of arm
- Musculocutaneous – flexors of arm and forearm
- Radial – muscles and skin of posterior arm and forearm, skin of lateral hand and some fingers
- Median - muscles of anterior forearm, some muscles of palm, skin of lateral palm and fingers
- Ulnar – anteromedial muscles of the forearm, most muscles of the palm, skin of medial hand and fingers

3. Lumbar Plexus

Origin of Nerves: Ventral rami of **L1-L4**
Position: On either side of the first four lumbar vertebrae.
Supplies: The anterolateral (front and side) **abdominal wall**, **external genitals** and some of the **lower extremities**.
Major Nerves:

- Iliohypogastric nerve – muscles of anterolateral abdominal wall, skin of lower abdomen and buttocks
- Ilioinguinal – muscles of anterolateral abdominal wall, skin of upper medial thigh and external genitals
- Genitofemoral – skin over middle anterior thigh, external genitals
- Lateral femoral cutaneous – skin over lateral, anterior and posterior thigh
- Femoral – flexor muscles of thigh, skin on front and medial aspect of thigh, and skin on medial side of leg and foot
- Obturator – adductor muscles of leg, skin over medial thigh

4. Sacral Plexus

Origin of Nerves: Ventral rami of **L4-L5** and **S1-S4**
Position: In front of the sacrum.
Supplies: Buttocks, **perineum** (the entire outlet of the pelvis between the thighs and the buttocks) and the **lower extremities.**
Major Nerves:

- Sciatic (the largest nerve in the body) – posterior thigh
- Common peroneal – peroneal muscles of lower leg, skin over lower anterior leg and top of foot
- Tibial – posterior lower leg muscles, some muscles of the foot, skin of plantar foot
- Posterior femoral cutaneous – skin over anal area, lower lateral buttock, upper posterior thigh, upper calf and genitals
- Superior and inferior gluteal – gluteal muscles

5. Coccygeal (Superficial) Plexus

Origin of Nerves: Ventral rami of **S4-S5** and **coccygeal** ventral ramus
Position: Small plexus, low in the pelvis.
Supplies: Skin over the **coccyx**.
Major Nerve: Anococcygeal – skin over the coccyx

Autonomic Nervous System

Much of the peripheral nervous system is concerned with **voluntary** responses. However, the peripheral nervous system is **also** concerned with the body's many **involuntary**, **automatic** responses to stimuli.

The peripheral nervous system supplies the motor nerves to the **smooth muscle** of the internal organs, the **heart** and **glands**. This part of the peripheral nervous system is called the **autonomic nervous system**, as it deals with the body's 'automatic' responses.

The autonomic nervous system comprises of the **sympathetic** and **parasympathetic** nervous systems. They both supply motor nerves to the smooth muscle of the internal organs, heart and glands. The main **difference** is the **responses** they generate.

The **sympathetic** nervous system is responsible for the '**fight or flight**' reactions that prepare the body for action.

Stimulation of the smooth muscle by the sympathetic nervous system **increases** the **heart rate**, increases the **respiratory rate** and increases the **blood pressure**. It also speeds up the **conversion** of **glycogen** in the liver to create energy, **increases tension** in the urethral and anal **sphincters**, **dilates** the **pupils**, and causes contraction of the arrector pili muscles to **raise** the **hair** on the skin. It also **slows down digestion**, so that the blood can be diverted away from the digestive system to other needy areas of the body.

The motor nerves of the sympathetic nervous system originate from the **spinal nerves** in the **thoracic** and **lumbar** regions. The nerve endings release **noradrenaline** that creates these 'fight or flight' reactions.

The **medulla** of the **adrenals** is supplied with **sympathetic** fibres. These trigger the release of **adrenaline** into the blood, so enhancing the effect of this system.

The **parasympathetic** nervous system **opposes** the sympathetic nervous system. The **motor** nerves of the parasympathetic nervous system originate from **cranial nerves** (especially the vagus nerve) and a few of the spinal nerves in the **sacral** region. The nerve endings release **acetylcholine** that **decreases** the **heart rate**, **respiratory rate** and **blood pressure**, and **promotes digestion**. As you would expect from an opposing system, parasympathetic responses also include a **decrease** in the **speed** in which **glycogen** is converted to energy, **relaxation** of the **sphincter** muscles, **constriction** of the **pupils** and a **relaxation** of the **arrector pili** muscles.

Each organ receives **input** from **both** the parasympathetic and sympathetic nervous system. The **response** created depends on the **relative** stimulation received from each.

The autonomic nervous system also incorporates the **solar plexus**. The solar plexus is a **network** of nerves that is located **behind** the **stomach**. It supplies nerves to the abdominal organs below the diaphragm and regulates the functions of these organs.

When emotionally stressed or shocked, the solar plexus may give rise to a feeling of nausea stemming from the stomach.

Summary

➢ The nervous system senses changes in the external and internal environments, analyzes these changes, decides how to respond and then responds.

➢ Nerve cells capable of transmitting nerve impulses are called neurons.

➢ Sensory (afferent) neurons transmit information received from the sensory organs to the central nervous system.

➢ The central nervous system consists of the brain and the spinal cord. It analyzes sensory information and responds by generating nerve impulses.

➢ Nerve impulses, generated by the central nervous system, are transmitted by motor (efferent) neurons to the muscle or gland that has to respond to the original sensory stimulus.

➢ The peripheral nervous system consists of all components of the nervous system except the brain and spinal cord.

➢ The autonomic nervous system is the part of the peripheral nervous system that deals with the body's many involuntary or automatic responses to stimuli.

➢ The autonomic nervous system consists of the sympathetic and parasympathetic nervous systems, which generate opposite responses.

➢ The sympathetic nervous system increases the heart rate, respiratory rate and blood pressure. It slows digestion.

➢ The parasympathetic nervous system decreases the heart rate, respiratory rate and blood pressure. It promotes digestion.

Questions (Answers: Page 396)

1. Which nerve cells are specialized to transmit nerve impulses?

2. Which nerve cells perform the role of connective tissue in the nervous system?

3. Which type of neuron receives information from the sensory receptors?

   a. sensory
   b. motor
   c. association

4. Fill in the missing word:

   _____ neurons transmit information to the effector that has to respond to the sensory stimulus.

5. Which is the most common type of neuron?

6. What is another term for sensory neurons?

   a. afferent
   b. efferent

7. What term is given to the junction between two neurons?

8. True or False?

   Synapses occur only between two neurons.

9. Which neuron carries the nervous impulse to the synapse?

   a. presynaptic
   b. postsynaptic

10. In which form of synapse is contact made between the neurons by tubular protein structures at a gap junction?

    a. electrical
    b. chemical

11. What term is given to the type of chemical released at a chemical synapse?

12. Which neuron releases the neurotransmitter at a chemical synapse?

     a. presynaptic
     b. postsynaptic

13. Fill in the missing word:

     The neurotransmitter diffuses across the extracellular fluid that fills the synaptic
     _____ .

14. What type of synapse occurs at a neuromuscular junction?

     a. electrical
     b. chemical

15. What part of the neuromuscular junction contains acetylcholine receptors?

     a. muscular end plate
     b. motor end plate
     c. sensory end plate
     d. motor start plate

16. Which part of the neuron receives the nerve impulse?

     a. dendrites
     b. axon
     c. axon terminal

17. What is the long, thin part of the neuron called?

18. What is the name of the insulating lipid and protein coating on the axon?

     a. melanin sheath
     b. myelin sheath
     c. marrow sheath
     d. merkel sheath

19. In which part of the axon terminals are the synaptic vesicles that store a chemical
     neurotransmitter?

20. True or False?

     The axon terminals of the presynaptic neuron meet the dendrites of the postsynaptic
     neuron.

21.   What type of neuron is this?

22.   What type of neuron is this?

23.   What type of neuron is this?

24.   True or False?

       The brain and spinal cord make up the central nervous system.

25.   What is the main artery that supplies blood to the brain?

26.   What name is given to the semi-permeable barrier that selectively allows, slows or prevents substances passing from the blood to the brain cells?

27.   Which type of tissue comprises of bundles of myelinated axons?

           a. white matter
           b. grey matter

28.   How many meninges surround the brain and spinal cord?

           a. 1
           b. 2
           c. 3
           d. 4

29. Starting from the outer membrane, what is the correct order of the meninges?

     a. pia mater, arachnoid, dura mater
     b. pia mater, dura mater, arachnoid
     c. dura mater, pia mater, arachnoid
     d. dura mater, arachnoid, pia mater

30. What is the name of the fluid that continuously flows in the subarachnoid space to protect and nourish the brain and spinal cord?

31. How many ventricles in the brain contain cerebrospinal fluid?

     a. 1
     b. 2
     c. 3
     d. 4

32. Which part of the brain consists of two cerebral hemispheres, joined by a band of nerve fibres?

33. What name is given to the surface of the cerebrum consisting of grey matter?

34. How many main lobes does each cerebral hemisphere have?

35. Which part of the brain consists of the thalamus and the hypothalamus?

36. Which structure of the diencephalon relays sensory and motor impulses to and from the appropriate centres in the cerebral hemispheres?

     a. thalamus
     b. hypothalamus

37. True or False?

The hypothalamus plays a major role in homeostasis and is known as the master of the endocrine system.

38. Which part of the brain occupies the inferior and posterior part of the cranial cavity?

39. Which of the following is NOT controlled by the cerebellum?

    a. fine muscle movement
    b. posture
    c. body temperature
    d. balance

40. The brain stem consists of three areas. Working down from the brain towards the spinal cord, which is the correct order?

    a. pons, medulla oblongata, midbrain
    b. midbrain, pons, medulla oblongata
    c. midbrain, medulla oblongata, pons
    d. medulla oblongata, pons, midbrain

41. Which part of the brain stem relays motor impulses from the cerebral cortex to the pons?

42. Which area of the brain stem, consisting of a thick band of nerve fibres, literally means 'bridge'?

43. Which part of the brain stem has areas that control heart rate, diameter of the blood vessels and the rhythm of breathing?

44. Where are the sensory and motor nerve tracts?

    a. in the white matter
    b. in the grey matter

45. Which nerve tracts are also known as ascending tracts?

    a. sensory
    b. motor

46. What is another name for motor tracts?

47. What term is given to the process involving the analysis and (if necessary) storage of sensory information, and the subsequent decision making function?

48. True or False?

    All nerve cells and nervous tissue, except that of the brain and spinal cord, make up the peripheral nervous system.

49.   True or False?

        The peripheral nervous system processes information received from the sensory organs.

50.   Fill in the missing word:

        The route taken through the nervous system from the sensory stimulus to the effector is called a reflex _____.

51.   A reflex arc has 5 components. Which component of the reflex arc is missing from here?

        1. Receptor
        2. Sensory neuron
        ?
        4. Motor neuron
        5. Effector

52.   How many pairs of cranial nerves originate from the brain?

             a. 6
             b. 12
             c. 18
             d. 31

53.   The optic nerve is tagged with the Roman numeral II (two). The vagus nerve is tagged with the Roman numeral X (ten). Which nerve emerges from the brain anterior to the other?

             a. optic
             b. vagus

54.   How many pairs of spinal nerves originate from the spinal cord?

             a. 6
             b. 12
             c. 31
             d. 42

55.   What type of fibres do all spinal nerves contain?

             a. only sensory
             b. only motor
             c. both sensory and motor

56. What generic name is given to the branches of the spinal nerves?

57. Which type of rami form plexuses?

    a. ventral
    b. dorsal

58. Which plexus supplies the skin and muscles of the head, neck and upper part of the shoulder?

59. Which plexus serves the buttocks, perineum and the lower extremities?

60. Which plexus serves the anterolateral abdominal wall, external genitals and some of the lower extremities?

61. From which plexus does the sciatic nerve arise?

62. Which plexus is responsible for the nerve supply to the shoulder and upper limb?

63. What part of the peripheral nervous system deals with the body's involuntary, automatic responses?

64. The autonomic nervous system comprises of the sympathetic nervous system and the parasympathetic nervous system. Which increases the heart rate, respiratory rate and blood pressure?

    a. sympathetic
    b. parasympathetic

65. Which nervous system slows down digestion?

66. Which nervous system causes a decrease in the speed in which glycogen is converted to energy, relaxation of the sphincter muscles, constriction of the pupils and a relaxation of the arrector pili muscles?

67. Where do the motor nerves of the parasympathetic nervous system originate?

    a. spinal nerves in the thoracic and lumbar regions
    b. cranial nerves and a few of the spinal nerves in the sacral region
    c. the solar plexus

This page has intentionally been left blank.

Chemistry

This page has intentionally been left blank.

The anatomy and physiology of the body results from the numerous reactions that take place at the chemical level of structural organization. All the life processes depend on the success of this chemistry.

It is not the intention of this section to transform you into a Chemist! It is purely to introduce a few basic terms and concepts that you may come across during your study.

Chemistry is the science that is concerned with the composition of '**matter**' (everything that makes up the universe!) and the changes that take place in it under certain conditions.

All matter can exist as a **solid**, **liquid** or **gas**, according to changes in temperature or pressure, and is made up of **atoms**.

Atoms are the **smallest** and **simplest** units of matter that can take part in a chemical reaction. They are too small to be seen even using a high-powered microscope and are in constant motion.

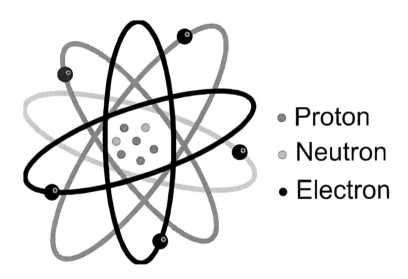

• Proton
◦ Neutron
• Electron

An atom has a **nucleus** (central part) containing **protons** (positively charged particles) and **neutrons** (particles with no electrical charge). The nucleus is surrounded by a number of **electrons** (negatively charged particles).

The number of **protons** (positively charged) in an individual atom always **equals** the number of **electrons** (negatively charged). Each atom therefore is **electrically neutral**.

Science recognizes **109** different types of atom, each with its own chemical behaviour.

The number of protons in the nucleus allows one atom to be distinguished from another. The number of protons gives the atom its **atomic number**. For example, oxygen has 8 protons. The atomic number for oxygen is therefore 8.

Atoms can combine with one another to form a **molecule**.

Atom + Atom = Molecule

Molecules that contain atoms of only **one type** are called **elements**. For example, oxygen exists in the atmosphere as a molecule of two oxygen atoms and is therefore an element.

Elements, being composed of just one type of atom, are the simplest substances that exist. They cannot be broken down into anything simpler and are the building blocks of chemical reactions.

In chemistry, **elements** are given letters as abbreviations called **chemical symbols**. For example, oxygen is denoted as O and carbon is C.

Two letters are sometimes used. For example calcium is Ca. Calcium couldn't be just C as that is taken by carbon. Notice that when two letters are used, the first is in uppercase and the second is in lowercase.

The most common elements in the body are oxygen, carbon, hydrogen, nitrogen, calcium, potassium and sodium. The chemical symbol and general features/functions of each of these elements are shown below.

Element	Chemical Symbol	Features/Functions
Oxygen	O	Essential to life. Constituent of water, carbohydrates, fats and proteins. Vital for respiration.
Carbon	C	Forms the basis of all living matter.
Hydrogen	H	Constituent of water and all foods.
Nitrogen	N	Component of all proteins and nucleic acids.
Calcium	Ca	Needed for many body processes, including building the hardness of bones and teeth, blood clotting and muscle movement.
Potassium	K	Plays an important part in the conduction of nerve impulses and muscle contraction.
Sodium	Na	Essential in blood to maintain water balance. Needed for conduction of nerve impulses and muscle contraction.

We have mentioned so far that atoms can combine with one another to form a molecule, and molecules containing atoms of **only one kind** are called **elements**.

Molecules that contain atoms of **different kinds** are called **compounds**. Water is an example of a compound. A water molecule contains two hydrogen atoms (H) and one oxygen atom (O), hence its chemical formula H_2O.

You will often see the word 'compound' preceded by either '**organic**' or '**inorganic**'. Don't be put off by this terminology. These terms can be distinguished by two words – **life** and **carbon**.

Organic compounds form the chemical **basis for life**. The main feature of all organic compounds is the presence of **carbon**. All matter that **is living** or **has once lived** will consist of carbon. Charcoal for example (live matter in the form of a tree before heating) is a simple carbon compound. Humans are no more than a highly complex carbon compound!

Needless to say, organic compounds are more **complex** and **abundant** than **inorganic** compounds that do **not** contain carbon and have **never** been 'alive'.

As well as carbon, **organic** compounds commonly contain **oxygen** and **nitrogen**. The ability of carbon atoms to react with other atom types, as well as with themselves, enables the body to build many **complex** compounds. Organic compounds can also be broken down quite easily to **release energy** from the molecules.

There are 4 main groups of organic compounds.

1. Carbohydrates
Carbohydrates contain carbon, hydrogen and oxygen. This group includes **sugars**, **starches**, **glycogen** and **cellulose** and forms 2-3% of body weight. Carbohydrates provide a readily available source of **energy**. They are rarely used as structural units.

2. Lipids
Lipids (fats) contain carbon, hydrogen and oxygen and make up 18-25% of the body weight. They are **insoluble** in water and so they can't travel freely in the blood, although they can combine with proteins to form water-soluble lipoproteins. Lipids form **steroids** and **vitamins** A, E and K. Lipids produce more **energy** than carbohydrates and the body has a virtually unlimited ability to **store** some forms of fat in the **adipose** tissue.

3. Proteins
Proteins are more **complex** than carbohydrates or lipids and make up 12-18% of the body weight. Some proteins have a **structural** role, e.g. building blocks for cells. Proteins form **enzymes** that act as catalysts to speed up chemical reactions, **antibodies** that play a part in immunity, and **hormones** that regulate the body processes.

4. Nucleic Acids
Nucleic acids are huge organic molecules containing carbon, hydrogen, oxygen, nitrogen and phosphorus. **Deoxyribonucleic acid** (DNA) forms the genetic code within each cell. Each **gene** is a segment of the DNA molecule. **Ribonucleic acid** (RNA) relays instructions from the genes to govern protein synthesis.

The most **abundant inorganic** compound in the body is **water** (H_2O). Water plays vital roles in the life processes and has many valuable properties. Water:

- ✓ is an excellent solvent. This property allows many chemical reactions to take place.
- ✓ participates in chemical reactions. Water can be added to break down large molecules or produced when molecules are built up.
- ✓ absorbs and releases heat very slowly. The presence of water in the body therefore lessens the effects of external temperature changes.
- ✓ requires much heat to change from a liquid to a gas. It therefore provides a good cooling medium.
- ✓ serves as a lubricant. It helps organs slide over each other, eases friction at joints and moistens food during digestion.

The body also contains **inorganic acids**, **bases** and **salts**. These are defined in the ionization topic later in this section.

Chemical Bonding

When atoms combine to form a molecule – an element or a compound - or when the atoms in a molecule break apart, a **chemical reaction** occurs. Chemical reactions create new products with different properties.

The chemistry of life is dependent on the ability of atoms to create and destroy **bonds** with other atoms. Let's look at the ways in which this bonding takes place. The **electrons** (negatively charged particles) are key players...

Electrons **orbit** the atom in **up to 8 circles**. These 8 circles are positioned at **varying distances** from the nucleus. Each circle is capable of holding a set number of electrons. The innermost circle can hold 2, the second circle can hold 8 and the third can hold up to 18. The electrons fill the innermost circle(s) first and then the remainder are situated on the outer circle. For optimum chemical stability, the **outermost** circle needs to be **complete** with the maximum number of electrons.

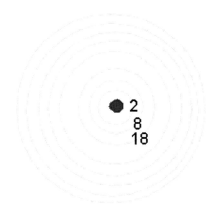

To achieve a full outer circle and, in doing so, gain chemical stability, the atom either;

- **accepts** an electron(s) from another atom;
- **gives up** an electron(s) to another atom; or
- **shares** an electron(s) with another atom.

The atom will take the **easiest** route it can to fill its outer circle.

Prior to any bonding, an atom is electrically neutral because the number of protons (positively charged particles) equals the number of electrons (negatively charged particles). However, when an atom **accepts** or **gives up** an electron this **balance** is **lost**.

When an atom accepts an electron it acquires a negative charge. This is because the number of electrons then exceeds the number of protons.

Atoms with either negative or positive charges are called **ions**.

Ions in solution are called **electrolytes**. As the name suggests, an ionic solution is capable of **conducting** an **electric** current.

Let's look at an example of an ion…

Sodium is an example of how an atom gives up an electron to become a positively charged ion. Sodium has an atomic number of 11 and so it has 11 protons and 11 electrons. 2 electrons are on the innermost circle, 8 orbit on the second circle and the outer circle has just 1. For maximum stability the sodium atom has to find a way of achieving a full outer circle. So, it either needs to accept some more electrons to complete the third circle, or give up 1 electron so that the second circle becomes the new, complete outer circle. Giving up an electron is the easiest option and so the sodium atom becomes a sodium ion with a positive charge. This is denoted by the chemical symbol Na^+.

Conversely, the chlorine atom (atomic number 17) achieves its stability by accepting an electron. The chlorine ion therefore has a negative charge. It is denoted by the chemical symbol Cl^-.

The plot doesn't stop there!

Positive and negative **ions**, such as sodium and chlorine, can **bond** with each other. **Opposites attract**, and this attraction, called an **ionic bond**, bonds the two ions together.

In the case of sodium and chlorine, the two ions combine to produce a molecule of sodium chloride (table salt). The chemical formula for this is NaCl. Notice that there are no longer any + or − signs. This is because this molecule is neutral. The positive and negative charges are counterbalanced.

Another type of chemical bond is the **covalent bond**. It is more common in the body than the ionic bond and is created when atoms **share electrons**.

Electrons are always shared in **pairs**. One, two or three pairs may be shared to fulfil the need for a full outer circle. Let's look at an example...

A hydrogen atom (H) has just 1 proton and 1 electron. Therefore there is just 1 circle with 1 orbiting electron. This circle is incomplete as it can hold a maximum of 2 electrons.

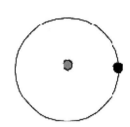

To increase stability, one hydrogen atom combines with another hydrogen atom and they share the pair of electrons. Each atom then has one of its own electrons and a shared electron. This forms a hydrogen molecule, symbol H_2.

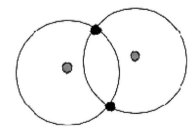

When **one pair** of electrons are shared the bond is called a **single covalent bond**.

The last type of bond to look at is **hydrogen bonds**. They are quite different to ionic or covalent bonds.

Hydrogen bonds occur between **molecules** and these 'bonds' are very **weak**.

In hydrogen bonding, two molecules, already formed by covalent bonding, are attracted and held together by **electrostatic** forces. One of these molecules will contain **hydrogen** and usually oxygen or nitrogen. The other molecule usually consists of oxygen or nitrogen.

Hydrogen bonds serve as **bridges** between molecules or between parts of a molecule. Water molecules are bonded to each other in this way. Large, complex molecules may contain hundreds of hydrogen bonds.

Ionization

Water is often referred to as the universal solvent. This is because it provides the ideal medium into which other substances can dissolve. When **inorganic** molecules dissolve in water a process called **ionization** occurs. This means that the molecules dissociate (split down) into **ions** again.

As we have seen, ions are either positively or negatively charged. When after ionization there is an **excess** of positively charged **hydrogen** ions (H^+), the fluid becomes acidic. A substance that dissociates to create hydrogen ions is categorized as an **acid**.

Substances called **bases** dissociate to form **hydroxide** ions (OH^-). These consist of oxygen and hydrogen and are **negatively** charged. An excess of hydroxide ions in the fluid will cause it to become **alkaline** or **basic**.

Salts when dissolved in water do **not** produce either **hydrogen** ions or **hydroxide** ions. For example, sodium chloride (NaCl) dissociates into its originating sodium (Na^+) and chlorine (Cl^-) ions.

Many salts occur in both intracellular and extracellular fluids. The ions produced when they dissociate provide many essential chemicals.

The **balance** of hydrogen and hydroxide ions in the body fluids must be **regulated**. An excess of hydrogen ions creates a more acidic fluid. If there is an excess of hydroxide ions the fluid will be more alkaline (basic).

The acidity or alkalinity of a solution is measured on the **pH scale**.

The pH scale runs from **0 – 14**. A pH of **0** represents the extreme of **acidity** and a pH of **14** denotes the extreme of **alkalinity**. The midway point is **pH7**. This is where the concentrations of hydrogen ions and hydroxide ions are equal and this is the pH of pure water.

pH 14

pH 7

pH 0

Homeostatic mechanisms maintain the pH level of the various body fluids.

Each body fluid has its own optimum pH value. For example, the blood is slightly alkaline and is maintained between pH 7.35 and 7.45. Semen is slightly alkaline (7.20 – 7.60) whilst vaginal fluid is quite acidic (3.5 – 4.5). Saliva is slightly acidic (6.35 – 6.85) and bile is very alkaline (7.6 – 8.6).

We have now completed our look at some basic chemistry. We hope that you will now feel more confident when dealing with chemical terms as you continue your study in anatomy and physiology. Here's a summary…

Summary

➢ Atoms are the smallest and simplest units of matter that can take part in a chemical reaction.

➢ Atoms consist of protons (positively charged), neutrons (neutral) and electrons (negatively charged).

➢ Atoms combine to form a molecule.

➢ Molecules containing atoms of only one kind are called elements.

➢ Molecules containing atoms of different kinds are called compounds.

➢ Organic compounds contain carbon. The four main groups are carbohydrates, lipids, proteins and nucleic acids.

➢ Water is the most abundant inorganic compound.

➢ Atoms can bond with each other by accepting, giving up or sharing electrons.

➢ Atoms with either a negative or positive charge are called ions.

➢ Ionic bonds are formed when atoms either accept or give up an electron(s).

➢ Covalent bonds are created when atoms share one, two or three pairs of electrons.

➢ Hydrogen bonds are formed by electrostatic forces between molecules.

➢ When inorganic compounds dissolve in water their atoms dissociate. This process is called ionization.

➢ Acids dissociate to form an excess of positively charged hydrogen ions and therefore create an acidic solution.

➢ Bases dissociate to form an excess of negatively charged hydroxide ions and therefore create an alkaline solution.

➢ Salts dissociate to form neither hydrogen ions nor hydroxide ions.

➢ Acidity/alkalinity is measured on the pH scale.

➢ pH0 represents the extreme of acidity.

➢ pH14 represents the extreme of alkalinity.

➢ The pH of pure water is 7.

Questions (Answers: Page 398)

1. What is the name given to the smallest and simplest unit of matter that can take part in a chemical reaction?

2. Atoms are made up of three types of particle. Which type is not found in the atom's nucleus?

   a. proton
   b. neutron
   c. electron

3. Which particle has a positive electrical charge?

4. Which particle has a negative electrical charge?

5. True or False?

   Neutrons exist in the nucleus of an atom but do not have an electrical charge.

6. A hydrogen atom has one proton. How many electrons does it have?

7. What is created when two or more atoms combine?

8. True or False?

   Elements are molecules made up of just one type of atom.

9. Which TWO elements play an important part in the conduction of nerve impulses?

10. Which element forms the basis of all living matter?

11. Carbon dioxide is made up of one carbon atom and two oxygen atoms. Its chemical formula is CO_2. Is carbon dioxide an element or a compound?

12. What atom is always present in an organic compound?

13. Which group of organic compounds is commonly called fats?

    a. carbohydrates
    b. lipids
    c. proteins
    d. nucleic acids

14. Which group of organic compounds includes sugars, starches, glycogen and cellulose?

    a. carbohydrates
    b. lipids
    c. proteins
    d. nucleic acids

15. What type of organic compound forms enzymes, antibodies and hormones?

16. True or False?

Proteins form steroids.

17. Which huge organic molecule forms the genetic code?

18. What is the most abundant inorganic compound in the body?

19. What charge will an atom hold if it gives up an electron?

    a. positive
    b. negative

20. What term is given to an atom which has either a positive or negative charge?

21. Which type of atomic particle is given up or accepted to produce an ion?

    a. proton
    b. neutron
    c. electron

22. Which circle of electrons needs to be complete for the atom to achieve optimum stability?

23. True or False?

Any ions, irrespective of electrical charge, can bond with each other.

24. How many pairs of electrons do you think are shared when a triple covalent bond is formed?

25. True or False?

Hydrogen bonds are formed between molecules.

26. What is known as the universal solvent?

27. What is the process in which inorganic compounds dissociate in water?

    a. diffusion
    b. hydrolysis
    c. lubrication
    d. ionizaton

28. What substances dissociate to produce hydrogen ions?

    a. acids
    b. bases
    c. salts

29. What substances dissociate to produce negatively charged hydroxide ions?

    a. acids
    b. bases
    c. salts

30. True or False?

When salts dissociate they produce neither hydrogen nor hydroxide ions.

31. What scale is used to measure the level of acidity/alkalinity?

32. True or False?

The greater the excess of hydrogen ions, the greater the pH value.

33.   What is the pH value of pure water?

This page has intentionally been left blank.

Answers

This page has intentionally been left blank.

Introduction

1. chemical
2. metabolism
3. plasma membrane
4. cytoplasm
5. nucleus
6. a - mitochondrion
7. nucleolus
8. smooth
9. oxygen
10. false
11. osmosis
12. false
13. b - pinocytosis
14. false
15. b - 2
16. c - they replicate
17. prophase
18. c - they align down the centre of the cell
19. yes
20. nuclear
21. cell/plasma membrane
22. tissue
23. a - simple
24. b - simple cuboidal
25. a - squamous
26. goblet cells
27. transitional epithelium
28. c - see graphic
29. c - columnar
30. b - adipose
31. areolar
32. false
33. lymphoid/lymph
34. a - hyaline
35. true
36. c - synovial
37. serous
38. true
39. epithelial
40. connective
41. muscle
42. nervous
43. organ
44. false
45. b – chest
46. c - abdomen
47. c - The head is superior to the pelvis.
48. lateral
49. distal

50. Transverse => Superior/Inferior   Frontal => Anterior/Posterior   Sagittal => Left/Right
51. false
52. nervous and endocrine
53. a - negative
54. digestion of food
55. false
56. metabolic
57. basal metabolic rate
58. true
59. hypothalamus
60. b - When the body is too warm.
61. adrenals

Skeletal System

1. b - 206
2. d - calcium
3. a - axial skeleton
4. c - The red marrow in the bones consists of fat which is used as an energy store.
5. true
6. c - diaphysis
7. marrow cavity or medullary cavity
8. epiphyses
9. metaphysis
10. articular/hyaline cartilage
11. false
12. Volkmann's or perforating
13. c - mineral salts
14. c - osteocytes
15. b - osteoblasts
16. d - osteoclasts
17. a - Haversian (central) canals
18. a - lamellae
19. c - osteocytes
20. canaliculi
21. osteon
22. cancellous
23. true
24. red bone marrow
25. plate
26. true
27. epiphyseal line
28. d - osteoclasts
29. b - short
30. flat
31. sesamoid
32. irregular
33. body
34. arch
35. a - spinal process

36. c - articular processes
37. a - cervical
38. b - chest
39. lumbar
40. d - 5
41. coccyx
42. occipital
43. d - radius, ulna, humerus
44. c - shoulder blade
45. c - 10
46. a - carpals, metacarpals and phalanges
47. radius
48. c - femur
49. lateral longitudinal arch
50. flexion
51. c - abduction
52. a - syndesmosis
53. articular
54. c - pivot
55. gliding (plane)
56. hinge
57. shoulder and hip
58. b - saddle

Skin, Nails and Hair

1. false
2. d - D
3. true
4. epidermis
5. a - keratinocytes
6. keratin
7. melanocytes
8. bone marrow
9. Merkel cells
10. basale or germinativum
11. d - keratinocytes
12. d - stratum spinosum (prickle cell layer)
13. c - stratum granulosum
14. b - stratum lucidum
15. stratum corneum (horny layer)
16. papillary region
17. reticular region
18. eccrine
19. apocrine
20. temperature control
21. subcutaneous layer
22. adipose tissue
23. areolar tissue
24. melanin

25. a - epidermis
26. false
27. carotene and haem
28. true
29. a - dry
30. c - living
31. c - nail root
32. c - hyponychium
33. lunula
34. stratum corneum (horny layer)
35. true
36. matrix
37. follicle
38. bulb
39. papilla
40. matrix
41. sebum
42. arrector pili
43. cuticle
44. cortex
45. false
46. c - lanugo
47. terminal
48. melanin
49. b - anagen
50. telogen
51. catagen

Respiratory System

1. a - pulmonary ventilation
2. b - external respiration
3. c - internal respiration
4. b - external respiration
5. a - pulmonary ventilation
6. carbon dioxide
7. d - pharynx
8. b - trachea
9. a - primary bronchi
10. bronchioles
11. b - alveoli
12. oxygen
13. carbon dioxide
14. b - pleural membrane
15. diaphragm
16. b - external intercostals
17. brain (pons and medulla oblongata)
18. b - expiration
19. true
20. expiration

21. a - chemoreceptors
22. true
23. decrease
24. pulmonary arteries
25. pulmonary veins

Senses - Sight

1. a - sclera
2. b - choroid
3. iris
4. retina
5. lens
6. optic

Senses - Sound

1. a - outer ear
2. ear-drum
3. c - ossicles
4. c - oval window
5. b - cochea
6. vestibulocochlear (auditory) nerve
7. balance

Senses - Taste

1. four
2. c - posterior
3. gustatory
4. gustatory pore

Senses - Smell

1. olfactory
2. olfactory hairs
3. olfactory
4. a - frontal
5. d - cerebral cortex
6. limbic system

Senses – Touch

1. dendrites
2. free nerve endings
3. d - parietal
4. false
5. a - corpuscles of touch

6. root hair plexuses
7. discs
8. c - end organs of Ruffini
9. b - lamellated corpuscles
10. a - corpuscles of touch
11. false
12. nociceptors

Urinary System

1. ureter
2. micturition
3. c - external urethral sphincter
4. true.
5. right
6. d - renal veins
7. c - medulla
8. renal pelvis
9. b - nephrons
10. a - Bowman's capsule
11. false
12. b - when the water concentration in the blood is low
13. decreasing

Reproductive System

1. b - vas deferens
2. prostate
3. false
4. a - follicle
5. b - fallopian tube
6. uterus
7. a – vulva
8. a – labia majora
9. c – greater vestibular glands
10. a - reduction in oestrogens and progesterone
11. c - oestrogen
12. areola
13. b - 15-20
14. c - alveoli
15. d - secondary tubule, mammary duct, lactiferous duct, nipple
16. true
17. axillary
18. c - 23
19. b - haploid
20. b - females
21. false
22. b – meiosis

Answers

23. a - meiosis I
24. c - replicate
25. true
26. b - metaphase I
27. false
28. b - 2 haploid cells
29. true
30. c - spermatogonia
31. a - mitosis
32. d - haploid secondary spermatocytes
33. spermatids
34. epididymis
35. oogonia
36. b - meiosis I
37. b - primordial follicle
38. a - primary follicles
39. a - secondary oocyte
40. fertilization
41. a - the largest
42. a - 1
43. segmentation
44. a - blastomeres
45. morula
46. b - blastocyst
47. embryonic

Lymphatic System

1. tissue
2. true
3. B-cells
4. true
5. capillaries
6. no
7. true
8. lacteals
9. lymph nodes
10. true
11. popliteal
12. b - lymph ducts
13. false
14. spleen
15. b - white pulp
16. a - cortex
17. a - non-specific
18. a - mechanical
19. sebum or perspiration
20. d - attraction, attachment, engulfing
21. chemicals
22. b – neutrophils

23. macrophages
24. true
25. antigen
26. c - surface proteins
27. b - T-cells
28. false
29. a - B-cells
30. plasma cells
31. false

Muscular System

1. skeletal
2. smooth
3. heart
4. tendons
5. a - motor
6. true
7. a - fascia
8. true
9. c - endomysium
10. a - sarcolemma
11. myofibrils
12. false
13. b - myosin filaments
14. false
15. calcium
16. b - when the muscle is contracting
17. true
18. diphosphate
19. glucose
20. b - anaerobic
21. lactic acid
22. false
23. c - mitochondria
24. myoglobin
25. d, c, b, a - uses the ATP, uses creatine phosphate, anaerobic, aerobic
26. true
27. true
28. c - intermediate
29. hormones
30. b - skeletal and cardiac
31. a - skeletal
32. a - aerobic
33. false
34. a - The attachment that remains unmoved during the muscular contraction.
35. a - agonist
36. b, c, a - adductors/abductors, depressors/levators, extensors/flexors
37. a - isotonic
38. orbicularis oculi

39. occipitofrontalis
40. buccinator
41. masseter
42. c - platysma and sternocleidomastoid
43. orbicularis oris
44. trapezius
45. deltoid
46. levator scapulae
47. true
48. a - coracobrachialis
49. c - supraspinatus, infraspinatus, teres minor, teres major
50. anterior
51. infraspinatus, subscapularis, supraspinatus and teres minor
52. true
53. d - triceps brachii
54. b - brachialis
55. a - biceps brachii
56. d - flexor digitorum superficialis
57. c - palmaris longus
58. a - humerus
59. e - extensor digiti minimi
60. c - extensor digitorum
61. a - extensor carpi radialis longus
62. b - hypothenar
63. a, b, g and h - opponens pollicis, abductor pollicis brevis, flexor pollicis brevis and adductor pollicis
64. false
65. a - rectus femoris
66. vastus intermedius
67. sartorius
68. a and d – pectineus and gracilis
69. femur
70. b - abduction and flexion
71. d - extensor hallucis longus and flexor hallucis longus
72. true
73. c - tibialis anterior
74. gastrocnemius
75. soleus
76. tibialis posterior
77. peroneus brevis
78. g - rectus abdominis
79. c - external oblique, internal oblique, transversus abdominis
80. increases
81. a - pectoralis major
82. e - latissimus dorsi
83. c, e and f - psoas major, iliacus and piriformis
84. gluteus minimus
85. a - quadratus lumborum

Cardiovascular System

1. lymphatic
2. true
3. plasma
4. water
5. liver
6. a - albumins
7. c - immunoglobulins
8. fibrinogen
9. erythrocytes
10. red bone marrow
11. d - late erythroblast
12. d - late erythroblast
13. false
14. liver or spleen
15. leucocytes
16. false
17. a - granular leucocytes
18. a - neutrophils
19. b - eosinophils
20. basophils
21. a - lymphocytes
22. a - B-cells
23. monocytes
24. thrombocyte
25. true
26. c - platelets (thrombocytes)
27. calcium
28. fibrin
29. a - arteries
30. b - veins
31. b - veins
32. c - capillaries
33. b - tunica media
34. a - heart, arteries, arterioles, capillaries, venules, veins, heart
35. pericardium
36. myocardium
37. coronary
38. aorta
39. vena cavae
40. 4
41. a - atriums
42. true
43. a - right atrium
44. right ventricle
45. b - pulmonary arteries
46. pulmonary veins
47. c - left atrium
48. left ventricle
49. aorta
50. a - pulmonary circulation

51. portal
52. b - sinoatrial node
53. a - systole
54. a - systole
55. true
56. a - decreases it
57. c - medulla oblongata
58. baroreceptors
59. b - vasoconstriction
60. b - 120/80 mm Hg 70-80 beats per minute

Digestive System

1.   a - polysaccharides
2.   disaccharides
3.   a - glycerol and fatty acids
4.   amino acids
5.   c - alimentary canal
6.   b - 3
7.   b - starches
8.   a - pharynx
9.   oesophagus
10. a - acidic
11. c - trypsin
12. pyloric sphincter
13. duodenum
14. d - duodenum, jejunum, ileum
15. a - lipase
16. pancreatic amylase
17. proteins
18. a - acini
19. b - hormones
20. a - nervous
21. b - cholecystokinin
22. secretin
23. a - hepatic artery
24. c - inferior vena cava
25. digestive organs and spleen
26. bile
27. a - duodenum
28. c - fats
29. secretin
30. Vater
31. true
32. amino acids
33. villi
34. c - 90%
35. ileocaecal
36. false

Endocrine System

1. true
2. pituitary
3. b - posterior
4. b - antidiuretic hormone
5. c - adrenocorticotrophic hormone
6. e - gonadotrophic hormones
7. b - prolactin
8. hypothalamus
9. thyroid stimulating hormone
10. thyroxine
11. calcitonin
12. four
13. b - adrenal medulla
14. adrenaline or noradrenaline
15. false
16. false
17. insulin
18. liver
19. oestrogen
20. a - progesterone
21. c - relaxin
22. d - luteinizing hormone and follicle stimulating hormone
23. oestrogens
24. progesterone
25. true
26. oxytocin
27. true
28. oxytocin
29. testosterone
30. inhibin
31. luteinizing

Nervous System

1. neurons
2. neuroglia
3. a - sensory
4. motor
5. association
6. a - afferent
7. synapse
8. false
9. a - presynaptic
10. a - electrical
11. neurotransmitter
12. a.- presynaptic
13. cleft
14. b – chemical

Answers

15. b - motor end plate
16. a - dendrites
17. axon
18. b - myelin sheath
19. synaptic end-bulbs
20. true
21. association
22. sensory
23. motor
24. true
25. carotid
26. blood-brain barrier
27. a - white matter
28. c - 3
29. d - dura mater, arachnoid, pia mater
30. cerebrospinal fluid
31. d - 4
32. cerebrum
33. cerebral cortex
34. four
35. diencephalon
36. a - thalamus
37. true
38. cerebellum
39. c - body temperature
40. b - midbrain, pons, medulla oblongata
41. midbrain
42. pons
43. medulla oblongata
44. a - in the white matter
45. a - sensory
46. descending
47. integration
48. true
49. false
50. arc
51. integration centre
52. b - 12
53. a - optic
54. c - 31
55. c - both sensory and motor
56. rami
57. a - ventral
58. cervical
59. sacral
60. lumbar
61. sacral
62. brachial
63. autonomic nervous system
64. a - sympathetic
65. sympathetic
66. parasympathetic

67. b - cranial nerves and a few of the spinal nerves in the sacral region

Chemistry

1. atom
2. c - electron
3. proton
4. electron
5. true
6. one
7. molecule
8. true
9. potassium and sodium
10. carbon
11. compound
12. carbon
13. b - lipids
14. a - carbohydrates
15. proteins
16. false
17. deoxyribonucleic acid
18. water
19. a - positive
20. ion
21. c - electron
22. outer
23. false
24. three
25. true
26. water
27. d - ionization
28. a - acids
29. b - bases
30. true
31. pH
32. false
33. 7

Unlabelled Graphics

399

This page has intentionally been left blank.

Cell

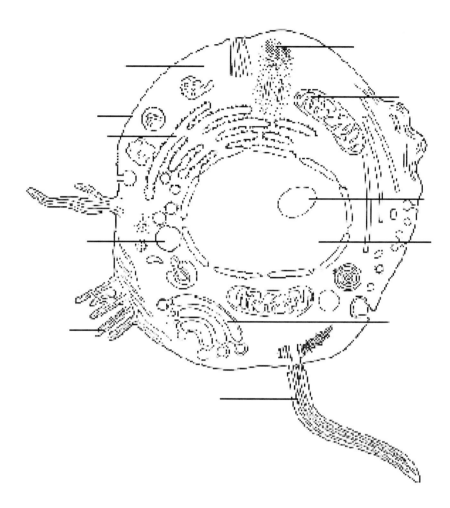

Skeleton – anterior

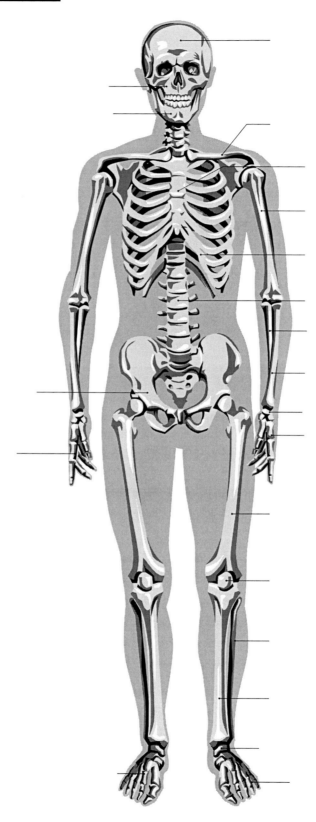

Skeleton – posterior

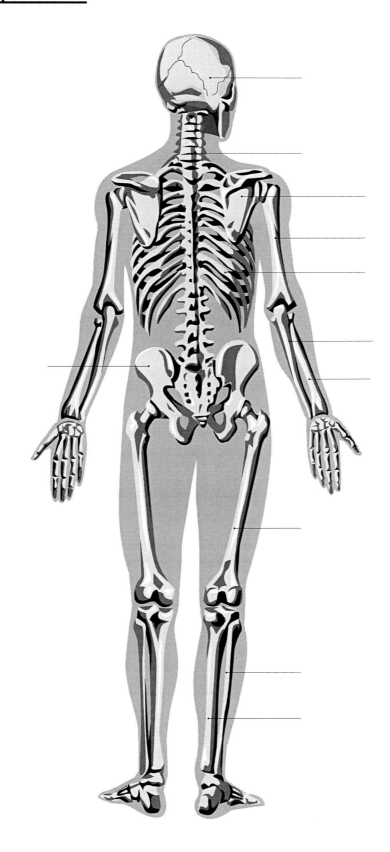

Long Bone

Vertebral Column

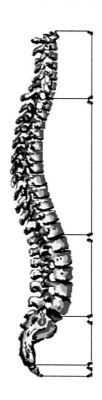

Vertebra

POSTERIOR

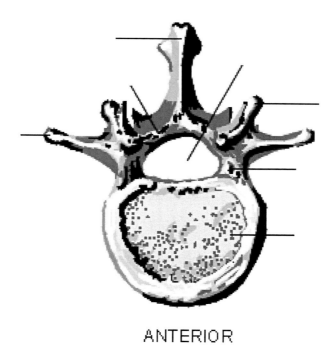

ANTERIOR

Skull and Face

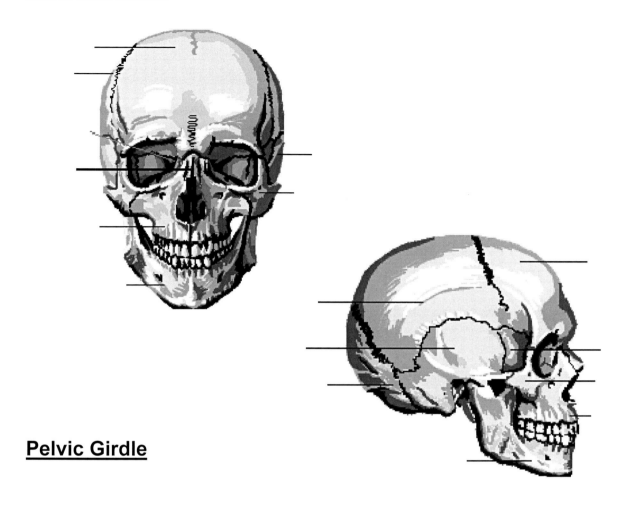

Pelvic Girdle

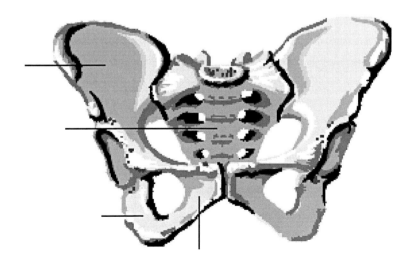

<u>Skin</u>

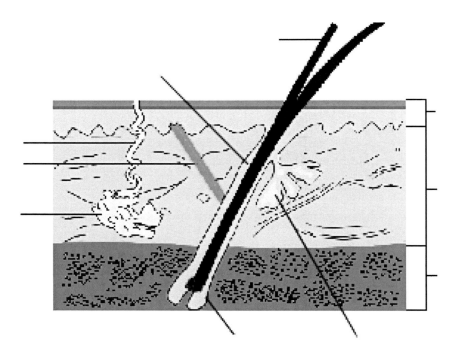

<u>Hair</u>

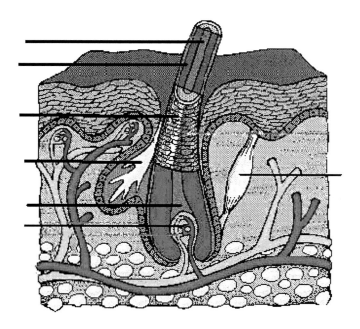

406

Nails

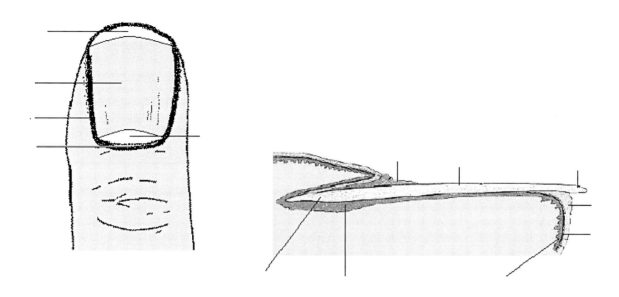

Cutaneous Receptors

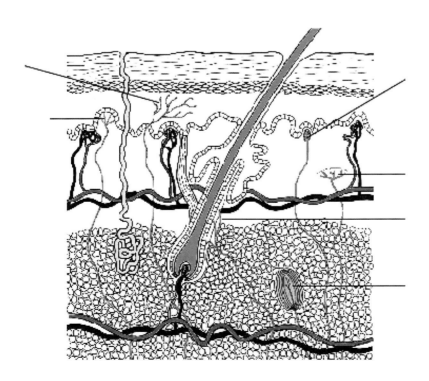

Upper Respiratory Tract

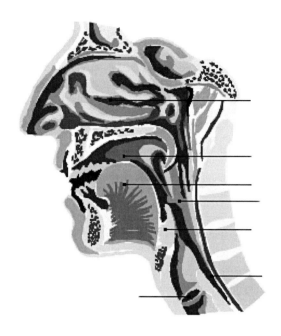

Bronchi

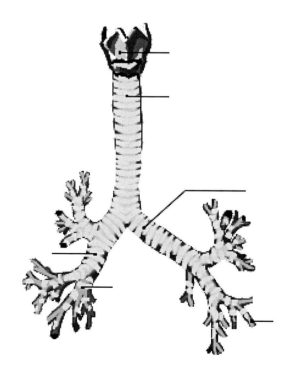

Eye

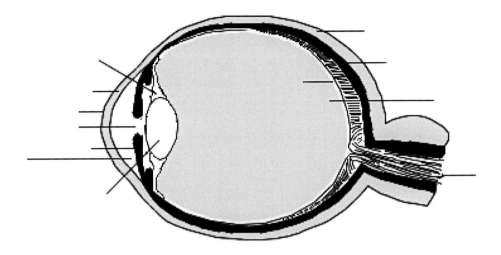

Ear

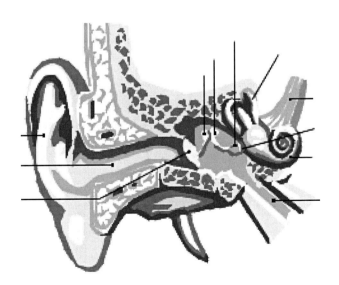

Urinary System

Kidney

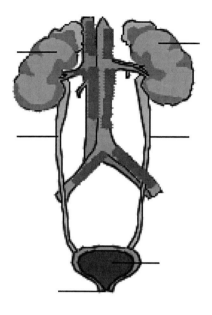

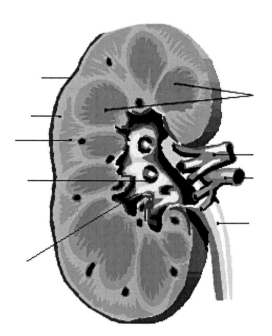

Nephron

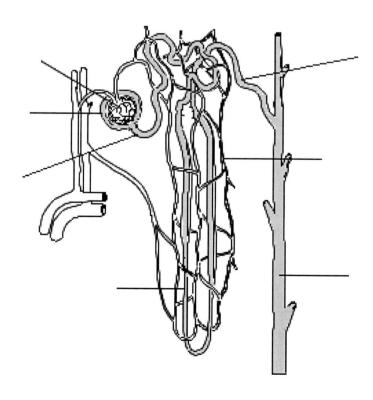

Male Reproductive System

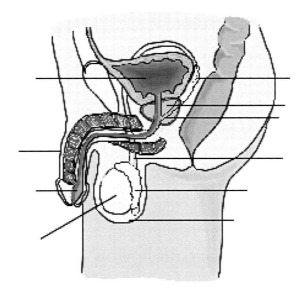

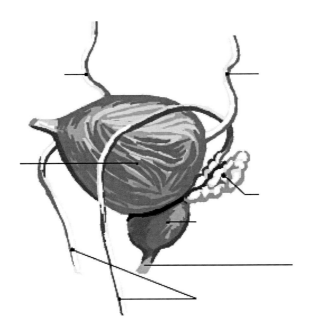

Female Reproductive System

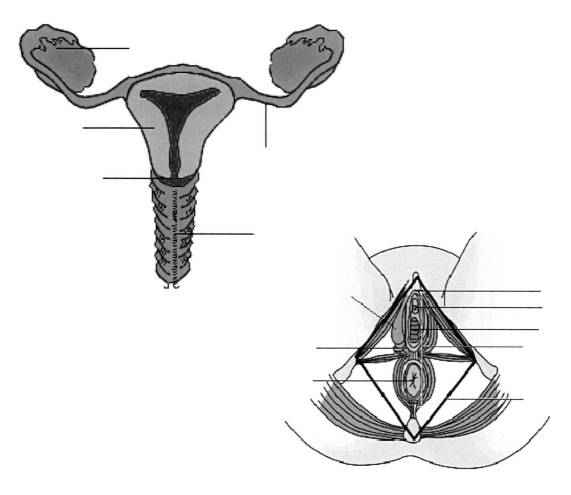

Breast

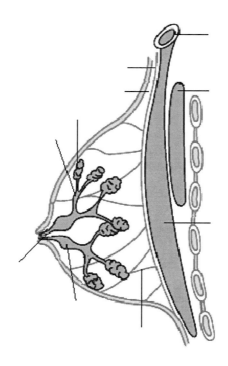

412

Lymphatic System

Lymph Node

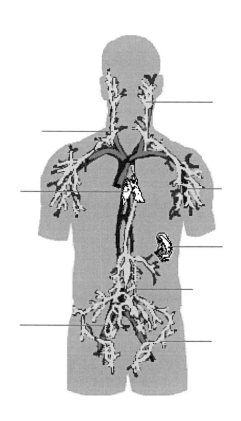

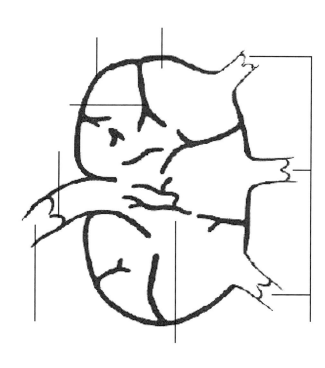

Lymph Nodes – Head and Neck

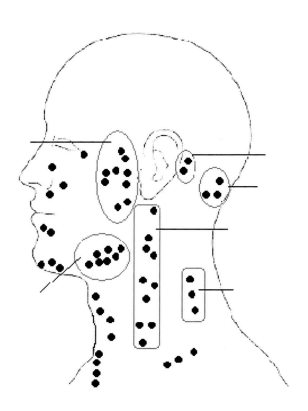

<u>Skeletal Muscle – cross–section</u>

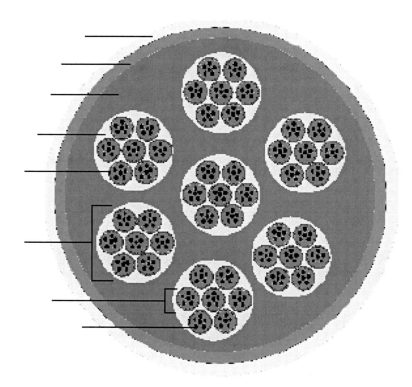

<u>Myofibril</u>

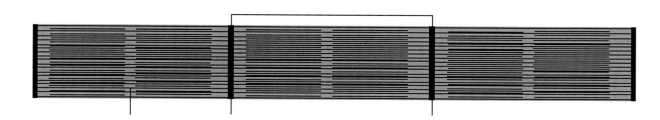

Face, Head and Neck Muscles

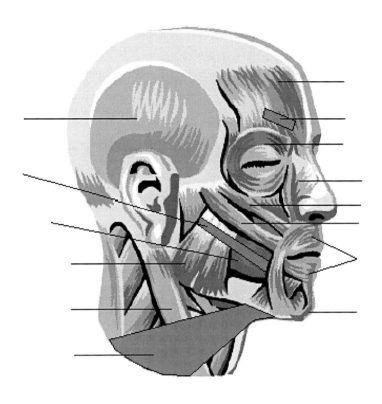

Shoulder Muscles - anterior

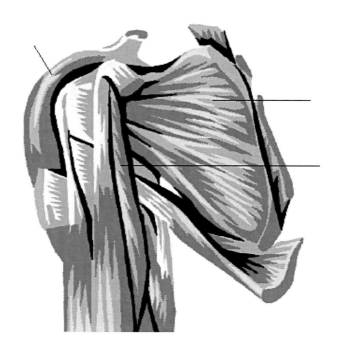

Shoulder Muscles - posterior

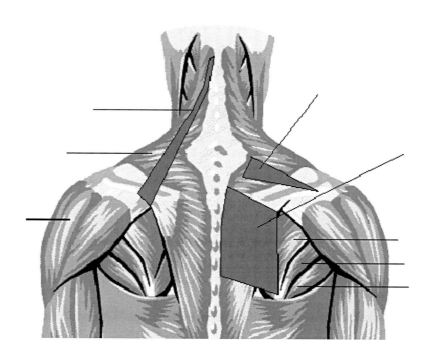

Arm Muscles - anterior

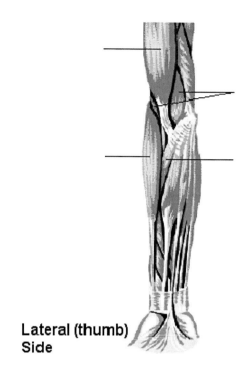

Lateral (thumb)
Side

Arm Muscles – anterior flexors

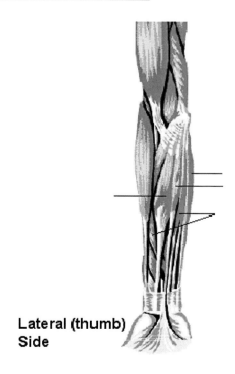

Lateral (thumb)
Side

Arm Muscles – posterior

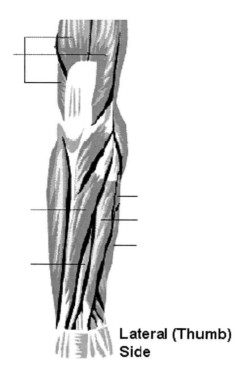

Lateral (Thumb)
Side

Hand Muscles – palmar view of left hand

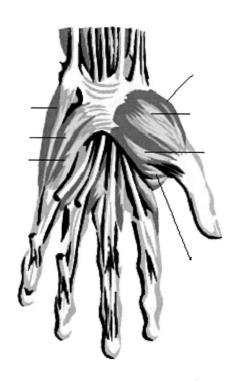

<u>Thigh Muscles - anterior</u>

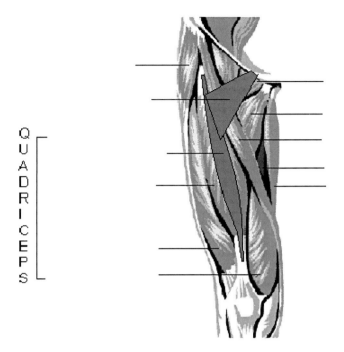

QUADRICEPS

<u>Thigh Muscles - posterior</u>

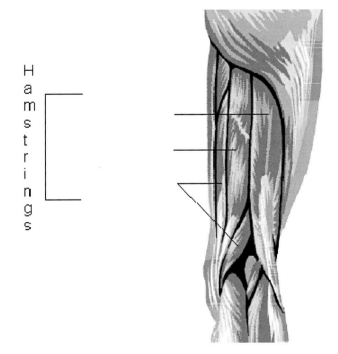

Hamstrings

Lower Leg Muscles – anterior

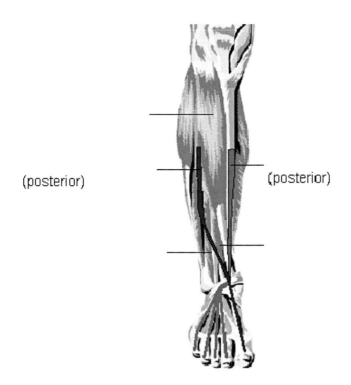

(posterior)

(posterior)

Lower Leg Muscles - posterior

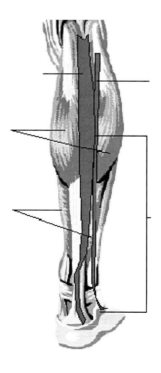

Trunk Muscles - anterior

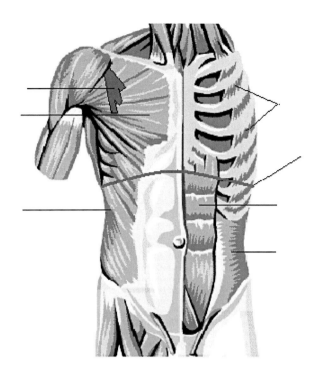

Trunk Muscles – posterior

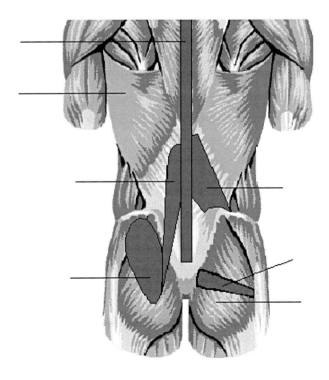

421

Heart

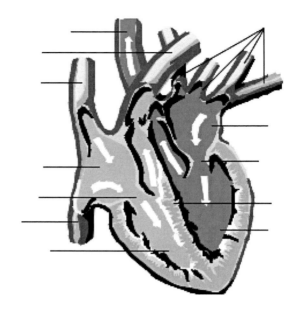

Major Arteries and Veins

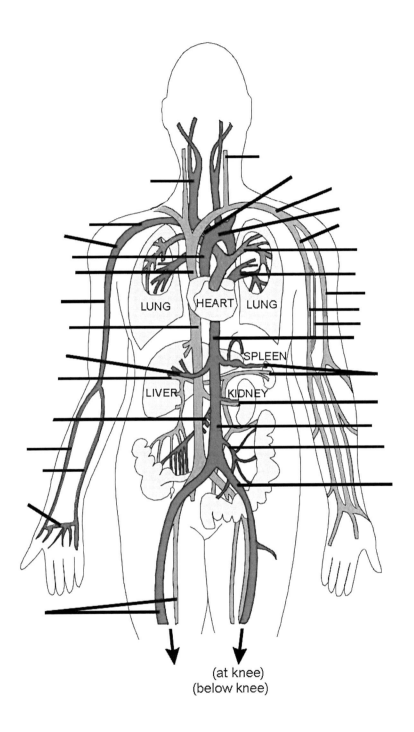

LUNG HEART LUNG

SPLEEN

LIVER KIDNEY

(at knee)
(below knee)

Note: The darker vessels shown here carry oxygenated blood.

423

Salivary Glands

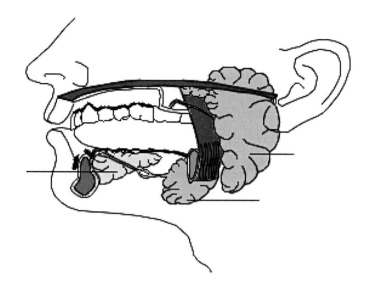

Pancreas

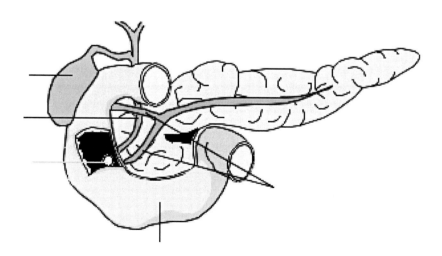

Digestive Organs

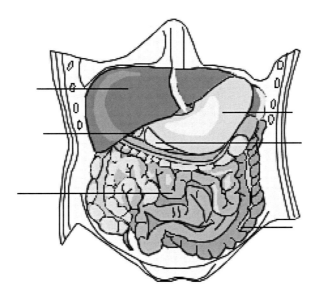

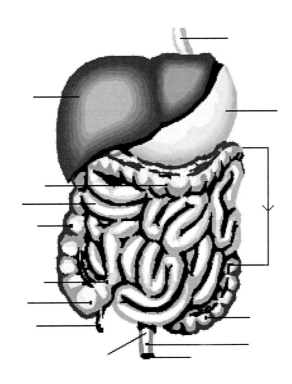

Sensory Neuron (assuming in PNS)

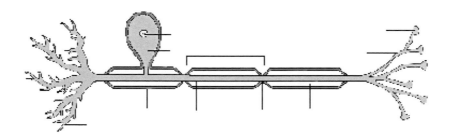

Motor Neuron

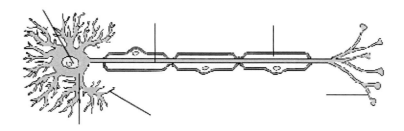

Association Neuron

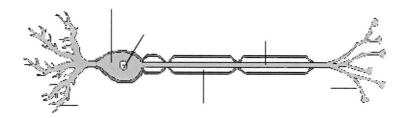

Brain

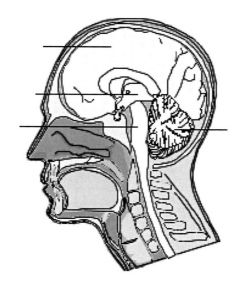

Glossary

This page has intentionally been left blank.

Abductors: Move a bone away from the midline.

Accommodation: A change in the curvature of the lens of the eye to adjust for vision at various distances.

Acetylcholine: A neurotransmitter released at a neuromuscular junction.

Acid: Dissociates in water to form hydrogen ions (positively charged).

Acini: Clusters of pancreatic epithelial cells that produce pancreatic juice.

Actin: A contractile protein that makes up the thin filaments in the myofibrils of muscle fibres.

Active transport: The way in which substances can, with the use of energy, be pushed, pumped or carried into and out of a cell.

Acute condition: A worse than chronic disorder, possibly leading rapidly to death.

Adductors: Draw a bone closer to the midline.

Adenoids: An overgrowth of the glandular tissue, naturally found in small amounts, on the back of the upper part of the throat.

Adenosine diphosphate (ADP): A molecule that can take on another phosphate group to become the energy-carrying molecule adenosine triphosphate (ATP).

Adenosine triphosphate (ATP): The energy carrying molecule, used to capture and store energy.

Adipose tissue: A "fatty" semi-solid connective tissue. The cells are specialised for the storage of fat. Adipose tissue supports, protects and insulates. It also provides a store of energy.

Adrenal glands: Endocrine glands located on the top of the kidneys. They produce a variety of hormones including adrenaline.

Adrenaline: The 'fight or flight' hormone produced by the adrenal glands. It prepares the body for an emergency. Adrenaline causes an increase in heart rate, dilation of the pupils and an increase in the metabolic rate. Also called epinephrine.

Adrenocorticotrophic hormone: Secreted by the anterior lobe of the pituitary gland, it stimulates secretions from the adrenals.

Aerobic: With oxygen.

Aerobic cellular respiration: The breakdown of glucose, in the presence of oxygen, into carbon dioxide and water. The reaction produces heat and energy.

Afferent: Conveys from the outer part of the body to the inner.

Agonist: The muscle that is contracting to perform the movement. It is opposed by the antagonist.

Agranular leucocyte: White blood cell that does not have cytoplasmic granules. Lymphocytes and monocytes are agranular leucocytes.

Albumins: Plasma proteins that regulate osmotic pressure.

Aldosterone: Hormone secreted by the adrenal cortex that controls sodium and potassium concentrations.

Alimentary canal: The digestive tract that runs from the mouth to the anus.

Alkaline: Containing more hydroxide ions (OH^-) than hydrogen ions (H^+) to produce a pH higher than 7. Also called 'basic'.

Alveoli: A cluster of air sacs found in the lungs at the end of the finest bronchioles. Also the term given to the clusters of milk-secreting glands in the lobules of the breast.

Alveolus: A small opening or cavity. An air sac found in the lungs.

Amino acid: An organic acid that is the building block for proteins.

Ammonia: Pungent smelling nitrogen compound. Ammonia is given off by urea in the presence of water.

Ampulla of Vater: The area at which the bile duct and the pancreatic duct meet to jointly enter the duodenum.

Anabolism: The metabolic process in which energy (from catabolism) is used to build up structural and functional components.

Anaemia: Deficiency of red blood cells or haemoglobin.

Anaerobic: Without oxygen.

Anaerobic cellular respiration: The break down of glucose by glycolysis into pyruvic acid. Two molecules of adenosine triphosphate are produced from each glucose molecule.

Anaphase: The third phase of mitosis in which the chromosomes split into two groups and move to opposite ends of the cell.

Anatomy: The structure (or study of structure) of the body.

Androgens: Substances that produce or stimulate male characteristics.

Antagonist: The muscle that could oppose the movement of the agonist but, in relaxing, allows the movement to take place.

Anterior: Nearer to the front of the body than its comparative component. Also called ventral.

Antibody: A protein produced by the body to neutralize the effect of antigens.

Antibody-mediated immunity: The part of immunity in which B-cells develop into plasma cells that produce antibodies to destroy antigens.

Anticoagulant: A substance that is able to delay or prevent blood from clotting.

Antidiuretic hormone (ADH): Hormone produced by the hypothalamus and stored and secreted from the posterior lobe of the pituitary gland. It stimulates water reabsorption from the nephrons of the kidney, so decreasing urine production.

Antigen: A foreign, invading substance (usually a protein) capable of inducing a specific immune response.

Apocrine glands: Sweat glands that open onto hair follicles.

Aponeurosis: A sheet-like tendon joining one muscle with another or with bone.

Appendicular skeleton: The shoulders, arms, hands, pelvis, hips, legs and feet.

Appendix: A small blind tube protruding from the caecum in the large intestine. It no longer has a digestive function.

Arachnoid: The middle membrane of the three membranes that constitute the meninges.

Areola: The slightly raised pink or brown pigmented area that surrounds the nipple.

Areolar tissue: The most widely distributed connective tissue. It consists of large, flat cells in a watery gel supported by a network of fine, white collagen fibres and elastic fibres. This white tissue surrounds blood vessels, nerves and muscles and connects the skin to the underlying tissues and muscles.

Arteriole: Created when an artery branches to form very small blood vessels. Arterioles divide further to become capillaries.

Artery: A thick walled vessel that carries blood away from the heart.

Articular capsule: Encapsulates the bone ends at a synovial joint to form the synovial cavity. Consists of the synovial membrane and a fibrous outer layer.

Articular cartilage: The most common cartilage type, also called hyaline cartilage. It is firm, elastic and reduces shock and friction in the joints. It is also used to connect bone to bone in joints such as those between the ribs and the sternum. It also forms the rings that keep the trachea open.

Articular process: One of 4 bony structures of a vertebra that form joints with neighbouring vertebrae.

Articulate: Connect by joints.

Ascending colon: A part of the large intestine that runs up the right side of the abdomen from the caecum to the transverse colon.

Ascorbic acid: Vitamin C. A water-soluble vitamin needed for many metabolic processes.

Association neurons: Carry nerve impulses from one neuron to another. They do not contact sensory receptors or effectors. Also called connecting neurons.

Astrocyte: A neurological cell having a star shape that supports neurons in the brain and spinal cord and attaches the neurons to blood vessels.

Atlas: The top cervical vertebra (C1), which permits the nodding movement.

Atom: The smallest and simplest matter that can take part in a chemical reaction. An atom has a nucleus (central part) containing protons (positively charged particles) and neutrons (particles with no electrical charge). The nucleus is surrounded by a number of electrons (negatively charged particles).

Atrium: One of the two superior chambers in the heart.

Autonomic nervous system: Part of the peripheral nervous system that regulates the activity of smooth muscle (found in the walls of hollow structures), cardiac muscle (found in the heart) and glands. It comprises of the sympathetic and parasympathetic nervous systems.

Axial skeleton: The skull, spine, ribcage and the sternum (breast bone).

Axilla: Commonly called the armpit. It is the hollow underneath the arm where the arm joins the side of the chest.

Axis: The second cervical vertebra (C2). The pivot joint between C1 and C2 allows the head to rotate from side to side.

Axon: The long, thin part of the neuron that conducts the nerve impulse from the dendrites to the axon terminals.

Axon terminal: An end branch of a neuron. Each has a synaptic end-bulb.

Bacteria: Micro-organisms with the capability of causing disease.

Baroreceptors: Pressure receptors situated in the walls of the blood vessels.

Base: Dissociates in water to form hydroxide ions (oxygen and hydrogen, negatively charged).

Basophil: White blood cell that ingests bacteria. They can release heparin and histamine, both of which intensify the inflammatory reaction.

B-cells: Lymphocytes that develop into antibody-producing plasma cells.

Bicarbonate: Salt containing a double proportion of carbon dioxide.

Bile: A secretion of the liver, stored in the gall bladder, which enters the duodenum via the bile duct. It consists of salts, pigments, cholesterol and traces of other substances. Bile aids digestion by emulsifying fats.

Bile salts: Components of bile that aid digestion in the duodenum. They emulsify fats and facilitate the digestive action of lipase.

Bladder (urinary): A thin-walled muscular sac used to temporarily store urine. The urine is drained from the kidneys to the bladder by the ureters, and leaves the bladder via the urethra.

Blastocyst: A hollow ball of cells that develops from the morula about 4-5 days after fertilization of the ovum. The blastocyst attaches to the uterine lining.

Blastomeres: Small cells produced by cleavage of a fertilized ovum.

Blood-brain barrier: A barrier, consisting of specialised brain capillaries that are less leaky than others, astrocytes and a continuous basement membrane, which prevents the free passage of materials from the blood to the cerebrospinal fluid and brain.

Body (vertebral): Thick, disc shaped, weight bearing part of the vertebra that contacts on either side with the intervertebral discs.

Bone marrow: A connective tissue within certain parts of the bone. Red bone marrow consists of immature red blood cells, adipose cells and macrophages. Red bone marrow produces red blood cells, white blood cells and platelets. Yellow bone marrow contains mainly fat.

Bowman's capsule: A part of the kidney involved in filtering the blood.

Brachiocephalic veins: Formed by the merging of the jugular and subclavian veins. They lead into the superior vena cava. The lymphatic ducts drain lymph into the brachiocephalic veins.

Brain stem: The part of the brain at the top of the spinal cord. It includes the midbrain, pons and medulla oblongata.

Bronchiole: A third or greater branch of the bronchus. The many bronchioles carry air to all areas of the lung. The finest bronchioles end in alveoli.

Bronchus (primary): One of the two large branches of the trachea. The bronchi take air into the lungs. They branch into secondary bronchi, tertiary bronchi and then into bronchioles.

Calcitonin: Hormone secreted by the thyroid gland. It lowers the blood levels of calcium and phosphates in the blood.

Calcium: A mineral salt essential for growth. It is found in bones and teeth. Calcium ions are important in triggering muscular contractions. Calcium is needed during the blood clotting process to convert prothrombin to thrombin.

Canaliculi: Minute canals, filled with extracellular fluid, that radiate from the lacunae in bone.

Cancellous bone: Forms the epiphyses and metaphyses in the long bones. It also forms short bones, flat bones, sesamoid bones and irregularly shaped bones. The bone tissue is arranged in an interlacing network in which red bone marrow may be found in the spaces. Also called spongy bone.

Capillary: One of numerous tiny blood vessels. They have thin walls that allow the exchange of gases and other substances between the blood and the tissues.

Carbohydrate: Energy producing compound of carbon, oxygen and hydrogen, e.g. sugars, starches, glycogen and cellulose.

Carbon: Element that forms the basis of all living matter.

Cardiovascular system: Responsible for supplying blood to the tissues. It consists of the blood, heart and the network of vessels.

Carotene: A yellow, orange or red pigment. The most widespread is beta-carotene, the orange pigment in carrots.

Carpals: The eight short bones that make up the wrist.

Carpus: The collective term for the 8 short bones (carpals) of the wrist.

Cartilage: Thick, fibrous connective tissue found in a number of locations in the body, e.g. lining the end of the bones in joints, between the vertebrae, in the outer ear and at the end of the nose. There are 3 main types – hyaline, white fibrous and yellow elastic.

Casein: Protein of milk.

Catabolism: The metabolic process in which large, complex molecules are broken down releasing energy.

Catalyst: A substance that increases the rate of a chemical reaction without being used up in it. Enzymes are catalysts.

Cell-mediated immunity: A part of immunity in which T-cells attach to antigens to destroy them.

Cell membrane: The membrane that surrounds the cell, forming a barrier between the cell and the extracellular fluid. It is also called the plasma membrane.

Cells: The basic structural and functional units that make up the body.

Cellular respiration: The oxidation of glucose, often expressed as the equation Glucose + Oxygen = Energy + Carbon Dioxide + Water.

Cellulose: A carbohydrate found in the cell walls of plants. It is an important source of carbohydrate in the human diet.

Central nervous system: Comprises of the brain and the spinal cord. It receives sensory information from all parts of the body, analyzes the information and then responds by sending impulses to stimulate muscles or glands.

Centromere: The portion of the chromosomes where the two chromatids join.

Cerebellum: Area of the brain inferior to the cerebrum and posterior to the brain stem.

Cerebral cortex: The surface of the cerebral hemispheres consisting of grey matter. It is responsible for the senses of vision, hearing, smell and touch, for stimulating the contraction of voluntary muscles, and for higher brain activities such as language and memory.

Cerebral hemispheres: The two halves of the forebrain that make up the cerebrum, the largest part of the brain.

Cerebral ventricle: One of the four cavities in the brain filled with cerebrospinal fluid.

Cerebrospinal fluid: The fluid that circulates in the ventricles of the brain and in the sub-arachnoid space around the brain and spinal cord. It protects, nourishes and acts as a shock absorber.

Cerebrum: The largest area in the brain. It is composed of two cerebral hemispheres.

Cervical vertebra: One of the seven bones that make up the neck area of the vertebral column (spine). The first cervical vertebra is called the atlas. The second is called the axis.

Cervix: Neck of the uterus.

Chemoreceptor: A receptor that responds to chemicals.

Chloride: Ion that, due to the ease at which it diffuses between extracellular and intracellular fluids, plays an important part in balancing osmotic pressure. Regulated by aldosterone.

Chlorine: Mineral found in extracellular and intracellular fluids. Plays a role in acid-base balance of blood, water balance and formation of hydrochloric acid in the stomach.

Cholecystokinin hormone: Secreted by the small intestine to stimulate pancreatic secretions that are rich in digestive enzymes. Also stimulates the contraction of the walls of the gall bladder and relaxes the sphincter at the ampulla of Vater.

Cholesterol: A fat derivative found in animal cells that is insoluble in water. Its presence on the inside of the walls of blood vessels is thought to contribute to hypertension and thrombosis. It can also accumulate in the gall bladder as gall stones.

Chondrocyte: Cartilage cell.

Chromatid: One of a pair of identical strands of genetic information. Chromatids separate during cell division and each forms a chromosome in the daughter cell.

Chromosome: A structure in the cell nucleus (centre) that carries the genes. Each chromosome consists of one very long strand of deoxyribonucleic acid (DNA). Humans usually have 23 pairs of chromosomes.

Chronic condition: A severe, long lasting disorder.

Chyme: Semi-fluid mixture of food and gastric juices.

Cilia: Tiny hairs that line many body cavities.

Circumduction: A circular movment created by a combination of flexion, extension, abduction and adduction.

Cleavage: Rapid mitotic divisions following fertilization of a secondary oocyte resulting in smaller cells called blastomeres.

Coccyx: The triangular bone at the tail of the vertebral column (spine), consisting of four fused coccygeal vertebrae.

Collagen: The protein of fibrous connective tissue.

Compact bone: Forms the external layer of all bones and most of the diaphysis in long bone. Characterized by the arrangement of osteons.

Conduction: Heat loss when the warmer body comes into physical contact with a cooler object.

Conjunctiva: The delicate membrane covering the eyeball and lining the eye.

Connective tissue: The most abundant tissue type. It binds, supports and connects structures within the body. It consists of cells within a matrix of ground substances and fibres. The main types are areola, adipose, white fibrous, yellow elastic, lymphoid, blood, bone and cartilage.

Convection: Heat loss when the warmer body comes into contact with a liquid or gas. The liquid or gas gets heated by conduction, expands and becomes less dense. The warmed substance then rises and is replaced.

Corpuscles of touch: Egg-shaped receptors for discriminative touch and low-frequency vibration. The dendrites are encapsulated by connective tissues and are located in the dermal papillae. They transmit impulses rapidly and are most abundant in the fingertips, palms of the hands and soles of the feet.

Corticosterone: A hormone produced by the adrenal cortex that stimulates the conversion of fats and proteins to glucose.

Cortisone: A steroid hormone produced by the adrenal cortex or synthetically. It has anti-inflammatory properties and stimulates the conversion of fats and proteins to glucose.

Covalent bond: Formed when atoms share either one, two or three pairs of electrons.

Cranial nerves: The twelve pairs of nerves that originate from the brain.

Creatine: An amino acid found in muscles. It combines with phosphoric acid to form creatine phosphate.

Creatine phosphate: A unique molecule found in muscles capable of transferring its phosphate group to adenosine diphosphate to form adenosine triphosphate and creatine.

Cremaster muscle: Surrounds the testis and runs up through the spermatic cord. It raises the testis during sexual stimulation and exposure to the cold.

Crude touch: When there is an awareness that the body has been touched, but the exact location of the contact is unknown.

Cytokinesis: Division of the cytoplasm that takes place during mitosis and meiosis.

Cytology: The study of cells.

Cytoplasm: Semi-fluid within the cell membrane that surrounds the organelles.

Deep: Internal, away from the surface of the body.

Dendrites: The end processes of a neuron that receive the nerve impulses.

Dense bodies: Areas in the sarcoplasm of a smooth muscle cell to which intermediate filaments attach to facilitate the shortening of the muscle.

Deoxyribonucleic acid (DNA): A complex two-stranded molecule, found in chromosomes, that contains all the information needed to build, control and maintain a living organism. It forms the basis for genetic inheritance.

Dermal papillae: Finger-like projections of the dermis that indent the epidermis. They can contain loops of capillaries and nerve endings that are sensitive to touch.

Dermis: The dermis is the second major layer of the skin. It is situated under the epidermis.

Descending colon: A part of the large intestine that runs down the left side of the abdomen from the transverse colon to the sigmoid colon.

Diaphragm: A dome-shaped sheet of muscle and tendon that divides the thorax from the abdomen. It plays a major role in respiration. During inspiration it contracts, drawing air into the lungs. During expiration the diaphragm relaxes, forcing air to be expelled.

Diaphysis: The main shaft of the bone.

Diencephalon: Part of the brain posterior to the midbrain. It includes the thalamus and the hypothalamus.

Diffusion: The passive movement of a solute from an area of greater concentration to an area of lower concentration through a semi-permeable membrane.

Digestion: The mechanical and chemical breakdown of food into molecules that can be absorbed and used by the body.

Digestive system: The organs responsible for the ingestion, digestion, absorption and elimination of food. The digestive system runs from mouth to anus, a route often referred to as the alimentary canal.

Diploid: A cell with the full genetic complement of 23 pairs of chromosomes.

Disaccharides: Formed by the chemical linking of two monosaccharides. Disaccharides include sucrose (table sugar) and lactose (milk sugar).
Discriminative touch: When the exact point of contact is known.
Distal: Further from the attachment of a limb to the trunk of the body than its comparative component. For example, the wrist is distal to the elbow.
Dorsal: Pertains to the back or posterior.
Duodenum: The first and shortest part of the small intestine.
Dura mater: The outermost of the three membranes that constitute the meninges.
Eccrine glands: Release sweat directly onto the surface of the skin.
Effector: A muscle or gland that responds to nerve impulses from a motor neuron.
Efferent: Conveys from the inner part of the body away to the outer.
Electrolytes: Ions in solution.
Electron: Negatively charged particle that orbits the nucleus of an atom.
Element: Molecule consisting of atoms of the same type.
Emulsification: The break down of large fat globules into smaller ones in the presence of bile.
End organs of Ruffini: Sensory receptors in which the dendrites are located deep in the dermis and in the deeper tissues of the body. They detect heavy and continuous touch sensations.
Endocardium: The layer of the heart wall that lines the inside of the heart.
Endocrine gland: A ductless gland that secretes hormones into the blood.
Endocrine system: The system in which ductless endocrine glands (e.g. hypothalamus, pituitary, adrenals, thymus, testes, ovaries, thyroid, parathyroids, pancreas and pineal) secrete hormones into the blood to regulate many body functions.
Endometrium: The mucous membrane that lines the uterus.
Endomysium: The layer of connective tissue that surrounds the muscle fibres within a fascicle.
Endoplasmic reticulum: A network of channels that runs through the cytoplasm of the cell. It performs many roles including intracellular transport and support. It also provides the surface area for many types of chemical reactions. Its surface is often covered with protein-synthesizing ribosomes, forming "rough" endoplasmic reticulum. It is here that most of the cell's enzyme activity takes place under the influence of ribonucleic acid. Endoplasmic reticulum lacking ribosomes is called "smooth" and is involved in lipid (fat) synthesis, including steroids.
Endosteum: Lining of the medullary (or marrow) cavity of the bone.
Endothelium: The layer of epithelial cells that lines the cavities of the heart, blood vessels and lymphatic vessels.
Energy: The capacity to do work.
Enzyme: Biological catalyst produced in cells, capable of speeding up chemical reactions. Enzymes are large, complex proteins and are not destroyed during the chemical reactions that they promote.
Eosinophil: Granular leucocyte thought to release enzymes that counteract the effects of histamine.
Epicardium: The thin, outer layer of the heart wall.
Epidermis: The outer layer of the skin, comprising of 5 strata.
Epididymis: An organ situated on the posterior border of the testis in which the sperm mature.
Epiglottis: A flap of tissue that prevents food entering the trachea during swallowing, so allowing the food to pass safely into the oesophagus.
Epimysium: Layer of connective tissue that surrounds the whole muscle. It is located underneath the fascia.

Epiphyseal plate: Cartilaginous area running across the epiphysis that is responsible for the lengthwise growth of long bones.

Epiphysis: The area at each end of a long bone.

Epithelial tissue: Forms glands and the outer part of the skin. It lines the blood vessels, hollow organs and passages that lead out of the body. There are two main types – simple and compound.

Eponychium: A narrow band of epidermis that extends from the proximal nail wall to the base of the nail.

Erythrocytes: Red blood cells, responsible for transporting the gases of respiration.

Eustachian tube: The passage that leads from the pharynx to the middle ear.

Evaporation: Turning from a solid or liquid into a vapour.

Excretion: The process of eliminating waste products from a cell, tissue, or the entire body; or the products excreted.

Exocrine gland: A gland that secretes substances into ducts that empty to an epithelial surface.

Extensors: Cause extension, so increasing the angle at a joint.

External respiration: The diffusion of gases between the lungs and the blood.

Extracellular: Outside the cell.

Extracellular fluid: The fluid that fills the spaces between the cells. It is constantly moving and bathes and nourishes the cells. Also called tissue fluid, interstitial fluid and intercellular fluid.

Facets: The 4 articulating surfaces of a vertebra.

Faeces: Undigested food, waste products and bacteria that is eliminated from the body by the digestive system.

Fallopian tube: One of two funnel-shaped tubes, each leading from an ovary to the uterus. The fallopian tubes transport the ova to the uterus and provide the site for fertilization.

Fascia: Sheet of fibrous connective tissue beneath the skin or around muscles and other organs.

Fascicle: In the muscle, this is the name given to a bundle of muscle fibres. Generally, it means a small bundle or cluster.

Fat: An oily or greasy energy-providing food source. Saturated fats are derived from animal fats and dairy products. Unsaturated fats include vegetable oils (soya bean, maize and sunflower) and marine oils from fish.

Femur: Thigh bone.

Fibrin: Formed by the interaction of thrombin and fibrinogen, fibrin is an insoluble protein that forms the basis of a blood clot.

Fibrinogen: Plasma protein that plays a vital role in blood clotting.

Fibula: One of the two long bones of the lower leg.

Filtration: The way in which substances may be forced across the cell membrane by gravity or water pressure.

Flat bones: Thin bones composed of 2 layers of compact bone sandwiching a layer of spongy bone. For example, the scapula and the sternum.

Flexors: Cause a limb to bend, decreasing the angle at a joint.

Follicle: A small secretory cavity.

Follicle stimulating hormone: Abbreviated to FSH, this hormone is secreted by the pituitary gland. It initializes the development of ova and stimulates the ovaries to secrete oestrogens (in females) and stimulates the production of sperm (in males).

Free nerve ending: Unspecialized sensory receptor capable of detecting either hot, cold or pain.

Fungi: Plants lacking chlorophyll (the pigment that gives plants their characteristic green colour). Includes mushrooms, toadstools and moulds.

Gall bladder: A small sac, located behind the liver, that stores bile and secretes it into the duodenum via the bile duct.
Gamete: Sex cell. The female sex cell is the ovum. The male sex cell is the spermatozoon. Gametes contain half the genetic information found in other cells.
Ganglion: A group of nerve cell bodies that lie outside the central nervous system.
Gastric juices: Acidic secretions from the stomach. Gastric juices include mucus, hydrochloric acid, pepsinogen, rennin, intrinsic factor and gastrin.
Gastrin: Hormone secreted in gastric juices that stimulates the secretion of hydrochloric acid and pepsinogen. It increases the muscular activity of the stomach and relaxes the pyloric sphincter.
Gene: Unit of inherited material located on a chromosome that, by itself or with other genes, determines a characteristic in an organism.
Germinal: In the earliest stage of development, or productive.
Gestation: The time that the zygote, embryo and foetus is carried in the female.
Globulins: Plasma proteins that include antibodies (immunoglobulins) and alpha and beta globulins that transport iron, fats and fat-soluble vitamins.
Glucagon: A hormone secreted by the islets of Langerhans in the pancreas. It increases the blood-glucose level.
Glucose: A form of sugar that circulates in the blood. It is a monosaccharide and the building block of all carbohydrates.
Glycerol: Colourless, sweet, viscous liquid formed by the break down of fats.
Glycogen: The form in which carbohydrates are stored in the liver and muscle. Glycogen is converted into glucose as the body needs it.
Glycolysis: A series of chemical reactions in which a molecule of glucose is split into two molecules of pyruvic acid. Two molecules of adenosine triphosphate are produced in this anaerobic process.
Goblet cells: Found in columnar epithelium. They secrete mucus which serves to protect and lubricate the tissue.
Goitre: The swelling on the front of the neck, caused by the enlargement of the thyroid gland.
Golgi-body: A cell organelle that looks like a stack of plates. It processes proteins and lipids, and controls the enzyme activity of the endoplasmic reticulum.
Gonad: Gland that produces gametes and hormones. The testes are the gonads in the male and the ovaries are the gonads in the female.
Gonadotrophic hormone: A hormone that regulates the functions of the gonads.
Granular leucocyte: White blood cell with a lobed nucleus and granules in the cytoplasm. Neutrophils, eosinophils and basophils are granular leucocytes.
Grey matter: Area of the central nervous system and ganglia consisting of non-myelinated nervous tissue. It provides the site for integration.
Growth hormone: Produced and secreted from the anterior lobe of the pituitary. It controls body growth.
Gynecomastia: The excessive benign growth of the male mammary glands.
Haem: A red pigment found in haemoglobin. It contains iron.
Haemoglobin: A substance in red blood cells, consisting of a protein (globin) and a red pigment (haem) that contains iron.
Haemorrhage: The escape of blood from a vessel.
Hair follicle: Surrounds the hair root. It comprises of an external root sheath and an internal root sheath. The external root sheath is a downward continuation of the epidermis.
Haploid: A cell with half the genetic complement of diploid cells. Haploid cells contain 23 chromosomes. Gametes are haploid cells.
Haversian canals: Canals, containing blood vessels, that run longitudinally through compact bone. Also called central canals.

Heart: The main organ of the cardiovascular system, responsible for pumping the blood around the body.

Heparin: A substance that prevents blood from clotting.

Histamine: Substance found in many cells that is released when the cell is injured. It causes the blood vessels to dilate and the bronchioles to constrict.

Histology: The study of the structure of tissues.

Homeostasis: Maintenance of a stable internal environment.

Homologous chromosomes: The two chromosomes that make up a pair. There are 23 homologous pairs in a diploid cell.

Hormones: Chemical messengers, secreted into the blood by the endocrine glands. They control many body processes including growth, metabolism, sexual development and reproduction.

Human chorionic gonadotrophic hormone: Hormone produced by the placenta that mimics luteinizing hormone. It therefore stimulates the secretion of oestrogens and progesterone from the ovaries.

Humerus: Long bone of the upper arm.

Humour: A fluid or semi-fluid substance in the body often used to support organs, e.g. aqueous humour and vitreous humour support the eye.

Hyaline cartilage: The most common cartilage type, also called articular cartilage. It is firm, elastic and reduces shock and friction in the joints. It is also used to connect bone to bone in joints such as those between the ribs and the sternum. Hyaline cartilage also forms the rings that keep the trachea open.

Hydrochloric acid: Secreted in the gastric juices, it kills bacteria, neutralizes saliva, inhibits the secretion of gastrin and acts on pepsinogen.

Hydrogen: Element that is a constituent of water and all foods.

Hydrogen bond: Formed by the electrostatic forces between certain molecules.

Hyperventilation: Increased respiratory rate.

Hyponychium: The epidermis that is located beneath the nail plate at the junction between the free edge and the skin of the fingertip.

Hypothalamus: Situated at the base of the brain, the hypothalamus is involved in many regulatory and metabolic activities, e.g. body temperature, hormone release, heart rate, respiratory rate, blood pressure, hunger and digestion. It also acts as an emotional regulator capable of alleviating anxiety and depression.

Ileocaecal sphincter/valve: The point at which the ileum of the small intestine meets the caecum of the large intestine.

Ileum: The final and longest part of the small intestine. The ileum joins the large intestine at the ileocaecal valve.

Immunity: The ability to withstand harmful infection agents and toxins. Non-specific immunity includes mechanisms such as phagocytosis and the protective properties of the skin. Specific immune responses involve the body's ability to form antibodies in response to antigens.

Inferior: Away from the head, towards the lower part of the body. Literally means 'below'.

Inhibin: Hormone secreted by the ovaries and testes. It inhibits the secretion of follicle stimulating hormone.

Innominate bone: Formed by the fusion of the ilium, ischium and pubis. The 2 innominate bones join anteriorly at the pubic symphysis and posteriorly at the sacrum to form the pelvic girdle.

Inorganic compound: Substance not containing carbon that is non-living or has never lived.

Insertion: The attachment to the bone that the muscular contraction intends to move.

Insulin: A pancreatic secretion that enables the muscles and other tissues to utilize the sugar in the blood. It decreases the blood-glucose level.

Integration: The analysis and (if necessary) storage of sensory information, and the subsequent decision making function performed by the grey matter of the central nervous system.

Integumentary system: Comprises of the skin and its associated components such as the nails and hair.

Intercellular fluid: The fluid that fills the spaces between the cells. It is constantly moving and bathes and nourishes the cells. Also called tissue fluid, interstitial fluid and extracellular fluid.

Intercostal: Between the ribs.

Intercostal muscles: Muscles located between the ribs.

Internal respiration: The diffusion of gases between the blood and the cells.

Interphase: The resting phase of cell division. Cells are said to be in interphase when they are carrying on their usual processes but not dividing.

Interstitial: Between the cells.

Intervertebral disc: A pad of white fibrous cartilage located between two vertebrae.

Intracellular: Within the cell.

Intrinsic factor: Secreted in the gastric juices, it allows the absorption of vitamin B12.

Iodine: An essential trace element, mainly found as a constituent of the thyroid hormones. Iodine deficiency causes the thyroid to enlarge.

Ion: A charged atom, usually formed when inorganic substances such as salt dissolve.

Ionic bond: Created when atoms either give up or accept an electron(s) to form a molecule.

Ionization: The dissociation of organic molecules in water.

Iris: The coloured portion of the eyeball.

Iron: Mineral found predominantly in the haemoglobin. The remainder is in the skeletal muscles, liver, spleen and enzymes. Iron is necessary for the transportation of oxygen in the blood. Also involved in the formation of adenosine triphosphate (ATP), a chemical used to capture and store energy.

Irregular bones: Have complex shapes and vary in the quantities of compact and spongy bone present. The vertebrae are examples of irregular bones.

Islets of Langerhans: A cluster of endocrine cells in the pancreas. They secrete insulin and glucagon, the two hormones involved in blood-sugar regulation.

Jejunum: The middle part of the small intestine, between the duodenum and the ileum.

Keratin: A protein that helps to waterproof and protect the skin.

Keratinocytes: Cells that make up about 90% of the epidermis. They produce keratin.

Kidney: A bean-shaped excretory organ of the urinary system, responsible for controlling the composition, volume and pressure of the blood. The kidneys absorb excessive materials and waste products from the blood and form urine.

Labia: Folds of skin in the female genital area.

Labour: The process by which the foetus is expelled from the uterus, via the vagina.

Lactation: The secretion and ejection of milk from the mammary glands.

Lacteal: A lymphatic vessel embedded in villi of the small intestine.

Lactic acid: A colourless, syrupy, sour liquid, produced in the body during muscular activity. Muscle fatigue and cramp are associated with an accumulation of lactic acid in the muscles.

Lacunae: Spaces between the lamellae in bone. They contain osteocytes.

Lamellae: Hard, calcified matrix in bone.

Lamellated corpuscle: Sensory receptor in which the dendrites are enclosed in an oval, layered capsule composed of connective tissue. They are located in the subcutaneous layer of the skin, under mucous membranes, around joints, tendons and muscles, in the mammary glands and in certain organs. They detect pressure and high-frequency vibration.

Laminae: Parts of the vertebra which, with the pedicles, make up the bony vertebral arch that surrounds the spinal cord.

Langerhans cells: Originate in the bone marrow and migrate to the epidermis. They are involved in immune responses.

Large intestine: The part of the digestive tract that extends from the ileocaecal sphincter to the anus. It incorporates the caecum, appendix, ascending colon, transverse colon, descending colon, sigmoid colon, rectum and anal canal. The large intestine receives chyme from the small intestine. It continues the absorption of water and nutrients from the digested food and prepares undigested food and waste for expulsion as faeces.

Larynx: Voice box, situated at the top of the trachea.

Lateral: Pertaining to the side. Further from the midline of the body or structure than its comparative component.

Lens: The transparent, biconvex disc in the eye, situated posterior to the pupil and iris. Adjustments in the curvature of the lens play a part in the production of a focused image.

Leucocyte: White blood cell that plays a part in the body's natural defenses and immunity against disease. Leucocytes occur in the blood, lymph and elsewhere in the body's tissues. Some engulf invading micro-organisms and some kill infected cells, but lymphocytes (a type of white blood cell) produce more specific immune responses.

Leukaemia: A disease in which the number of white blood cells is permanently excessive. It is characterized by the enlargement of the spleen and the lymph glands. Changes also occur in the bone marrow. The cause is unknown.

Ligament: Tough, elastic, white fibrous connective tissue that connects two bones at a joint.

Limbic system: A portion of the brain concerned with various aspects of emotional behaviour.

Lipase: Enzyme in pancreatic juice that digests fats.

Lipid: Fat or fat-like organic substance composed of carbon, hydrogen and oxygen. Lipids are insoluble in water. Steroids are lipids.

Liver: The heaviest organ in the body, located to the right of the upper abdomen, just below the diaphragm. Its many functions include regulating the composition of the blood, producing bile, removing toxic substances and breaking down used blood cells. It also creates much heat and manufactures and stores certain substances.

Liver spot: Light brown-black, flat skin patches caused by clusters of melanocytes.

Long bones: Have a greater length than width and have a shaft. They are slightly curved and consist mostly of compact bone. For example, the femur and humerus.

Lumbar vertebra: One of the five bones that make up the lower back area of the vertebral column (spine). The lumbar vertebrae are the largest and strongest of the vertebrae.

Lumen: The space within a blood vessel through which the blood flows.

Lung: A major organ of the respiratory system, situated in the thorax. The lungs receive 'new' air, provide the site in which gaseous exchange can take place in the blood, and expel 'old' air.

Luteinizing hormone: Abbreviated to LH, this hormone is secreted by the pituitary gland. In females, it stimulates ovulation and the production of oestrogen and progesterone. It also prepares the mammary glands for milk secretion. In males, it stimulates the production of testosterone by the testes.

Lymph: The used and excess tissue fluid that is drained from the intercellular spaces into the vessels of the lymphatic system. Also called lymphoid tissue.

Lymph nodes: Small, round bodies that occur at intervals along the lymphatic vessels. They are usually found in clusters, particularly in the axilla (armpit), neck, thorax, abdomen and groin. The lymph nodes are packed with lymphocytes and so have a valuable part to play in dealing with infection. When the lymph nodes are particularly active in this role they may swell.

Lymphatic system: A series of vessels and associated lymph nodes in which lymph is transported from the tissue fluids into the bloodstream. Lymph is drained from the tissues by lymph capillaries, which empty into larger lymph vessels. The lymph vessels lead to lymph nodes (found mainly in the neck, axilla, groin, thorax and abdomen) which process the lymphocytes produced by the bone marrow and filter out harmful substances and bacteria. From the lymph nodes the lymph is carried in larger vessels called lymphatic trunks. The lymphatic trunks join to form lymph ducts. The lymph ducts join the cardiovascular system and the lymph is drained into large veins that transport the blood to the heart. The tonsils, spleen and thymus comprise of lymphatic tissue and are included in this system.

Lymphocyte: Agranular white blood cell produced in the red bone marrow, lymph nodes, tonsils, spleen and thymus. They play key roles in immune responses. There are 2 main types of lymphocyte, B-cells and T-cells. B-cells form plasma cells that produce antibodies, and T-cells directly destroy foreign particles. Natural killer cells are lymphocytes.

Lymphoid tissue: Commonly called lymph, a semi-solid connective tissue containing cells called lymphocytes. This tissue forms a part of the lymphatic system which is concerned with the control of disease.

Lysosome: A single membraned organelle that contains digestive enzymes.

Lysozyme: Enzyme capable of breaking down the cell walls of certain microbes.

Macrophage: Phagocytic cell formed from monocytes (agranular leucocytes).

Matrix: Ground substances and fibres that lie outside of the cells in connective tissue.

Medial: Nearer the midline of the body or structure than its comparative component.

Medulla: Middle layer of an organ. Also an abbreviation for 'medulla oblongata'.

Medulla oblongata: The lowest part of the brain stem. It connects with the spinal cord. Sometimes abbreviated to simply 'medulla'.

Meiosis: Nuclear division in sex cells. In this process, the resulting cells have half the genetic complement of the parent cell. In non-sex cells, nuclear division is called mitosis.

Meiosis I: The first meiotic nuclear division that produces two haploid cells.

Meiosis II: The second meiotic nuclear division, similar to mitosis, in which the two haploid cells (produced in meiosis I) produce a total of 4 haploid cells.

Melanin: Brown-black pigment that contributes to skin colour.

Melanocytes: Make up about 8% of the epidermis. They produce melanin.

Melatonin: Hormone produced by the pineal gland, thought to induce sleep and inhibit sexual activity.

Meninges: Membranes surrounding the brain and spinal cord. The outer meninge is the dura mater, the middle membrane is the arachnoid and the inner membrane is the pia mater.

Meningitis: An inflammation of the meninges surrounding the brain and/or spinal cord.

Menopause: The cessation of the menstrual cycle.

Menstruation: The monthly menstrual flow caused by the breakdown and expulsion of the lining of the uterus, together with much bleeding. The uterine lining regenerates after menstruation in preparation for the reception of a fertilized ovum. In the absence of this, it breaks down again and the cycle continues. The monthly menstrual cycle begins with the onset of puberty and continues until the menopause.

Merkel cells: Found in the deepest layer of the epidermis of hairless skin. They make contact with sensory neurons and are thought to have a part to play in the sensation of touch.

Merkel discs: Flattened portions of dendrites that make contact with Merkel cells in the deepest layer of the epidermis. They function in discriminative touch.

Mesenchyme: The tissue from which all connective tissues are derived.

Metabolic rate: The rate at which heat is produced in the body.

Metabolism: The chemical reactions that take place in cells. It is metabolic reactions that keep cells alive. Metabolic reactions involve breaking down molecules to provide energy, and building up more complex molecules and structures from simpler molecules.

Metacarpals: Five bones in the hand that are situated below the phalanges (the bones that make up the fingers) and above the carpals (the eight bones that make up the wrist).

Metaphase: The second phase of mitosis in which chromosomes align down the centre of the cell.

Metaphysis: The area of bone that joins the diaphysis (shaft) and the epiphysis (bone end). It is the growing area of the bone.

Metatarsals: Five bones in the foot that are situated below the phalanges (the bones that make up the toes) and above the cuboid and the three cuneiforms (four of the seven bones that make up the ankle).

Microbe: Micro-organism, generally capable of causing disease.

Microvilli: Finger-like projections of the cell membrane that increase the surface area for absorption.

Micturition: Urination.

Midbrain: Part of the brain stem that extends from the pons to the lower portion of the diencephalon.

Mineral: Inorganic substance that may perform a function vital to life. Examples of minerals include calcium, potassium, iron, phosphorus and chlorine.

Mitochondrion: A double-membraned organelle, involved in the production of adenosine triphosphate (ATP). Known as the "powerhouse" of the cell.

Mitosis: Nuclear division in non-sex cells. In this process, cells replicate their chromosomes and then separate to form two cells, each with the same genetic information as the originating cell. In sex cells, nuclear division is called meiosis.

Molecule: Formed when two or more atoms combine.

Monocyte: Agranular leucocyte that becomes a macrophage.

Monosaccharides: The smallest carbohydrates. Glucose is a monosaccharide and provides the main source of energy in the body.

Morula: A solid mass of cells produced by successive cleavages.

Motor end plate: The part of the muscle that communicates with the motor neuron at a neuromuscular junction.

Motor neurons: Transmit information to the part of the body that has to respond to a sensory stimulus. These responsive body parts are called effectors and are muscles or glands. Also called efferent neuron.

Mucous membrane: Comprised of a layer of epithelial tissue and an underlying connective tissue. They secrete mucus and line body cavities that open to the exterior and line the entire digestive, respiratory and reproductive systems and most of the urinary system.

Mucus: A thick secretion from the mucous glands or membranes.

Muscle fatigue: The inability of the muscle to maintain its strength of contraction due to an insufficient supply of oxygen and the accumulation of lactic acid.

Muscle fibre: A single muscle cell. The sarcoplasm of the fibre is comprised of a number of threads called myofibrils. Myofibrils contain numerous tiny filaments capable of producing muscular contraction.

Muscle filament: Tiny protein structures within the myofibrils of the muscle cell. The muscle filaments are capable of causing muscular contraction. Filaments made up mainly of actin are thin and light in colour. Filaments mainly comprising of myosin are thicker and darker.

Muscle tissue: Characterized by its ability to contract. There are three main types: 1. Skeletal - this type is mainly attached to bones and it can voluntarily be made to contract and relax. 2. Smooth - this type is found in the walls of hollow structures such as blood vessels, the stomach and other internal organs. Its movement is involuntary. 3. Cardiac - this type of muscle tissue forms most of the heart. Its movement is involuntary.

Muscle tone: The firmness of a muscle at rest. This firmness is created by the contraction of a few muscle fibres while the majority are resting.

Myelin: Fatty material composed of lipid and protein.

Myocardium: The middle layer of the heart made up from cardiac muscle.

Myofibril: One of many thread-like structures within a muscle cell. Myofibrils contain the protein filaments capable of causing muscular contraction.

Myoglobin: An oxygen-carrying pigment in the muscles.

Myosin: A contractile protein that makes up the thick filaments in the myofibrils of muscle fibres.

Natural killer cell: Lymphocyte able to kill a wide range of infectious microbes. They are present in the spleen, lymph nodes, bone marrow and blood. They may release chemicals or they may cause the fatal damage by direct contact.

Negative feedback system: When the triggered response reverses the original stimulus.

Nephrons: The functional units of the kidney. They filter the blood during the production of urine.

Nerve tract: Bundle of nerve fibres having a common origin or destination and carrying similar information.

Nervous system: All components of the body made of nerve cells. Divided into the central nervous system (comprising of the brain and spinal cord) and the peripheral nervous system that includes all other nervous tissue.

Neuroglia: Nerve cells that support and protect the neurons.

Neurolemma: The peripheral, nucleated, cytoplasmic layer of the Schwann cell. It plays a part in neuron regeneration.

Neuromuscular junction: The area of communication between a motor neuron and a muscle. The synapse at a neuromuscular junction is chemical.

Neuron: A nerve cell capable of transmitting nerve impulses.

Neurotransmitter: A chemical released at chemical synapses to allow the nerve impulse to be transmitted.

Neutron: Particle with no electrical charge found in the nucleus of an atom.

Neutrophil: Granular leucocyte that engulfs foreign particles then releases destructive chemicals to digest them.

Nitrogen: Element that is a component of all proteins and nucleic acids.

Nociceptor: A pain receptor.

Non-specific resistance: Includes the defense mechanisms that provide general protection against a variety of pathogenic invasions. For example, the skin, in covering the body, provides general protection.

Noradrenaline: A hormonal neurotransmitter secreted by the medulla of the adrenals and from nerve endings supplied by the sympathetic nervous system. It increases heart rate, breathing rate and blood pressure and slows down digestion. Also called norepinephrine.

Nucleic acids: Huge organic molecules found in the nucleus of a cell. Include deoxyribonucleic acid and ribonucleic acid.

Nucleolus: A part of the nucleus that functions in the synthesis and storage of ribonucleic acid (RNA).

Nucleus: Central part. In a cell it is the organelle that contains the chromosomes and controls cellular activities.

Oesophagus: The tube that connects the throat to the stomach.

Oestrogens: Female sex hormones produced by the ovaries. Oestrogens are concerned with the development and maintenance of the reproductive system and the development of secondary sex characteristics (e.g. growth of the breasts). During the menstrual cycle, oestrogen prepares the body for the implantation and growth of the fertilized ovum.

Olfactory: Pertaining to smell.

Oogenesis: The formation of ova, the female gametes.

Oogonia: Diploid cells in the ovaries produced during early foetal development.

Organ: Made up of varying types of tissue. Organs have specific functions and usually have distinctive shapes.

Organelle: A structure within a cell that serves a particular function.

Organic compound: Contains carbon and forms the basis for life. All matter that is living or has once lived will consist of organic compounds.

Origin: The attachment to the bone that remains unmoved during the muscular contraction.

Osmosis: The movement of water from a diluted solution to a more concentrated solution through a semi-permeable membrane.

Osmotic pressure: The pressure required to prevent the movement of pure water into a solution containing solutes when the solutions are separated by a semi-permeable membrane.

Ossification: The formation of bone.

Osteoblasts: Cells that form bone. They secrete collagen and other organic components needed to build bone. As they surround themselves with matrix materials they become osteocytes.

Osteoclasts: It is believed that osteoclasts develop from monocytes. They play a part in the reabsorption of bone – a necessary function for growth and repair.

Osteocytes: The principal bone cells, derived from osteoblasts. They maintain the cellular activities of the bone tissue.

Osteon: A unit of compact bone consisting of a Haversian canal with its lamellae, lacunae, osteocytes and canaliculi.

Osteoprogenitors: Unspecialized bone cells that can divide mitotically to develop into osteoblasts.

Ovary: Principal structure of the female reproductive system. The two ovaries are suspended in the upper pelvic cavity, one either side of the uterus. They produce ova (eggs). The ovaries secrete hormones and so they are classified as endocrine glands.

Ovum: Egg cell, produced by the ovaries.

Oxidant: Oxidizing agent. Causes substances to combine with oxygen.

Oxidation: The removal of electrons and hydrogen ions from a molecule, or the addition of oxygen to a molecule, resulting in a decrease in the energy content of the molecule. Energy is therefore released during oxidation.

Oxygen: Element essential to life. Constituent of water, carbohydrates, fats and proteins. Vital for respiration.

Oxytocin: Hormone produced by the hypothalamus and stored and secreted from the posterior lobe of the pituitary gland. It stimulates uterine contractions and milk ejection from the mammary glands.

Pancreas: A gland located below and slightly behind the stomach. It secretes pancreatic juice (containing digestive enzymes) via ducts into the duodenum. It also secretes hormones into the blood. It is therefore both an exocrine and endocrine gland.

Pancreatic amylase: Enzyme in pancreatic juice that digests carbohydrates.

Parasympathetic nervous system: A part of the autonomic nervous system. The motor nerves originate from cranial nerves (especially the vagus nerve) and a few of the spinal nerves in the sacral region. The nerve endings release acetylcholine that decreases the heart rate, breathing rate and blood pressure, and promotes digestion. This system opposes the sympathetic nervous system.

Parathyroid glands: Four small endocrine glands attached to the rear surface of the thyroid. They produce parathyroid hormone which decreases the blood phosphate level and increases the blood calcium level.

Parathyroid hormone: Hormone secreted by the parathyroid glands that decreases the blood phosphate level and increases the blood calcium level.

Parietal lobe: One of the main lobes of the cerebrum responsible for sensory reception and perception.

Paronychium: The tissue on the lateral sides of the nail that forms the lateral skin folds.

Parotid glands: Salivary glands located inferior and anterior to the ears.

Pathogen: A disease-producing organism.

Pedicles: Parts of the vertebra which, with the laminae, make up the bony vertebral arch that surrounds the spinal cord.

Pelvis: The structure formed by the 2 hipbones, the sacrum and the coccyx.

Penis: The male reproductive organ, used to introduce spermatozoa into the female vagina.

Pepsinogen: Enzyme secreted in gastric juices which, on contact with hydrochloric acid, is converted into pepsin, a protein-digesting enzyme.

Peptides: Formed when amino acids bond. When two amino acids bond the structure is called a dipeptide. If a third attaches it is known as a tripeptide. When more than three amino acids bond the chain-like structure is called a polypeptide.

Perimysium: The connective tissue that separates bundles (fascicles) of muscle fibres.

Periosteum: The membrane that covers the surface of bone not protected by cartilage. It has two layers. The outer fibrous layer is comprised of dense connective tissue containing blood vessels, lymph vessels and nerves that pass into the bone. The inner layer contains elastic fibres, blood vessels and a variety of bone cells.

Peripheral nervous system: Includes all components of the nervous system except the brain and spinal cord. It is the system of nerves, originating at the cranial and spinal nerves, that runs to all organs and peripheral regions of the body. It also incorporates ganglia situated outside of the brain and spinal cord.

Peristalsis: Waves of muscular contraction. In the alimentary canal, peristalsis aids the movement of food. In the renal pelvis and ureters it promotes the flow of urine.

Permeable: Able to be penetrated.

Peyer's patches: Groups of lymph nodules in the small intestine, particularly in the lower part of the ileum. Their purpose is to prevent bacteria from entering the blood stream.

pH: A measure of the concentration of hydrogen ions in a solution.

pH scale: Measures the acidity or alkalinity of a solution. The pH scale runs from 0 – 14. A pH of 0 represents the extreme of acidity and a pH of 14 denotes the extreme of alkalinity. The midway point is pH7 - the pH of pure water.

Phagocytosis: The process by which some cells can ingest foreign particles and cell debris.

Phalanges: Long bones that comprise the fingers and toes.

Pharynx: Commonly called the throat. The pharynx connects the mouth and the nasal passage to the oesophagus and the trachea.

Phosphate: Salt of phosphoric acid. About 85% of phosphate in the body is present in bone as calcium phosphate salts. It is also in the teeth. The rest is combined with lipids, proteins, carbohydrates, nucleic acids and adenosine triphosphate (ATP).

Phosphorus: Non-metallic element that exists in many different forms, including a yellow wax-like substance. About 80% is found in bones and teeth. It plays a role in muscular contraction and nerve activity. It is involved with energy transfer and is a component of deoxyriboneucleic acid (DNA) and ribonucleic acid (RNA).

Physiology: The science of the function of living organisms and the function of their individual parts.

Pia mater: The inner membrane of the three membranes that constitute the meninges. The meninges surround the brain and spinal cord.

Pigment: Natural substance that gives colour.

Pineal gland: An endocrine gland located in the roof of the third cerebral ventricle of the brain. It secretes melatonin during darkness that may induce sleep and inhibit sexual activity.

Pinocytosis: Cell drinking. It is similar to phagocytosis but the cell engulfs droplets of extracellular fluid rather than solid particles.

Pituitary gland: An endocrine gland located just beneath the hypothalamus at the base of the brain. The anterior lobe produces, stores and secretes 6 major hormones. The posterior lobe stores and releases hormones produced in the hypothalamus.

Placenta: The structure that allows the exchange of materials between the foetus and the mother.

Plasma: The straw-coloured fluid that makes up about 55% of the blood. Makes up 20% of extracellular fluid.

Plasma cell: An antibody-producing cell that develops from a B-cell.

Plasma membrane: The membrane that surrounds the cell, forming a barrier between the cell and the extracellular fluid. It is also called the cell membrane.

Platelet: A type of blood cell. Platelets are also called thrombocytes. They are fragments of cytoplasm, enclosed by a cell membrane. They play an important part in the blood clotting process.

Plural membrane: A double layered membrane that surrounds the lungs. The space between the membranes is called the plural cavity. It is filled with air to help cushion the lungs. The membranes secrete lubricating plural fluid that reduces friction.

Polar bodies: Three cells produced during oogenesis that disintegrate.

Polysaccharides: The largest and most complex carbohydrates. The principal polysaccharide is glycogen. Glycogen is comprised of glucose units that are linked together and is stored in the liver and skeletal muscles.

Pons: The part of the brain stem that forms the bridge between the medulla oblongata and the midbrain.

Portal circulation: The circulation of venous blood from the digestive organs and the spleen to the liver before it is returned to the heart.

Positive feedback system: When the triggered response increases the original stimulus.

Posterior: Nearer to the rear of the body than its comparative component. Also called dorsal.

Potassium: Essential element required for the successful transmission of nerve impulses and muscle contractions.

Primary follicle: Produced from primordial follicles under the monthly influence of follicle stimulating hormone. One primary follicle, under the influence of luteinizing hormone, completes meiosis I to form a secondary oocyte and a polar body.

Primary oocyte: Produced by mitosis of the oogonia in the third month of foetal development. They begin meiosis I but do not complete it until after puberty.

Primary spermatocytes: Produced when spermatogonia divide by mitosis and differentiate. They undergo meiosis I to become secondary spermatocytes.

Primordial follicle: The primary oocyte surrounded by a single layer of epithelial cells.

Progesterone: A female sex hormone produced in the ovaries after ovulation. It helps to prepare the uterus for the implantation of the fertilized ovum, develops the placenta and prepares the mammary glands for milk secretion.

Prolactin: Hormone secreted by the anterior lobe of the pituitary gland. It stimulates the mammary glands to produce milk.

Proliferate: Reproduce many times to increase in numbers.

Prophase: The first phase of mitosis in which the chromosomes appear to shorten and thicken and the nuclear membrane disintegrates.

Proprioception: The receipt of information from muscles, tendons and the labyrinth (intricate passageway in the inner ear) that enables the brain to determine movements and position of the body and its parts.

Prostate gland: A large, oval gland in males, surrounding the urethra near the point where it leaves the bladder. It produces a fluid containing various substances that is incorporated into the semen during ejaculation.

Protein: An organic compound containing carbon, hydrogen, oxygen and nitrogen. It may include sulphur and phosphorus. Proteins form an important part of all living organisms and are an essential constituent of any animal's diet. Major sources of protein are meat, egg-white, gelatin and pulses.

Prothrombin: A protein that is changed into thrombin by the enzyme thromboplastin.

Proton: Positively charged particle found in the nucleus of an atom.

Proximal: Nearer to the attachment of a limb to the trunk of the body than its comparative component. For example, the elbow is proximal to the wrist.

Puberty: The time during which the secondary sex characteristics begin to appear and sexual reproduction is possible.

Pulmonary arteries: Blood vessels that transport deoxygenated blood from the right ventricle of the heart to the lungs. These are the only arteries that contain deoxygenated blood.

Pulmonary circulation: The flow of deoxygenated blood from the right ventricle to the lungs, and the return of oxygenated blood from the lungs to the left atrium.

Pulmonary veins: Blood vessels that transport newly oxygenated blood from the lungs to the left atrium of the heart. These are the only veins that contain oxygenated blood.

Pulmonary ventilation: The inhalation (inspiration) and exhalation (expiration) of air between the atmosphere and the lungs.

Pupil: The hole in the centre of the iris through which light penetrates the eyeball.

Pyloric sphincter: The muscle at the duodenal end of the stomach through which the stomach content passes into the duodenum.

Pyruvic acid: An acid created by glycolysis. If oxygen is available, pyruvic acid is broken down in the mitochondria to form large quantities of adenosine triphosphate. In the absence of oxygen, pyruvic acid is converted into lactic acid.

Radiation: Heat transfer by infra-red rays from the warmer body to a cooler object without physical contact.

Radius: One of the two long bones of the forearm.

Red blood cells: Also called erythrocytes, they are responsible for transporting the gases of respiration.

Reflex: Fast, automatic response to a change in the internal or external environment that attempts to restore homeostasis.

Reflex arc: The route taken through the nervous system from the sensory stimulus to the effector.

Relaxin: Hormone secreted by the ovaries that dilates the cervix and helps the pelvic girdle to widen during childbirth.

Renin: An enzyme secreted by the kidneys to help regulate blood pressure.

Rennin: Enzyme secreted in gastric juices that coagulates the milk protein casein.

Reproductive system: The organs involved in reproduction, the process by which new individuals are produced and the genetic information passed from generation to generation. The main reproductive structures are the testes and the ovaries in the male and female respectively.

Respiratory system: The organs involved in taking oxygen from the external environment, absorbing oxygen into the blood, removing carbon dioxide from the blood and expelling the carbon dioxide from the body.

Ribonucleic acid (RNA): A nucleic acid found mainly in the cytoplasm. It works with deoxyribonucleic acid (DNA) in protein synthesis.

Ribosome: An organelle in the cell that may attach to the endoplasmic reticulum. It contains ribonucleic acid and proteins. Ribosomes are the site of protein synthesis.

Ribs: Bones that make up the thoracic cavity. Each of the 12 pairs of ribs articulate posteriorly with the corresponding thoracic vertebra. Anteriorly, the top 7 pairs attach to the sternum and are referred to as "true" ribs. The remaining 5 pairs of "false" ribs either attach indirectly to the sternum or do not attach to it at all.

Root hair plexuses: Dendrites arranged in a network around the hair follicle. The movement of the hair stimulates the dendrites. This allows the detection of movement on the surface of the skin when the hair is disturbed.

Sacrum: The triangular bone at the base of the vertebral column (spine), consisting of five fused sacral vertebrae.

Saliva: Alkaline secretion consisting mainly of water and an enzyme called salivary amylase that begins the breakdown of starches.

Salivary glands: Three pairs of glands that secrete saliva into the mouth via ducts.

Salt: A compound that produces neither hydrogen nor hydroxide ions when it dissociates in water.

Sarcolemma: The cell membrane of a muscle fibre.

Sarcomere: A compartment within the myofibril of a muscle cell in which the filaments are arranged. Z lines are the cross-partitioning structures.

Sarcoplasm: The cytoplasm of a muscle cell.

Sarcoplasmic reticulum: A network of little sacs and tubes in muscle fibres. It is similar to the endoplasmic reticulum in other cells. The sarcoplasmic reticulum surrounds the myofibrils. It releases calcium to enable muscular contraction and absorbs calcium when the muscle is relaxing.

Scapula: Shoulder blade. Categorized as a flat bone.

Sciatic nerve: A large spinal nerve, originating in the lumbar region, which descends through the thigh.

Schwann cell: A neuroglial cell of the peripheral nervous system that forms the myelin sheath and neurolemma. Also called neurolemmocyte.

Sebaceous gland: An exocrine gland in the dermis of the skin, usually associated with a hair follicle, that secretes sebum. Also called oil gland.

Sebum: Secretion from the sebaceous glands. It prevents the skin from drying and makes the hair and skin waterproof. It also contains an anti-septic ingredient to kill bacteria.

Secondary follicle: The secondary oocytes surrounded by several layers of epithelial cells.

Secondary oocyte: Produced when the primary follicle, under the influence of luteinizing hormone, completes meiosis I. The secondary oocyte is the larger of the 2 cells produced. The smaller is the polar body that disintegrates. When the secondary oocyte is fertilized, an ovum is produced.

Secondary spermatocytes: Produced when primary spermatocytes undergo meiosis I. When the secondary spermatocytes undergo meiosis II they become spermatids.

Secretin: Hormone, secreted by the small intestine, that stimulates the production of alkaline pancreatic secretions. Also stimulates the liver to produce alkaline bile.

Secretion: Production and release from a gland cell of a fluid, especially a functionally useful product as opposed to a waste product.

Semen: The sperm and secretory fluids released via the penis during ejaculation.

Seminal vessels: A pair of convoluted, pouch-like structures that secrete a component of semen into the ejaculatory ducts.

Seminiferous tubules: Tightly coiled ducts, located in the testes, where spermatozoa are produced.

Sensory neurons: Transmit information received from the sensory receptors. They carry information about the internal or external stimuli. Also called afferent neurons.

Serous membranes: Comprised of a layer of epithelial tissue and an underlying connective tissue. They line body cavities that do not open to the exterior and cover many organs. The epithelial layer secretes lubricating serous fluid.

Sesamoid bone: Type of bone found in tendons. These bones prevent tendon damage by allowing the tendon to pass smoothly over the bone. The biggest sesamoid bone is the patella (knee cap).

Short bones: Nearly equal in length and width. They consist of spongy bone except for their thin outer layer of compact bone. For example, the carpals (bones of the wrist) and tarsals (bones of the ankle).

Sigmoid colon: A part of the large intestine that runs from the descending colon (on the left of the abdomen) to the anal canal.

Simple epithelium: Single layer of cells that lines body cavities. Simple epithelium allows substances to quickly move through them. The main types of simple epithelium are squamous (pavement), cuboidal and columnar (may be ciliated or have microvilli).

Sinus: A hollow in the bone, space or channel.

Skeletal system: In the human, the skeletal system consists of 206 bones, cartilage, bone marrow and the periosteum (the membrane around the bones).

Small intestine: Consists of the duodenum, jejunum and ileum. The small intestine runs from the pyloric sphincter at the base of the stomach to the ileocaecal valve at the entrance to the large intestine. It is the site of digestion and absorption.

Sodium: Element essential in blood to maintain water balance. Also needed for the conduction of nerve impulses and muscle contraction.

Solar plexus: A network of autonomic nerves located behind the stomach.

Solute: Dissolved substance.

Solvent: Dissolving agent.

Specific resistance: Involves the production of specific antibodies or the activation of T-cells against a particular pathogen.

Spermatids: Produced by meiosis II of the secondary spermatocytes. Spermatids develop into spermatozoa.

Spermatogenesis: The production of spermatozoa, the male gametes.

Spermatogonia: Immature stem cells that line the seminiferous tubules.

Spermatozoa: Sperm, the male gametes.

Sphincter: A circular muscle constricting an orifice.

Spinal cord: A mass of nervous tissue running through the vertebral column from which 31 pairs of spinal nerves originate.

Spinal process: Bony projection on the posterior side of the vertebra that provides a site for muscular attachment.

Spleen: An oval shaped organ located to the left of the abdomen. It is the largest mass of lymphatic tissue in the body. It produces lymphocytes, destroys worn out red blood cells and acts as a reservoir for blood.

Spongy bone: Forms the epiphyses and metaphyses in the long bones. It also forms short bones, flat bones, sesamoid bones and irregularly shaped bones. The bone tissue is arranged in an interlacing network in which red bone marrow may be found in the spaces. Also called cancellous bone.

Squamous: Scale-like.

Starch: A carbohydrate obtained mainly from cereals and potatoes. It is converted to sugar under certain conditions such as the presence of heat and certain chemicals.

Stem cell: An immature, undifferentiated cell that divides to replace lost or damaged cells.

Sternum: Breast bone. Categorized as a flat bone.

Steroid: The group name for organic compounds derived from cholesterol. Some hormones are included in this group.

Stomach: A muscular sac between the oesophagus and the duodenum. It holds food for 2-6 hours. The stomach churns food and secretes acidic gastric juices and enzymes to facilitate digestion.

Stratum: A layer.

Subarachnoid space: Area between the arachnoid and the pia mater, filled with cerebrospinal fluid.

Subcutaneous layer: The layer of skin that connects the dermis to the underlying tissues. It consists mainly of adipose tissue.

Sublingual glands: Salivary glands located superior to the submandibular glands.

Submandibular glands: Salivary glands situated beneath the base of the tongue.

Sugar: A carbohydrate containing carbon, hydrogen and oxygen. It has many forms, e.g. glucose (found in fruit and produced by the tissues), sucrose (found in sugar cane, beetroot and maple), lactose (found in milk) and maltose (produced from starch).

Superficial: External, located on or near the surface of the body.

Superior: Towards the head or upper part of the body.

Sweat glands: Secrete sweat (containing a mixture of water, salts, urea, uric acid, amino acids, ammonia, sugar, lactic acid and ascorbic acid) onto the surface of the skin (eccrine) or onto a hair follicle (apocrine).

Sympathetic nervous system: A part of the autonomic nervous system. It increases the heart rate, breathing rate and blood pressure, and slows down digestion. The motor nerves of this system originate from the spinal nerves in the thoracic and lumbar regions. The nerve endings release noradrenaline that creates these 'fight or flight' reactions. Sympathetic fibres also trigger the release of adrenaline.

Synapse: The junction between two neurons or between a motor neuron and an effector.

Synovial fluid: The lubricating fluid secreted by the synovial membrane into the synovial cavity of a freely movable joint.

Synovial membrane: The inner layer of the articular capsule composed of areolar connective tissue, elastic fibres and fat. Secretes lubricating synovial fluid into the synovial cavity.

System: Several related organs with a common function.

Systemic circulation: The route through which oxygenated blood flows from the left ventricle, through the aorta, to all the organs of the body, and deoxygenated blood returns to the right atrium.

Tarsals: Short bones in the ankle.

Tarsus: The collective term for the 7 bones (tarsals) of the ankle.

T-cells: Lymphocytes that function in cell-mediated immunity and directly destroy foreign particles. They originate in the bone marrow and then migrate to the thymus where they mature.

Telophase: The fourth phase of mitosis in which a nuclear membrane forms around the two groups of chromosomes formed in anaphase.

Tendon: Non-elastic, tough, white fibrous connective tissue that joins muscle to bone.

Testis: One of a pair of male reproductive organs. The testes (or testicles) descend from the abdomen into two sacs of skin called scrotal sacs. The testes are comprised of thousands of fine, coiled tubules in which the sperm are produced. The testes secrete hormones and are therefore classified as endocrine glands.

Testosterone: A male sex hormone secreted by the testes. It controls the growth and maintenance of the reproductive system and the development of secondary sex characteristics. It also stimulates the production of sperm and body growth. The level of testosterone is controlled by luteinizing hormone.

Tetanus: A sustained muscular contraction produced by a series of rapid stimuli. Tetanus is also an infectious disease, characterized by muscle spasms, exaggerated reflexes, lockjaw and arching of the back.

Thalamus: A large, oval structure located above the midbrain, consisting of two masses of grey matter covered by a thin layer of white matter.

Thermoreceptor: Receptor that detects changes in temperature.

Thoracic duct: Otherwise called the left lymphatic duct, this vessel receives lymph from the left side of the head, neck and chest, the left arm and all of the lower body. The lymph is then drained into venous blood via the left brachiocephalic vein.

Thoracic vertebra: One of the twelve bones that make up the chest area of the vertebral column (spine). Provide the posterior attachment point for the ribs.

Thorax: The section of the body containing the heart and the lungs, divided from the abdomen by the diaphragm.

Thrombin: Interacts with the protein fibrinogen to form fibrin, an insoluble protein that forms the basis of a blood clot.

Thrombocyte: A type of blood cell, also called a platelet. Thrombocytes are fragments of cytoplasm, enclosed by a cell membrane. They play an important part in the blood clotting process.

Thromboplastin: An enzyme, produced in response to an injury, that changes the protein prothrombin into thrombin in the presence of calcium.

Thymus: A lymphatic gland, consisting of two lobes located in the upper chest, between the sternum (breast bone) and the lungs. The outer layer is packed with lymphocytes. T-cell lymphocytes, produced in the bone marrow, migrate to the thymus for development. The thymus secretes hormones, a feature that classifies it as an endocrine gland.

Thymus stimulating hormones: Produced in the thymus, these hormones stimulate their originating gland, promoting the maturation of T-cell lymphocytes.

Thyroid: An endocrine gland situated just below the larynx. It secretes hormones that regulate growth and development and control the metabolic rate.

Thyroid stimulating hormone: Secreted by the anterior lobe of the pituitary gland, it controls secretions from the thyroid.

Thyroxine: A thyroid hormone, involved in regulating growth and development.

Tibia: One of the two long bones of the lower leg.

Tissue: Made up of cells of the same type, e.g. muscle tissue is made up of muscle cells only. There are four main types of tissue: epithelial, connective, muscle and nervous.

Tissue fluid: The portion of extracellular fluid that fills the spaces between the cells in tissues. Also called interstitial fluid and intercellular fluid.

Tonsils: Small bodies of lymphatic tissue located at the back of the throat.

Trabeculae: Irregular lace-work of spongy bone comprising of lamellae, lacunae and canaliculi. In some bones, red bone marrow is located in its meshes. Also the name given to fibrous cords of supporting connective tissue that extend into an organ/structure.

Trachea: Commonly called the windpipe. It extends from the pharynx (throat) down to the level of the 5th thoracic vertebra. It then branches to form the left and right primary bronchi.

Transverse colon: A part of the large intestine that runs across the abdomen from the ascending colon (on the right) to the descending colon (on the left).

Transverse process: One of two bony projections that extend laterally from a vertebra. They provide a site for muscular attachment.

Triglycerides: The fats and oils that we eat will usually be triglycerides. Triglycerides can be broken down into glycerol and fatty acids to provide the body's largest source of energy.

Trypsin: Enzyme in pancreatic juice that digests proteins.

Ulna: One of the two long bones of the forearm.

Umbilical cord: The long structure that provides the vascular connection between the placenta and the foetus.

Unmyelinated: Not covered in an insulating protein and lipid myelin sheath.

Urea: A water soluble nitrogen compound, that makes up 60-90% of all nitrogenous material in the urine. When in the presence of water it gives off ammonia.

Ureter: The tube that transports urine from a kidney to the bladder.

Urethra: The tube that transports urine from the bladder to the exterior.

Uric acid: A slightly soluble, crystalline substance that is present in the urine. It is formed by the liver and removed from the blood by the kidneys.

Urinary system: An excretory system responsible for the removal of urine from the body. It comprises of the kidneys, ureters, bladder and urethra.

Uterine tubes: Another name for the fallopian tubes. Each leads from an ovary to the uterus.

Uterus: A tough, muscular sac suspended by broad ligaments, situated between the bladder and the rectum in the female. If fertilization occurs, the uterus provides a source of attachment and nourishment for the fertilized ovum.

Vascular: Pertaining to or containing many blood vessels.

Vas deferens: A tube of the male reproductive system that transports sperm from the testis to the urethra, ready for ejaculation.

Vasoconstriction: A decrease in the diameter of the lumen of a blood vessel.

Vasodilation: An increase in the diameter of the lumen of a blood vessel.

Vein: A vessel that carries blood back to the heart.

Venous: Pertaining to the veins.

Ventricle: A cavity in the brain or one of the two inferior chambers of the heart.

Venule: Small vein that collects deoxygenated blood from the capillaries. Venules merge to become veins.

Vertebra: One of the 26 bones that makes up the vertebral (spinal) column. Categorized as an irregular bone.

Vertebral column: Commonly called the spine. The adult vertebral column comprises of 26 individual bones (vertebrae).

Vertebral foramen: The gap in the vertebra through which the spinal cord runs.

Villi: Finger-like projections of the inner layer of the small intestine. Each villus contains a network of capillaries and a lacteal.

Virus: A tiny infectious agent capable of causing a variety of diseases.

Viscous: Sticky, semi-fluid.

Vitamin: Essential organic chemical that acts as a catalyst in metabolic processes.

Vitamin A: Developed by plants as carotene, also found in egg-yolk, liver, milk, butter and many green vegetables. Plays a role in sight, growth of bones and teeth and general well-being.

Vitamin B12: Cyanocobalamin. Necessary for the formation of red blood cells and amino acids.

Vitamin C: Ascorbic acid. Water soluble vitamin needed for many metabolic processes.

Vitamin D: A fat-soluble vitamin found in fish oil, butter, milk, cheese, egg-yolk and liver. Its principal action is to increase the absorption of calcium and phosphorus from the intestine. Deficiency of vitamin D results in inadequate amounts of calcium in the bones.

Vitamin E: Found in fresh nuts, seed oils and green, leafy vegetables. It is involved in the formation of nucleic acids and red blood cells, and may promote wound healing, prevent scarring and function as an antioxidant.

Vitamin K: Phytomenadione. Found in spinach, cauliflower, cabbage and liver. Essential for blood clotting because it is involved in the synthesis of many blood clotting factors, including prothrombin.

Volkmann's canal: The space through which blood vessels, lymphatic vessels and nerves enter the bone from the periosteum. Also called perforating canal.

White fibrous cartilage: Made up of bundles of white collagenous fibres with chondrocytes in between. It is very strong but slightly flexible. It is found in some pelvic joints and makes up the intervertebral discs.

White fibrous connective tissue: Contains closely packed collagen fibres. It is strong and forms attachments. For example, white fibrous connective tissue is found in tendons (that attach muscle to bone) and ligaments (that attach bone to bone).

White matter: Bundles of myelinated axons in the brain and spinal cord. White matter conducts the nerve impulses.

Yellow elastic cartilage: Flexible cartilage consisting of yellow elastic fibres. It forms the epiglottis and can be found at the tip of the nose and in the upper part of the pinna (external part of the ear).

Yellow elastic connective tissue: Consists of yellow elastic fibres. It allows organs to stretch and then return to the normal size. For example, yellow elastic connective tissue is found in the walls of the arteries.

Z lines: The cross-partitioning structures that divide the myofibrils into compartments called sarcomeres. The thin, light, actin filaments attach to the Z lines. The Z lines are pulled closer during muscular contraction, so shortening the muscle.

Zygote: Fertilized ovum.

This page has intentionally been left blank.

Index

Product List

Essential Training Solutions offer a wide range of accredited and approved onlin
courses, complementary healthcare learning materials, online tutorials and questio
banks for colleges, plus business resources. The product list includes:

Accredited Courses:

Online VTCT Level 3 Certificate in Anatomy, Physiology and Pathology

FHT / AoR / IFPA / Bowen Ass'n Approved Online CPD Courses:

Anatomy and Physiology
Pathology
Further Pathology
Additional Pathology
Complete Pathology
Health and Safety

Complementary Healthcare Learning Materials:

Anatomy and Physiology
Pathology
Health and Safety
Aromatherapy
Reflexology

Please visit our web site for full details.

www.essential-training.co.uk

Tel: +44 (0)1279 726800